The Ultimate Personal Trainer Handbook

The Ultimate Personal Trainer Handbook

The comprehensive reference book for professional personal trainers

The Kinetic Pulse Collective

Copyright

Handbook purpose

This personal trainer handbook has been created to support certified personal trainers and personal trainers in training. KPC cannot be held responsible for individual interpretation of content and application of knowledge during any associated assessments.

Symbols used in handbook

Core information has been highlighted throughout this training manual using the following symbols:

- Personal trainers take note
- Activity
- See relevant document and section
- Further reading
- Tip
- Warning
- Checklist
- Recalling

Content

Content

Introduction to Personal Training

Chapters

Our Personal Trainer handbook is divided into four major chapters, each consisting of a series of sub chapters detailed below. Personal trainers should read the chapters in the respective order specified in this training manual.

Chapter 1: Anatomy and physiology for personal training

Chapter 1A: The human body - anatomy & physiology
Chapter 1B: Impact of exercise on the body

Chapter 2: Nutrition

Chapter 2A: Nutrition and healthy eating
Chapter 2B: Applying the principles of nutrition to training programs

Chapter 3: Introduction to personal training

Chapter 3A: Personal training overview
Chapter 3B: Knowing the client

Chapter 4: Delivering personal training sessions

Chapter 4A: Programming personal training with clients
Chapter 4B: Delivering personal training sessions
Chapter 4C: Training special populations

THE KINETIC PULSE COLLECTIVE

KPC

Chapter 1

ANATOMY AND PHYSIOLOGY FOR PERSONAL TRAINING

Chapter 1A: The human body - anatomy and physiology Chapter 1B: Impact of exercise on the body

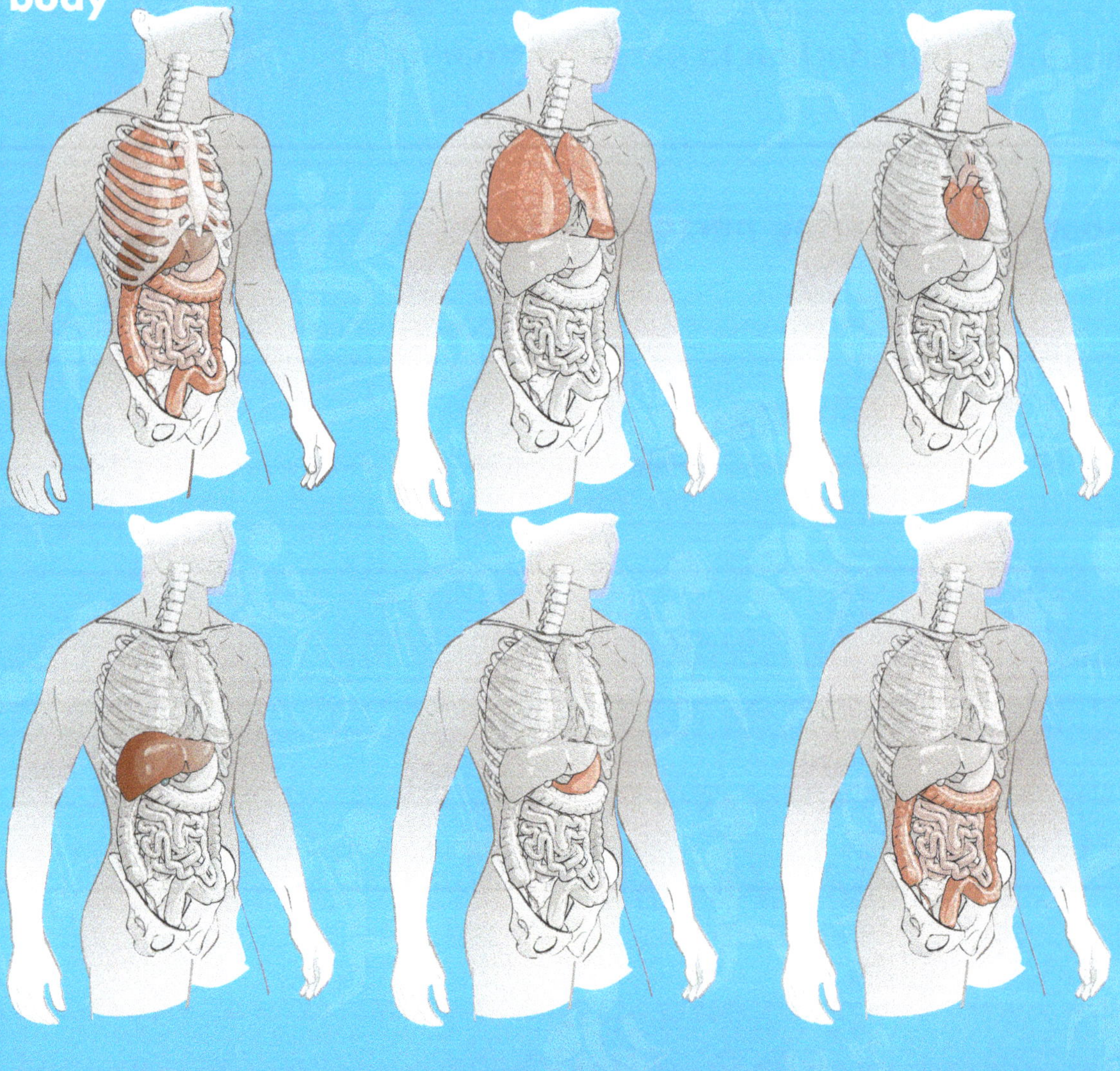

Chapter 1A: The human body - anatomy & physiology

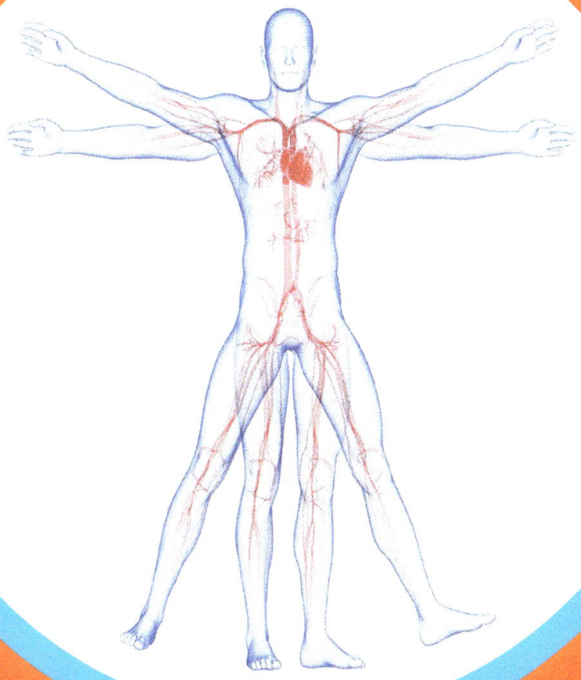

Chapter summary

This Chapter will build on the anatomy and physiology lessons completed during Fitness Instructor training, to develop and consolidate a student's knowledge of the human body and how the main biological systems work.

Aim

The aim of this Chapter is to allow personal trainers to confidently discuss with clients the main biological systems of human body and how they are connected in a healthy functioning body.

Learning objectives

After completing this Chapter, personal trainers will be able to:

1. Name the main biological systems in the body and discuss the role of each one in a healthy and functioning body.
2. Name the main organs in the body used during exercise.
3. Discuss the skeletal system and its composition.
4. Discuss core stability and its relevance to posture.
5. List the main components of a long bone.
6. Summarize the ossification process.
7. Summarize osteoporosis and how to maintain healthy bones.
8. Explain how force is generated by muscles.
9. List major joints in the body and the movement types possible at these joints.
10. Discuss the main anatomical planes.
11. Discuss the cardiac cycle and its role in the circulatory system.
12. Explain the role of the nervous system and the endocrine system and discuss how they differ.
13. Explain the digestive system and its connection to the energy systems.

Organs and biological systems

As a personal trainer, it is important to understand the human body and how it is impacted by exercise. A brief overview of the human body is provided below:

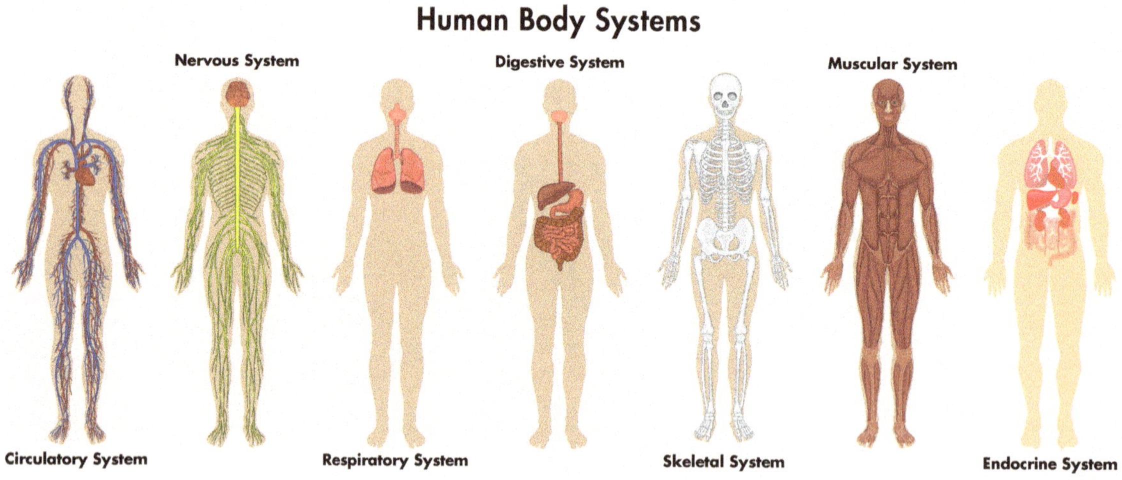

These are not the only systems in the body, but the main ones that will be looked at in this handbook.

Main organs

The human body has five main organs that are essential for survival. These are the heart, brain, lungs, kidneys and liver.

The brain is a kind of central power system of the body. It uses the nervous system and secreted hormones to transmit and receive signals to other organs. A person's thoughts, feelings, storage of their memory, and broad outlook of the world are all determined by the human brain.

The human heart has the function of supplying blood around the body through the arteries and veins.

The lungs take oxygen from the air and transmits it to our blood. From there, it is sent to our cells. Carbon dioxide, which is exhaled, is also removed by the lungs.

The role of the kidneys is to take away waste and excess fluid from the blood. The kidneys also remove urea from the blood and incorporate it with the water and other materials to make urine.

The liver has several functions which include 'detoxing' the body of injurious chemicals, breaking down drugs, filtering the blood, secreting bile and making blood-clotting proteins.

Biological systems

The human body is made up of several biological systems that undertake precise tasks which are vital for our daily lives.

The circulatory system carries blood, nutrients, oxygen, carbon dioxide and hormones around the body. It is made up of the heart, blood, blood vessels and veins.

The digestive system is made up of a number of organs that are linked together. They let the body break down food, allow it to be absorbed and for waste to be removed. The digestive system consists of the mouth, oesophagus, stomach, small intestine, large intestine, rectum and anus. The liver and pancreas are also constituents of this system as they make digestive juices.

A total of eight key glands make up **the endocrine system**. These emit hormones into the blood. The hormones eventually make their way to different tissues. They control many functions of the body such as metabolism, growth and sexual function.

The immune system protects the body against bacteria, viruses and other pathogens that could be injurious to health. Some of these are lymph nodes, the spleen, lymphocytes (including B-cells and T-cells), bone marrow and the thymus and leukocytes – these are white blood cells.

The main role of **the lymphatic system** is to create and circulate lymph, which is a transparent fluid. This fluid contains white blood cells. This helps the body to resist infection. The lymphatic system also takes away excessive lymph fluid from the tissues in the body and gives it back to the blood. The lymphatic system includes lymph nodes, lymph ducts and lymph vessels and plays a part in the body's defences.

The nervous system is responsible for voluntary actions like movement and involuntary behaviors like breathing. It also transmits signals to various parts of the body. The central nervous system consists of the brain and the spinal cord. The peripheral system is made up of nerves which link all other areas of the body to the central nervous system.

The muscular system of the body is made up of approximately 650 muscles. These help movement, flow of blood and other body functions. The three types of muscle are called skeletal muscle, smooth muscle and cardiac muscle. Skeletal muscle is joined to the bone and assists with voluntary movement. Smooth muscle is situated inside organs. It helps to move substances via the organs. Cardiac muscle, which is only found in the heart, assists in pumping blood around the body.

As the name suggests, **the reproductive system** enables us to reproduce. Body parts such as the penis and the testes make up the male reproductive system, which creates sperm. The female reproductive system is made up of the vagina, uterus and the ovaries which produce eggs. During the process of conception, the combination of an egg cell with a sperm cell helps to make a fertilized egg. This egg then embeds and starts to grow in the uterus.

Our bodies are held in place by **the skeletal system**. The teeth are also part of the skeletal system, but they are not commonly seen to be categorized as a form of bone.

The respiratory system permits the body to breathe in essential oxygen and exhale carbon dioxide (breathing). This system is made of mainly the trachea, the diaphragm and the lungs.

The urinary system helps to discard urea from the body. This is a waste product. It is produced when foods are broken down. The urinary system is made up of two kidneys, two ureters, the bladder, the urethra and two sphincter muscles. Urine made by the kidneys moves down to the bladder via the ureters, and leaves the body through the urethra.

By far the largest organ of the body is the skin, formally known as **the integumentary system**. It shelters us from the external environment and is the body's first port of call when it comes to fighting bacteria, viruses and other pathogens. Our body temperature and elimination of waste through perspiration is also regulated by the skin.

Personal training and the human body

A personal trainer needs to understand the human body to prescribe exercises that are suitable for the client's physiology.

Studying anatomy and physiology will provide personal trainers the knowledge to create exercises that use the right muscles at the right times. It will allow them to understand angles and ranges of motion to create personal training programs for clients who have different body alignments.

An understanding of the human body and the biological systems will also allow the personal trainer to recognize imbalances in strength and stability of muscle groups and prescribe exercises as well as provide other advice to treat these issues. The more a personal trainer knows and understands the body, the better they will be at creating successful training programs tailored for the client.

It is not possible to cover all the organs and biological systems in the human body in this course, but the following will be examined, building on what was covered in Fitness Instructor Handbook.

01 The skeletal system

02 The muscular system

03 The respiratory system

04 The circulatory system

05 The nervous system

06 The endocrine system

07 The digestive system

The skeletal system

The framework of the human body is called the skeletal system, constructed of bones, joints and cartilages. The skeletal system was covered in some detail in the Fitness Instructor Handbook but a summary is provided below.

The skeleton contains 206 bones of various sizes and has a number of important functions including:

- Giving the human body its shape and providing a framework for the development of the body
- Protecting the internal organs such as the heart and the lungs via the rib cage
- Facilitating movements through the bones and soft tissues
- Providing a surface for the attachment and growth of soft tissues to form muscles and ligaments
- Storing minerals within the bones for the body to consume quickly when required, such as calcium phosphorus and salt
- Producing blood cells (red and white) which are vital for the human body to function healthily and the immune system to operate

Axial skeleton

Body area	Name of bones	Number of bones
Skull	Cranial	22 (There are 8 cranial and 14 facial bones)
Spine	Cervical vertebrae Thoracic vertebrae Lumbar vertebrae Sacral vertebrae Coccygeal vertebrae	33-35
Chest	Costals (ribs)	12 pairs

Appendicular skeleton

Body area	Name of bones	Number of bones
Shoulders	Scapulae Clavicle	2 2
Pelvis	Ilium, Ischium and Pubis	6
Arms	Humerus, Radius and Ulna	6
Hands	Carpals Metacarpals Phalanges	16 10 28
Legs	Femur, Tibia, Fibula and Patella Tarsals Metatarsals Phalanges Calcaneus	8 14 10 28 2

Skeletal muscles

There are approximately 650 skeletal muscles in the human body. Throughout this course muscles will be referred to by their names and the figure below shows the main muscles and where they can be found in the body.

Frontal Muscle Anatomy

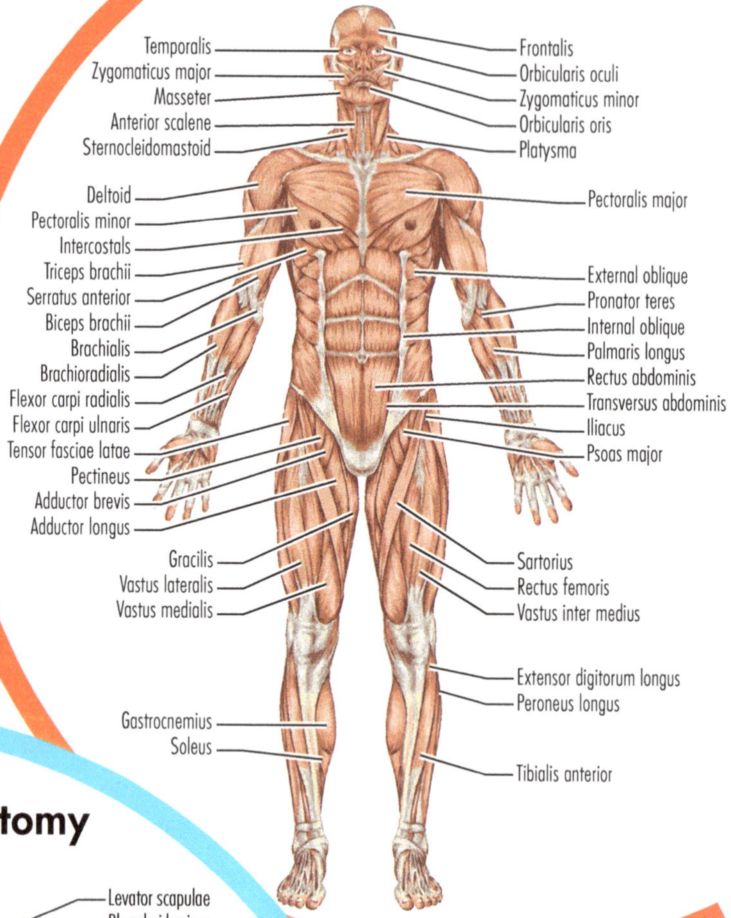

Back Muscle Anatomy

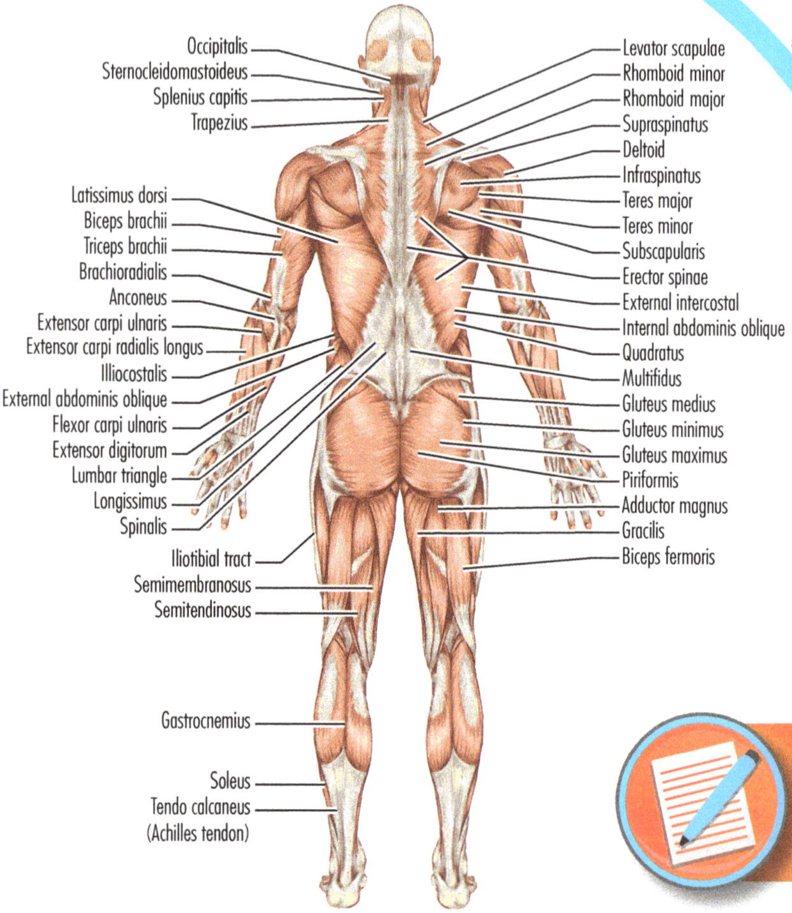

The figure above does not show all the muscles in the human body.

Girdles and limbs

Limbs are part of the body's appendicular or hanging skeleton. Each is a modular structure consisting of a number of bones and joints with muscles joining them to facilitate the various types of movements with arms, legs, hands and feet. Connecting the limbs to the rest of the body are the two girdles known as:

- Shoulder girdle which connects the upper limbs
- The pelvic girdle which attaches the lower limbs

The Pelvic Girdle

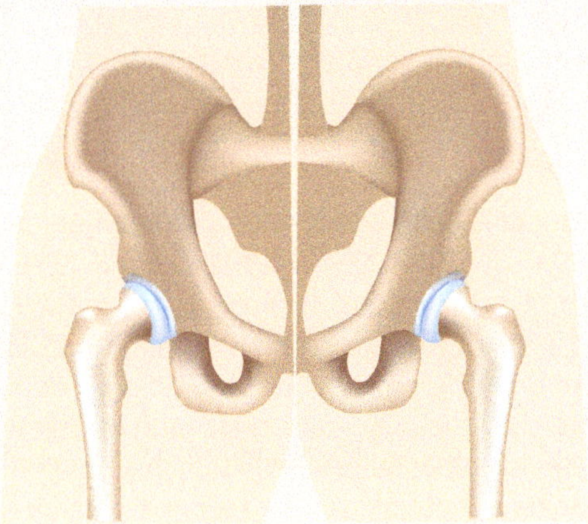

The Shoulder Girdle

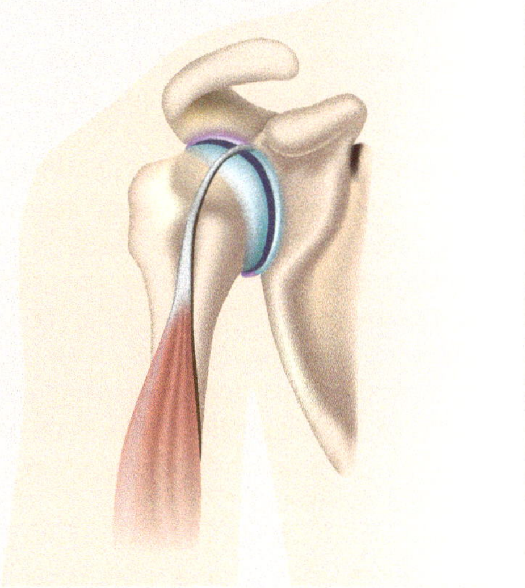

A human limb has three major segments. The arm stretches from the shoulder to the elbow, followed by the forearms and the hand. The thigh extends from the hip to the knee followed by the leg and foot. Each of the body's limbs has separate bones joining together to facilitate the various types of movements we can achieve.

The pelvic girdle

The Pelvic Girdle

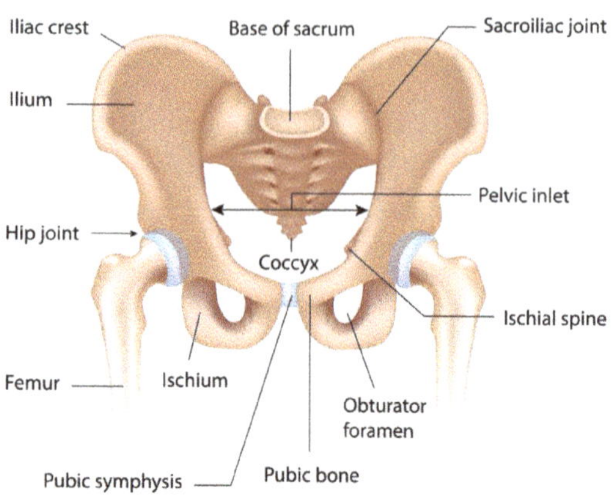

The pelvic girdle, also known as hip girdle, is very relevant in the context of personal training. This is because of its role in making the body stable. The pelvic girdle is made up from either a single bone, hip bone or the coxal (hip) bone. The latter bone functions as a joining area for each of the lower limbs. Each hip bone is securely connected to the axial skeleton via the sacrum in the vertebral column. Both hip bones meet each other in an anterior position in order to combine with each other. The bony pelvis forms the whole framework made up by the two hip bones, the sacrum, and fixed inferiorly to the sacrum, the coccyx.

The hip bone makes up the pelvic girdle part of the pelvis. Both hip bones are big in size and are curved. They make up the lateral and anterior parts of the pelvis. The adult hip bone is made up of three bones that merge with each other in older adolescents. These are called the ilium, ischium and pubis.

The pelvis is made up of four bones – right and left ilium, the sacrum and the coccyx. The pelvis has a number of roles. Its main purpose is to prop up the weight of the upper part of the body when in the sitting position. It also helps to carry this weight to the lower limbs when one is upright. Yet another function of the pelvis is to act as a connection point for the torso and lower limb muscles. The pelvis also helps to shield the internal pelvic organs. When standing anatomically, the pelvis is slightly slanted anteriorly. Whilst in this position, the anterior superior iliac spines and the pubic tubercles lay in the same upright plane. The sacrum's anterior surface looks forwards and downwards.

The three parts of the hip bone – the pubis, ischium and ilium meet in the middle in order to make a sunken impression called the acetabulum. This is situated beside the hip bone and is a portion of the hip joint. The obturator foramen is the big entrance in the anteroinferior hip bone. This is situated in between the ischium and pubis. This entrance area is mostly composed of a tier of connective tissue. It aids the joining of muscles on its internal and external surfaces.

Various ligaments combine the pelvis bones. The mostly static sacroiliac joint is held together by two firm ligaments which are joined between the sacrum and ilium parts of the hip bone. These parts are known as sacroiliac ligament (on the anterior side) and the posterior sacroiliac ligament (on the posterior side). There are an extra two ligaments which extend over the sacrum and hip bone. The sacrospinous ligament spans from the sacrum spine to the ischial spine, whilst the sacrotuberous ligament starts from the sacrum and ends at the ischial tuberosity. These ligaments help to hold up and restrict the sacrum as it holds the body's weight.

The pelvic bones are firmly bound with each other and make up a fixed structure which can bear weight. In contrast, the pectoral girdle bones are extremely versatile, enabling a wide range of movement to take place in the upper limbs. This is crucial to keeping the body stable and well balanced. This is because it allows the body's weight to transition sideways from the vertebral column, via the pelvic girdle and hip joints, into any of the lower limbs, when the other limb isn't holding any weight. So, the fixed nature of the pelvis is a solid base to the upper body because it lies on top of the movable lower limbs. A stable pelvic girdle therefore provides a stable foundation for 'core stability' (see *Posture and core stability* section).

Differences between men and women

The main difference between a male and female human skeleton is that the female has a more rounded pelvis with shorter pelvic bones and the surrounding bones are designed to be more flexible to accommodate gestation and child delivery. Male bones in general tend to be longer and heavier than the corresponding female bones. In males, the jaw bone is generally larger and more pronounced, and the brow is taller. Male skeletons also generally have longer, thicker bones in the arms, legs and fingers. However, despite these differences it is important to remember that male and female skeletons are much more alike than different.

The shoulder girdle

The **pectoral** is also known as the shoulder girdle. It is the set of bones that connects arms to the axial skeleton on each side. The pectoral girdle is formed by two sets of bones - the **scapulae** and the **clavicles**, which are connected to one another themselves. Each clavicle further connects to the sternum in the chest to form a **synovial gliding joint**. The scapula is further connected to the **humerus** which connects to the radius and ulna. At the end of the radius and ulna we have the **carpals**, followed by **metacarpals** and then the **phalanges**.

The clavicle, also known as the collar bone is an elongated, slender, curved bone lying horizontally at the root of the neck in the upper part of the thorax. Each collar bone articulates with the sternum and a scapula to form the anterior part of a shoulder.

The scapulae often referred to as the shoulder blades are thin and triangular in shape and partially cover the back of the ribs. Each scapula is fixed in place by the many muscles of the back and shoulder joint, making the whole shoulder girdle and associated limbs very mobile. The scapulae faciliates two unique movements. It allows movement sideways around the ribs during protraction and retraction movements and secondly it allows rotation during abduction and adduction movements.

The humerus is the only upper arm bone and the largest bone in the arm. It runs from the shoulder to the elbow, connecting the scapula with the lower arm bones. Many powerful muscles that contract to move the upper arm are anchored to the humerus. The humerus is fundamental to accomplish movements like lifting, writing, throwing and complete rotation of the arm.

The radius is a bone with a rounded head that connects to the humerus. Its round head pivots at the elbow to enable the arms to produce some hand movements without moving the elbows. Running parallel to the radius but also extending from the elbow to the wrist is the second bone in the forearm called the ulna. It is thinner than the radius on the side opposite the thumb.

The carpals are a cluster of bones between the wrist and fingers. These bones are very flexible which in return makes the hand very flexible with the ability to perform many types of movements.

Metacarpals are bones in our hands after the carpals on which our palm rests and finally the phalanges are the small bones at the end of the fingers.

The shoulder girdle

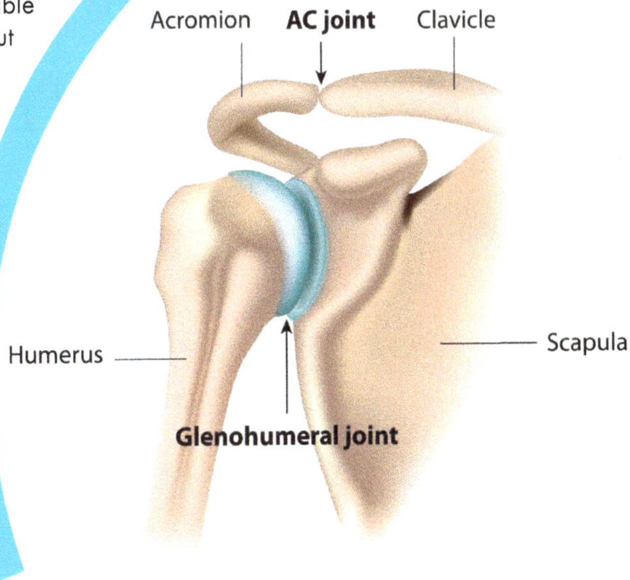

The vertebral column (spine)

The vertebral column also known as the spine was looked at in some detail in the Fitness Instructor Handbook, but it is worth taking another look at this special structure in the human skeleton, as it includes many unique features and acts as the main foundation for human framework, supporting other major bones and allowing movements such as turning the head and bending down to touch your toes.

The spine, curved in shape can be divided into five sections and within each section there are a number of individual vertebrae as shown in the figure below:

The structure of the segments of the spine

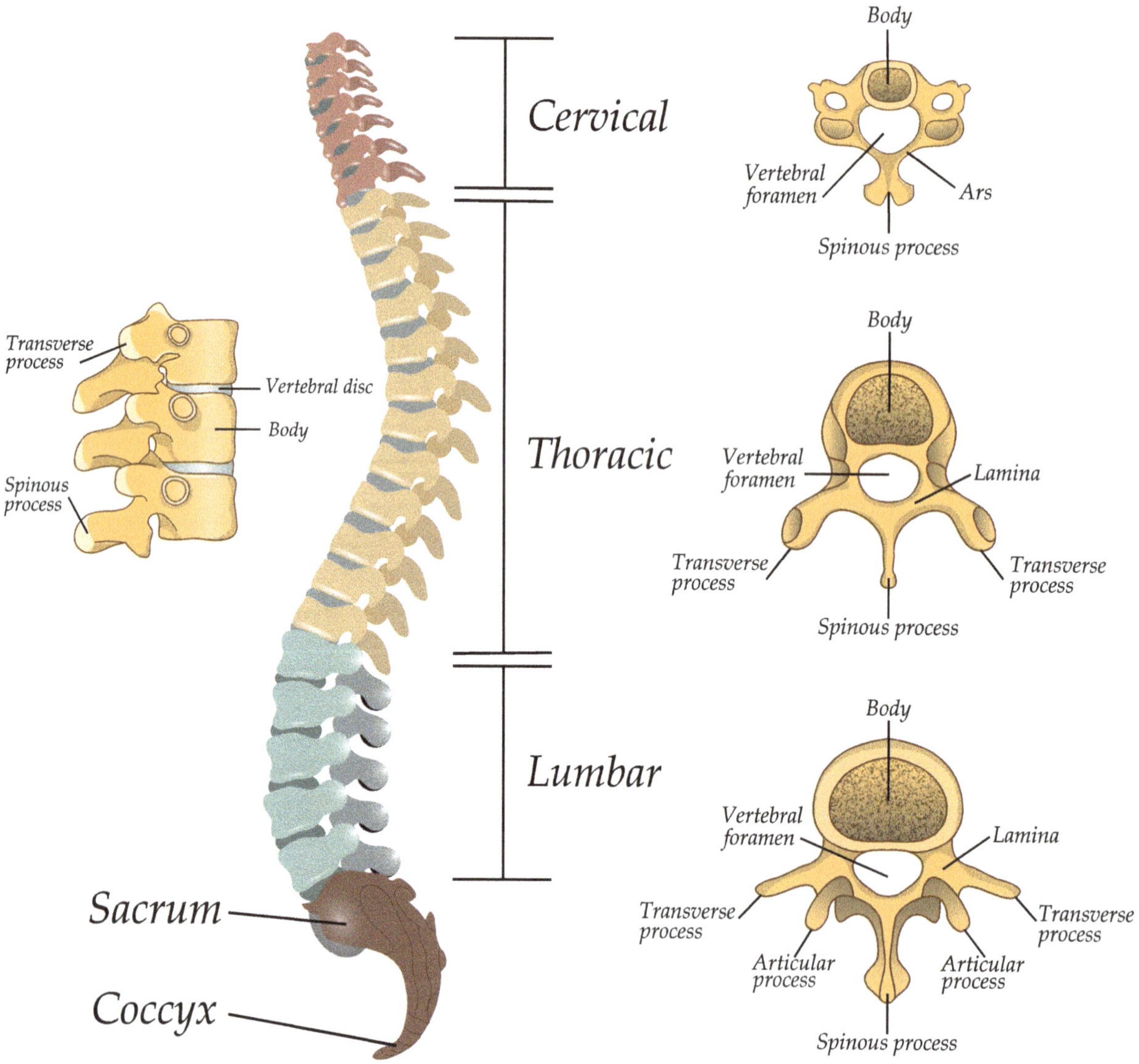

Differences between vertebrae

It is noted above how the vertebra hold the same essential attributes. However, there are significant anatomical and functional differences between the various areas of the spine. The table below outlines this:

Area	No. of vertabrae	Main Features
Cervical	7	• Smallest from all other vertebrae. • Encompasses and supports the spinal cord and skull. • Enables and facilitates various head movement (for example, rotation side to side, forwards and backward movement). • Facilitates load of the head which weighs 10-11 lbs (size of a bowling ball). • With correct posture, weight of head is positioned exactly above the center of gravity. • When the head is in a forward position, it is held ahead of the center of gravity. This results in physical pressure on the cervical spine. • Includes bigger and a higher amount of foramen (openings) to cater for nerves and blood vessels.
Thoracic	12	• Makes joints with the costal bones. • Can rotate notably more than the lumbar vertebrae.
Lumbar	5	• Is the biggest vertebrae in size and thus can support a larger load. • Has less capacity for flexion, extension and lateral flexion compared with the thoracic vertebrae.
Sacrum	5	• Forms a joint with the pelvis (SI Joint). • Is normally totally fused after 30 years of age.
Coccyx	3 to 5	• The most further down of all the vertebrae. • Is normally totally fused after 30 years of age.

Structure of the spine

Vertebral body is the thick oval segment of bone forming the front of the vertebra also called the centrum. The cavity of the vertebral body consists of cancellous bone tissue and is encircled by a protective layer of compact bone.

Collectively, the vertebral bodies comprise the bony building blocks of the spine. They are stacked on top of each other with a disc in between each one called the **intervertebral** disc. In the middle of each disc is a soft nucleus. The primary role of the intervertebral disc is to prevent the vertebrae from rubbing against each other and to absorb any shocks encountered from the impact of daily activities.

The **spinal cord** is the cylindrical bundle of nerve fibers and associated tissue which is enclosed in the spine and connects nearly all parts of the body to the brain, forming the central nervous system. Each vertebra has a hole in the body to allow the spinal cord to pass through and they also act as the outer protection layer of the spinal cord.

The **spinous process** is a slender bony projection from the back of a vertebra to which muscles and ligaments attach. It protrudes where the laminae of the vertebral arch join.

Human vertebrae anatomy

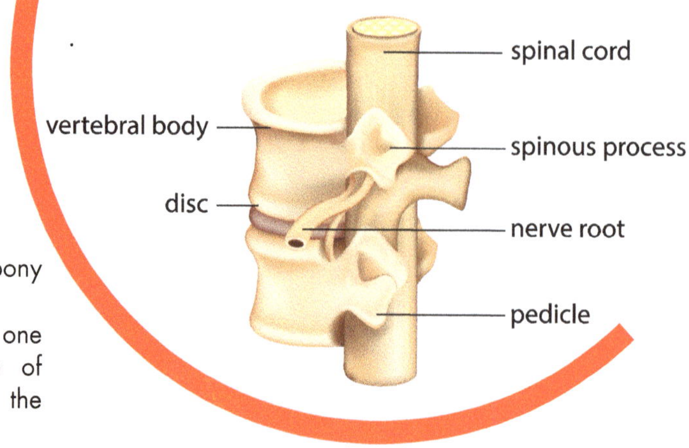

A **nerve root** is the initial segment of a **nerve** leaving the central **nervous** system.

The **pedicle** is a stub of bone that connects the lamina to the vertebral body to form the vertebral arch.

The spinal cord and nerve roots are enveloped within the secure framework of the spinal column. Paired nerves live in the intervertebral foramina (IVF). The spinal cord and nerve roots are most secure when the spine is in its optimum framework. The transmission of normal nerves is interrupted when any loss of this optimum spinal framework occurs.

Spinal curves

A 'normal' spine has four natural curves that are named after the vertebrae that form them: Cervical curve, Thoracic curve, Lumbar curve and Sacral curve.

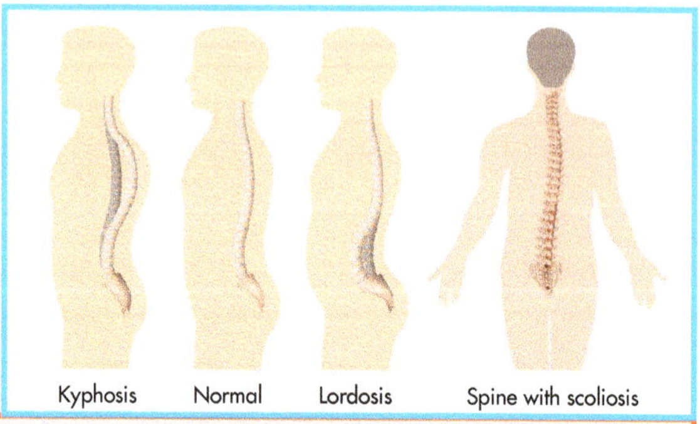

L2

Different types of spinal curves (kyphosis, normal, lordosis and scoliosis) and their impact on the body was covered in the Fitness Instructor Handbook. The curves of the vertebral column are significant for several reasons. They boost its strength, assist in keeping the balance upright, take the pressure of any shock whilst running and walking and assist in shielding the spinal column against fracture. The curves let the spine hold more weight and bear more pressure compared to when being upright. The reason for this is that the curves boost resistance to axial compression - in other words, the curves reduce the chances of squeezing of the spine from head-to-toe.

We have a C-shaped spine from birth. The spinal curves build resistance to various gravitational pressures that influence our body. The first spinal curve to grow in the womb is the cervical curve. It grows as the baby is learning to lift its own head.

Vertebral alignment and posture

It was stated previously that the likelihood of injury increases if the spine is held in a poor position. The standard curvature of the spine needs to be looked at so that what makes a 'good alignment' can be fully understood. The recommended state of curves is also known as a 'neutral spine'. This is where the vertebrae and linked structures have the least pressure on them. Excluding the sacrococcygeal, a typical adult's human spine has three considerable curvatures. These are known as:

- A posterior cervical curvature – a posterior concavity of the cervical spine
- An anterior thoracic curvature – a posterior convexity of the thoracic spine
- A posterior lumbar curvature – a posterior concavity of the lumbar spine

Deciding what the optimal posture is can be difficult because clothes and areas of the anatomy may conceal the vertebral column. Many specialists think that the ideal posture is when one can drop a line vertically from the ear through the middle of the shoulder and hip to an area near the ankle.

A healthy spinal curve is fundamental to core stability as covered in the *Posture and core stability* section.

Latest research has revealed that our healthcare system is evolving from one based on symptom and disease, to one that is function and performance-led. The latter focuses on the human body being renewed and preserved. Rectifying and preserving of the framework of the spine, especially the cervical spine, is most important when aiming to have the best health possible (Wassung, North-Rockland-Chiropractic-Life-Center).

The research journal 'Neurosurgery' conducted a study on patients who needed spondylotic myelopathy surgery. The findings from this study showed a marked improvement post-surgery, of patients who had a normal cervical lordosis before surgery, compared to patients who did not have a cervical curve pre-operation. (Naderi, cited in Wassung).

It is not within the scope of this course to go deeper into the anatomy of the vertebral column but further reading is recommended: Keith Wassung, Health Research Report #9 in https://www.nrchiro.com/.

Posture and core stability

The core is at the center of the whole body. It spans from the shoulders to the pelvis and it is often referred to as the body's 'center of power'. Core stability is the phrase used to describe one's capacity to make stable their core. So, if one has increased core stability, they have increased control over the status and movement of this particular part of their body. The majority of the movement power and stability stem from the core. As well as being the root cause of robust, focused movement, the core muscles provide a solid framework of stability. The core muscles provide security to the body, ensuring it is balanced when a person is moving and also when they are stationary.

It is fair to follow from this that the stronger one's core is, the more secure and balanced their movements will be. They will also be healthier. The more stable the core, the more control there is over one's status and movement of that part of the body. The core of the body often assists in movements in other areas, for example the limbs. So, improving the core will subsequently improve movements in other areas of the body. Core stability training for example, can help one's running capability. The core area is often referred to as a 'torso' or 'trunk', although the muscles that make up these parts are slightly different. Some of the main muscles attributed to core stability are transversus abdominis, multifidus, internal and external obliques, rectus abdominis, the pelvic floor muscles, erector spinae (sacrospinalis), and more so the longissimus thoracis, and the diaphragm. Some of the other muscles linked with core stability are gluteus maximus, latissimus dorsi and trapezius. Interestingly, the act of breathing, which includes activity of the diaphragm, can markedly affect the position and movement of the core. This is more notable when there is exaggeration in inhaling and exhaling. So how one breathes may have an effect on their capacity in regulating their core.

Core stability systems

Panjabi's model states that the core stability system is made up of three divisions. Panjabi states that spinal stability should be broken down into three subsystems. These are the active subsystem (muscles), the passive subsystem (joints and soft tissue) and the neural subsystem (neural conduction). It has been stressed that for the lumbar spine to experience long term stability, and to stop LBP from occurring, all the three subsystems must work well together.

Passive system

This category is made up of the most basic elements of the spine (Panjabi 1989).

- The lumbar vertebrae
- The joint capsules
- The intervertebral disc
- Ligaments surrounding the area

Many ligaments help with keeping the spine stable. The two key ligaments in play here are the posterior longitudinal ligament and the anterior longitudinal ligament. The posterior ligament spans across the spines length on the posterior areas. It helps to stop too much forward flexion. This is a fairly fragile ligament and tends to get injured if the forward flexion is abruptly executed. The anterior ligament runs along the spines length on the anterior areas and helps to deter the spine from hyperextending.

Active system

This system is made up of muscles which fix themselves to the spinal column, directly or indirectly. The muscles of the body are either classified as global (movement muscles) or local (stabilizers). Global muscles play an important role to facilitate movement of the limbs. They generate force to move the body (contract) and then relax.

The deep local muscles work independently from the global muscles. The main deep muscles are the transversus abdominus, pelvic floor, diaphragm and deep multifidus. These stabilizing muscles support the spine and pelvis by forming a muscular cylinder. They work together to stabilize the trunk. When the stabilizers can no longer work well together, muscle function changes. This could lead to pain around the lower back and pelvis. To compensate for the inefficiency of the deep muscles working together the global muscles are called upon by the brain for support. Without this support from the global muscles, the spine would not be able to resist the force of gravity and as a result collapse.

To relieve the body from back pain, the causes of the deep muscles failing to work well needs to be identified and fixed, usually through physiotherapy and specific exercises.

Neural Chapter

Neural control centers give neural responses from both systems and look after the timing of the core muscles which hold the spine. When a person goes to open a heavy door, a well-executed and relevantly timed chain of muscular contractions take place in the back to give the spine the stability it needs to open the door.

If the back is damaged after lifting or after a road traffic accident, the ligamentous system is injured. Subsequently, the active support system should be used to re-balance the spine. This entails making stronger, organizing and educating again, the musculature which surround this area. The muscles' capacity to contract and preserve stability is dependent on how fast and how accurate the information from joints and stretched ligaments is communicated.

Subsequently, the most relevant parts of the neural system are how accurate the movement is, and how fast the muscular contractions contract.

Core stability training

Core stability training focuses on both the local and global muscles. In short, good core stability assists in the reduction of injury caused by bad posture as well as reduce the chances of injury during physical activities.

Core stability exercise types will be covered later in *Chapter 4*.

Bones

There are five different bone types found in the human body as shown in the table below.

Classification	Description	Examples
Long bones 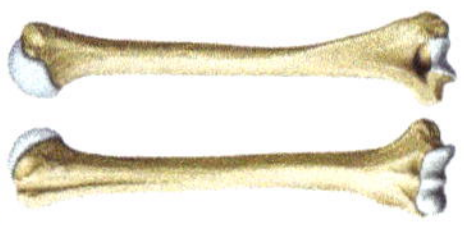	Long bones are hard, dense bones that are greater in length than width and slightly curved to give the body strength. They provide structure and mobility and act as levers. A long bone consists of a tubular shaft (diaphysis) and two extremities (epiphyses).	The tibia, fibula, femur, metatarsals, humerus, radius, ulna, metacarpals and phalanges.
Short bones 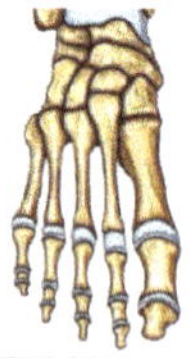	Short bones are almost equal in length and width, almost cube shaped and usually without epiphyses.	Carpals and tarsals.
Flat bones 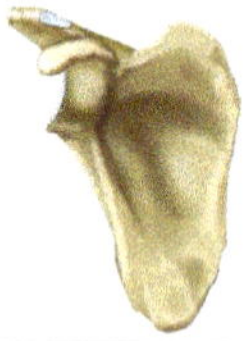	Flat bones are thin and sandwiched between two compact layers. They provide protection for internal organs and also allow muscle attachment.	Pelvis, sternum, scapula and crania.
Irregular 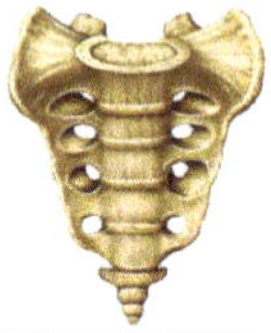	Irregular bones have complicated shapes and cannot be described as long, short or flat. Their shapes are due to the function they perform in the body, such as protecting an organ.	Facial bones and vertebral column or spine.
Sesamoid ('seed-like') 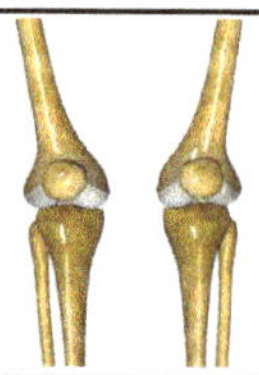	Sesamoid bones improve leverage and protect joints from damage. They tend to develop in areas where there is friction, tension and physical stress.	Patella.

The content of bone varies depending on its classifications. The image below shows structure of a long bone. The short and flat bone do not contain all the above.

Epiphysis is the expanded portion at each end of the bone. It consists of cancellous or spongy bone tissue giving the ability to endure compression.

Diaphysis is the shaft (longest part) of the bone. It is strong and dense and made up of compact bone, which makes this part resistant to bending.

Epiphyseal plate is a hyaline cartilage plate at each end of a long bone found in bodies that are still growing. Once a body reaches full maturity the plate is replaced by an **epiphyseal line**.

Articular (hyaline) cartilage is connective tissue covering the ends of the bone.

Periosteum is a tough fibrous sheath covering the entire bone, excluding the ends. It contains the supply for blood vessels that brings nutrients for bones and removes waste.

Endosteum is a soft thin connective tissue that lines the surface of the cavity of long bones.

Medullary cavity is the hollow tube down the center of the compact bone.

Bone marrow is the tissue comprising the center of large bones. There are two types – **yellow marrow** and **red marrow**. Yellow marrow facilitates storage of fat and the red bone marrow's primary role is the production of blood cells. Both types of bone marrow contain numerous blood vessels and capillaries.

Compact bone makes up the outer layer of all bones.

Spongy bone is also known as cancellous bone. These make up the inner layer of all bones. Spongy bone doesn't include osteons tissue. It is made up of trabeculae, which are lamellae. These are set out in the form of rods or plates.

Nutrient foramen is the external opening for the entry of blood vessels in a bone.

Nutrient vessel supply nutrition to certain special tissues, as arteries entering the substance of bone or the walls of large blood vessels.

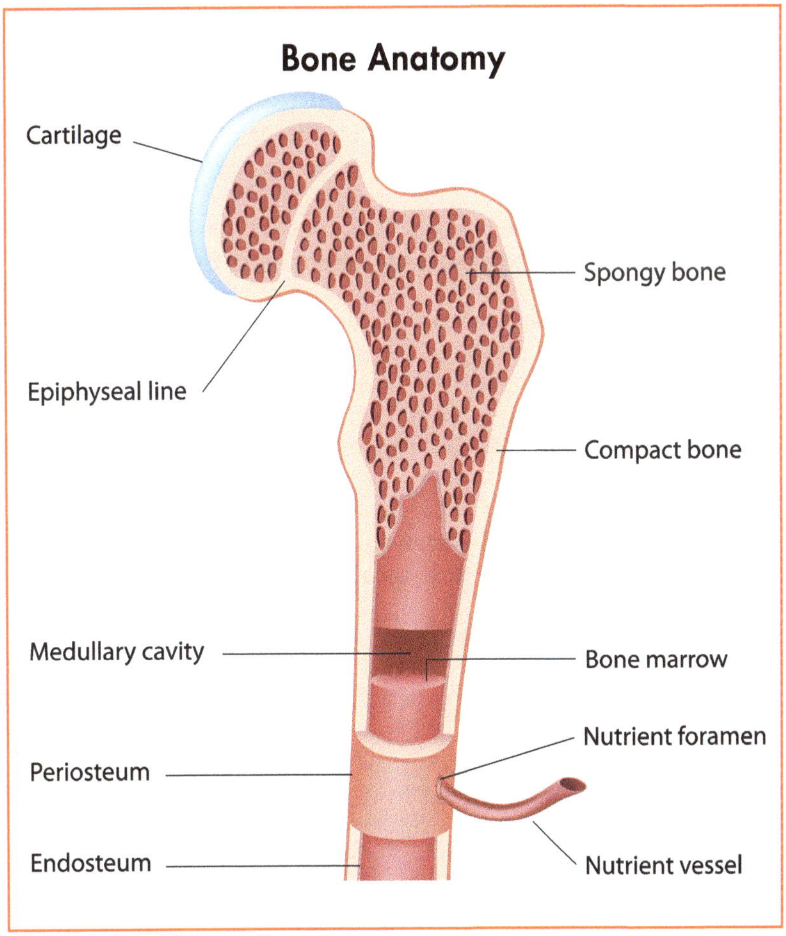

Ossification

The bone formation process is known as ossification which starts while a fetus is still in the womb.

Cells Of Bone Tissue

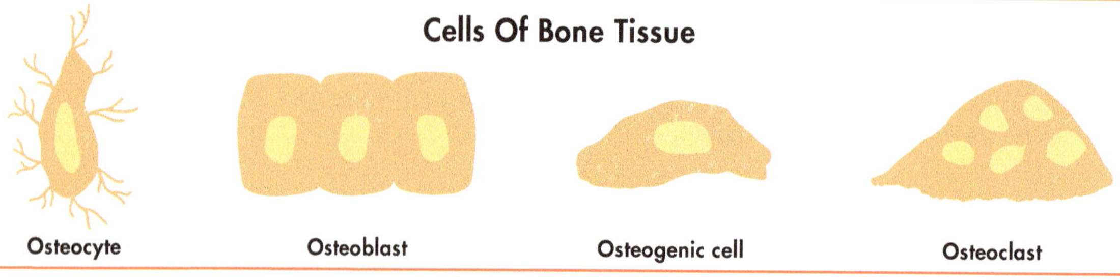

Ossification changes the different kinds of connective tissue into bone. The two key systems of ossification are known as intra-membranous and intra-cartilaginous ossification and these are dependent on which part of the body the cartilage is located at. Intra-membranous ossification is commonly referred to as mesenchymal ossification, as here, the bone is ossified from mesenchymal tissues. Membranous bones and dermal bones are just some examples of bones composed from intra-membranous ossification.

During intra-cartilaginous ossification, the mesenchyme has already been changed into a cartilaginous form. Here, ossification starts with the cartilaginous formations. These formations go through a process called chondrification. This is where the cartilaginous formation starts to harden as it grows and turns into bones. Intra-cartilaginous ossification takes place during a foetus' second month of existence and this process is maintained until birth.

Areas of the body known as 'centres of ossification' are where ossification begins. At each of these points, osteoblasts start the bone formation process. Osteoblasts can be defined as cells which form bones. They produce collagen and other materials that make up the bone material. Ossification is classed as either primary or secondary.

Primary: These centres of ossification first show before birth and are key in beginning the ossification process.

Secondary: The secondary centres of ossification most often show up after birth has taken place, but in some cases, they do appear before birth. Secondary centres are areas where the process of ossification occurs after it has begun in primary centres.

Elongation of long bones and remodeling

Long bones continue to elongate after birth through to adolescence. Elongation is achieved by the activity of two cartilage plates called epiphyseal plates, located between the shaft (the diaphysis) and the heads (epiphyses) of the bones. These plates expand, and cells multiply forming new cells, increasing the length of the shaft at both ends. The heads of the bone then move progressively apart. As growth proceeds, the thickness of the epiphyseal plates gradually decreases and fades, leaving a bony structure called the epiphyseal line, concluding the bone lengthening process.

The body continues to replace old bones with new ones throughout our lives maintaining the thickness and strength of bones. The osteoblasts and osteoclasts work hand in hand to accomplish this - bones are continually deposited by osteoblasts, while at the same time, they are broken down and digested by the body by osteoclasts.

Importance of calcium in bone development

Key to ossification are calcium compounds, without which ossification cannot take place.

Calcium is vital in preserving the amount of bone mass needed in order to support body structure. The body continuously uses calcium for organs like the heart, blood, muscles and nerves. The body loses calcium also, via processes, for example, hair loss, losing fingernails, sweat and skin. If one does not eat enough calcium to replenish what has been lost, the body removes calcium away from the bones. This makes the bones less strong, increasing the likelihood of fracture. It is also interesting to note that the diet of around 70% of the general public does not have enough calcium in it. This has varied repercussions depending on age and type of population group.

www.spine-health.com/conditions/osteoporosis

Calcium and osteoporosis

Children and teenagers in particular need to have sufficient calcium to help develop their growing bones and bone mass. Long term, a lack of the recommended amount of calcium significantly increases the risk of osteoporosis, a condition which causes the bone to thin and become brittle. Osteoporosis may also cause fractures to the bones in the spine. This can lead to chronic pain and even possible deformity. Osteoporosis progresses slowly over many years. Diagnosis is often delayed and only discovered when a person has a fall or unexpected pressure on it which causes a fracture.

Women and osteoporosis

Osteoporosis is more common in older females and so the risk of developing it is higher amongst this age group. The reason for this is oestrogen's major role in preserving bone strength. From the age of around 30, right through to the beginning of menopause, a small amount of bone is lost annually due to the effect of aging. Oestrogen levels are reduced when a woman reaches the menopause. The rate at which bone is lost increases now, for around eight to ten years. After this, the rate of bone loss reverts to the same rate as before menopause.

Injuries resulting from osteoporosis

The most common of these are fractures to the wrist, hip or spinal bones. Other bones it can affect are the arm and pelvis. Even a simple cough or sneeze can make the rib fracture or even cause a bone in the spine to be damaged.

The condition is not known to be painful for the sufferer, unless a fracture is caused by it. However, fractures to the spine are a usual cause of prolonged pain. The first sign of osteoporosis is often a fracture, and some elderly people develop a forward bending of their back, as spinal fracture makes it difficult to hold together the body's weight.

Causes of osteoporosis

As explained above, calcium deficiency is a major cause of osteoporosis as is menopause for women. But there can also be other reasons that can increase the risk of osteoporosis, as outlined below:

- Medical issues - e.g. inflammatory or hormone based ailments, or malabsorption issues
- If other family members (in particular parents) have had it
- Prolonged usage of certain medicines, may have an adverse effect on bone strength or hormone levels
- A low body mass index (BMI)
- Having a heavy drinking habit or being a heavy smoker

http://www.nhs.uk/conditions/Osteoporosis/Pages/Introduction.aspx

How to maintain strong bones

One should follow guidance below in order to keep bones strong:

- Consume sufficient calcium by eating calcium-rich food and drink
- Consume food that maximizes the absorption of calcium via the gut
- Maximize the retention of as much calcium in the bone as is possible
- Take steps to stop long term reduction of calcium from the bones

Joints

A joint is the connection of two bones, stabilized and held together by cartilage and ligament. There are a number of joints found in the body which allow us to accomplish movements on a day to day basis. Joints are surrounded by cartilage, ligaments and tendons.

Joints can be classified into three types depending on the degree of movement they allow.

Cartilaginous: Slightly movable bones like the vertebrae brought together by cartilage (fibrocartilage or hyaline). Cartilaginous joints allow more movement between bones than a fibrous joint but less than the highly mobile synovial joint.

Fibrous: Immovable and interlocking bones such as the plates in the skull. They hold bones tightly together usually with a thin layer of connective tissue. Example of a fibrous joint is the joint between our teeth and skull. The fibrous joints hold our teeth in their socket and unite the plates of the skull.

Synovial: The common and the most freely movable joints in the body are the synovial joints, which come in various sizes and configurations. Examples of synovial joint are knee joint, elbow joint and joint from thumb to wrist.

Synovial joints can be further broken down into six sub-groups as shown in the diagram below.

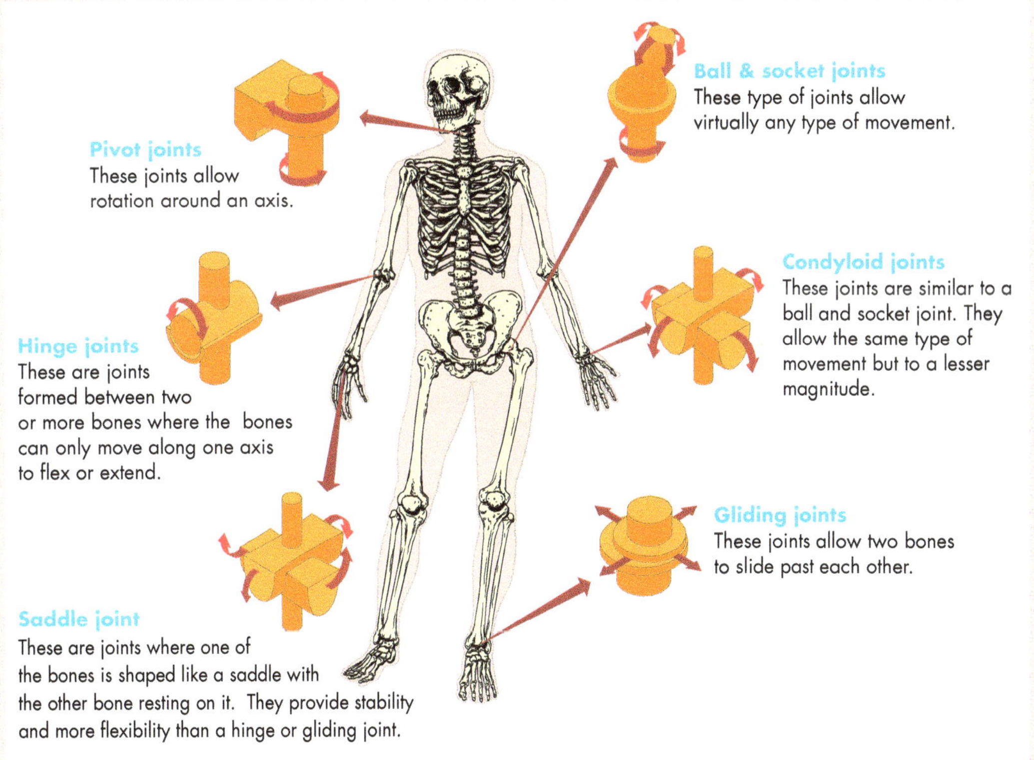

Activity

Activity 1.1: Add the missing labels

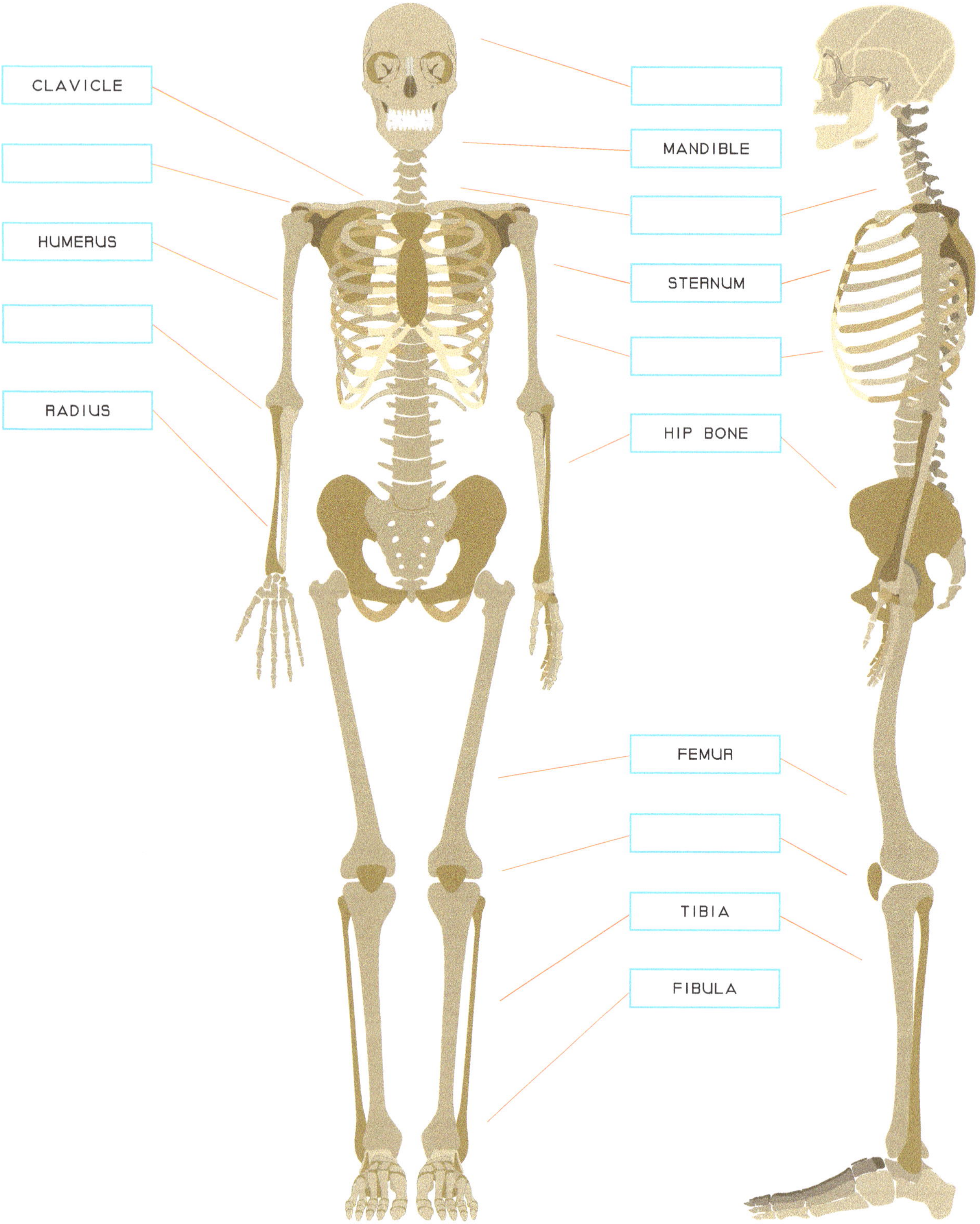

The muscular system

Muscles tissues are divided into three distinct categories, each of which performs a different function.

- Skeletal muscle (striated)
- Smooth muscle
- Cardiac muscle (myocardium)

Each muscle type contains cells that contract and relax in a rhythm that allows the muscle to perform the assigned tasks correctly. Each muscle type and its features were covered in level 2 but a closer look at the skeletal muscle system is required for certification in Level 3.

Skeletal muscle system

Skeletal muscles are the largest group of muscles in our body and personal trainers are required to have an in depth understanding of this system to support clients. Skeletal muscles attach to bones and have the main function of stabilizing the body's movable joints, contracting to facilitate movement. They are regarded as voluntary muscles because we have direct control over them through the brain sending signals to them. Contractions between skeletal muscles can vary to produce powerful, fast movements or small precision actions.

The skeletal muscles are made up of two different fibers. The fibers vary in their color and speed of contraction. Hence, one is known as a fast twitch muscle fiber and the other is known as a slow twitch muscle fiber.

Slow twitch muscle fibers - Type I

Slow twitch muscle fibers are red in color and are good for endurance activities like long distance running or cycling or running on a treadmill as they can work for a long time without getting tired. Muscles that contain a lot of slow twitch fibers are red, because they contain lots of blood vessels. Slow twitch muscle fibers rely on a rich supply of oxygenated blood as they use oxygen to produce energy for muscle contraction.

Fast twitch muscle fibers - Type II

Fast twitch muscle fibers are white in color because they don't use oxygen to make energy, so they don't need such a rich blood supply. They contract quickly and produce small amounts of quick energy, but at the same time they get tired quickly. These fibers are good for rapid movements like jumping to catch a ball or sprinting to catch a bus. The reason they get tired quickly is because of how fast they are contracting and consuming energy and hence we tend to feel exhausted after a short period of rapid movements like running and jumping.

Intermediary muscle fiber

The human body has the ability to form an intermediary muscle fiber if an activity requires rapid contraction, but at the same time it needs a small supply of oxygen. This is known as fast oxidative glycolytic.

Fast oxidative glycolytic - Type IIa

These fiber types are pink in color and have a stronger contraction rate than the slow twitch fibers but a slower rate than the fast twitch fibers making them an intermediary between the two main fiber types. The intermediary fibers have the ability to work under endurance due to the high level of mitochondria and capillaries compared to the fast twitch fibers. The fibers types are created by the body to support the slow twitch muscle fibers during the difficult stages of endurance events

Muscle tones

When muscles are in a state of tension and ready for action we call this the muscle tone. Regular exercise and training tones muscles and improves your body posture. Toned muscles can also make physical tasks easier, such as carrying shopping bags or gardening. As muscle tones improve, the strain on muscles, tendons, ligaments and the chances of injuries during physical activities are reduced.

Most of your muscles however are made up of a mixture of both slow and fast twitch muscle fibers. But some muscles in your lower leg and muscles in your back involved in maintaining posture contain mainly slow twitch muscle fibers. Muscles that move your eyes are made up of fast twitch muscle fibers.

The entire combination of various voluntary muscles form the skeletal muscle system. There are approximately 650 skeletal muscles in the human body. In an average adult man, on average 40% of their body content is muscle and for women it is about 30%.

A deeper study of skeletal muscle shows that each group of fibers are themselves made up of smaller parallel fibers. Several collagen based membranes are situated around the muscles, acting as a protection for them. The most outer part of these membranes is called the epimysium (epi comes from the word 'upon') and this covers the whole muscle.

Fascicles are groups of muscle fibers which are located in the epimysium. Every fascicle has an outer layer called a perimysium (peri means 'around'). Inside each fascicle are further bundles of muscle fibers. These are sectioned against each other by another membrane called the endomysium (endo means 'inside'). This adjoining material is repeated throughout the muscle fiber and outside it, where it merges together to make the tendons. These are robust tissues that fix muscle to the periosteum. It is this special structure of skeletal muscles that allows force to be generated to cause movement.

Main functional properties of muscle tissue which work towards force generation are:

Extensibility: Muscles have the ability to extend to its normal resting length and beyond to a limited degree.

Contractibility: Muscles have the ability to shorten (contract) quickly pulling the muscle ends closer together. The muscle ends pull on the tendons and bones to which they are attached, causing movements.

Elasticity: Muscles like elastic muscles can stretch and then recoil to its original length. However, like thick elastics can tear if overstretched, muscles too can tear if it's stretched beyond their capability.

Excitability: Muscles have the ability to receive and respond to stimuli via generation of an electrical pulse (neurotransmitters or hormones).

Force generation by muscles

Muscles are able to endure large force over a short time or prolonged force over a long period of time because it is able to consume the exact level of energy demanded by an action or series of actions. The body needs to produce energy for muscles to contract and during this production of energy heat is generated which is distributed throughout the body via the skeletal muscles system's blood supply.

To better understand how muscles generate force, it is necessary to look even closer at the fine structure of muscle fibers. Below the endomysium are even smaller rows of fibers called myofibrils. Contained within these fibers are the structures which are responsible for force production. The fibers are arranged in repeating units to form fasciculi and the fasciculi are then grouped together to form the muscle. Each fiber is connected separately to the nervous system so each can contract on its own.

Force generation are two contractile proteins called myosin and actin, often referred to as thick and thin filaments respectively. These are arranged in a series of compartments called sarcomeres that run the length of the myofibril.

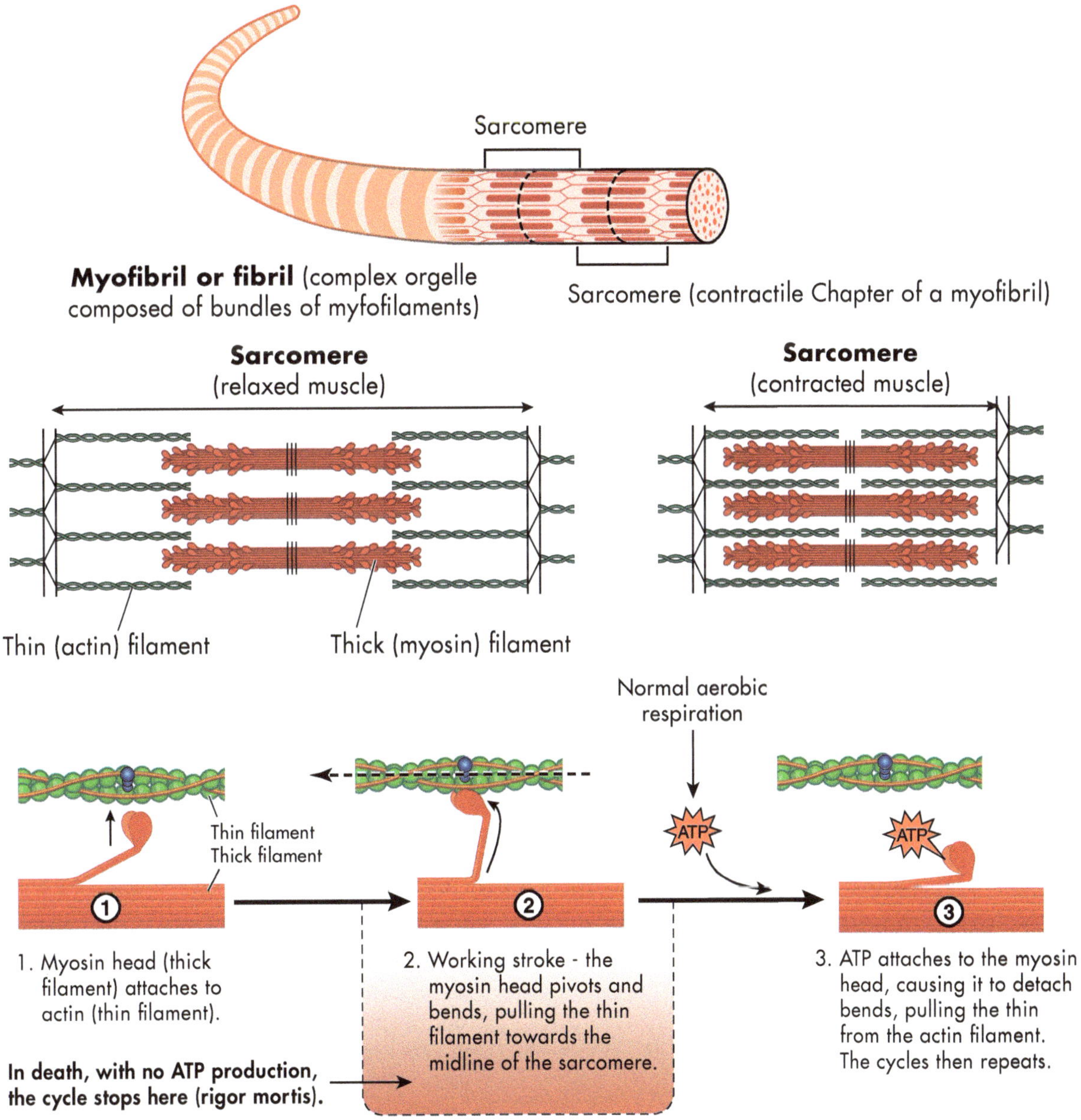

Myosin heads are hook shaped projections which hang off the myosin filament. When the muscle contracts, the heads latch themselves onto the actin filament as well as rotating. This results in the slimmer actin filaments being moved inwardly, moving the sarcomeres ends together. This process is known as the sliding filament mechanism.

Myosin and ATP

The force behind the myosin head is Adenosine Triphosphate (ATP – see *Unit 2B - Reaction of the energy systems to exercise*). The ATP molecule prepares the myosin for action by joining with the head straight away. The ATP's energy is shifted to the head. This action can be compared to a finger cocking a gun. In the appropriate setting, the myosin head will secure itself with the actin and will move around in a circle.

Troponin and tropomyosin

These are a fusion of other molecules that block the myosin connecting areas whilst they are in a calm state. These molecules need to be moved before the myosin can be connected.

Actin and calcium

The above action cannot happen without the presence of calcium. So even though the ATP may have supplied energy to the myosin head, it won't be able to connect with the actin without calcium.

Action potentials

The discharge of calcium is caused by the movement of electrical charges along the area of the muscle length (action potential). When dormant, the muscle membranes are negatively charged on the inside and have an exterior that is charged positively. The stored energy is released as required.

When an action potential reaches the point where the nerve joins the muscle (neuromuscular junction), the neurotransmitter (acetylcholine) is discharged. Subsequently, this has the effect of triggering sodium to drive through the muscle membrane., reversing the electrical action (depolarization). If sufficient enough, this would travel alongside the muscle fiber in the form of an action potential. This would prompt calcium to be discharged and the start of the sliding filament process.

Sarcoplasmic reticulum (SR)

These are an arrangement of tubes that circle the myofibrils. They operate as a storage unit to hold the calcium.

When provoked by an action potential, the SR discharges its calcium into the liquid around the myosin and actin (sarcoplasm). This calcium makes the molecule which is blocking the myosin to move away. This permits the 'prepared' myosin head to connect with the actin and rotate. This process cannot happen without the admission of calcium into the fiber. So, what prompts the SR to stream the myofibril with calcium? The stage at which nervous impulses arrive at the muscle needs to be looked at further in order to answer this question.

Muscular activity control

Understanding the core points of muscular contraction has enabled us to better understand how they produce force. However, some questions about the structure and how it is contained, remain unanswered. The following will seek to analyze the topic of muscular control systems.

Motor units

Muscles are composed of motor units; one motor unit is made up of a single motor neuron or nerve and the muscle fibers which it stimulates.

It was explained earlier how an action potential is triggered through the total length of muscle fiber, if the stimulus is strong enough. In particular, it will be dispersed through all the muscle fibers provided by one nerve. If therefore, the stimulus is not powerful enough, no action potential or muscle contraction will be produced.

Motor units can't change the level of force they trigger. They either contract as much as possible or not at all.

Muscle proprioceptors

The muscles hold two small neural sensors or proprioceptors. These assist in giving feedback and react to any changes from within the actual muscle. The first of these sensors is called a muscle spindle.

Muscle spindle

This is situated far down amongst the muscle fibers. It is attached firmly around each muscle fiber. As the length of the muscle changes, the 'coils' of the muscle spindle either come apart or are pushed towards each other, depending on whether the length is increasing or being reduced.

This change in length and subsequent variation in the muscle spindle encourages neural firing to the central nervous system (CNS) at the spinal position.

The outcome of an increased muscle and spindle length is a catalyst to contract that muscle. The extent of the contraction is dependent on the level of change in muscle length and the speed at which this change occurs.

Generally, the contraction will be greater as the range of motion increases and the quicker the muscle lengthens. This action is commonly known as the stretch reflex.

Golgi tendon organ (GTO)

The GTO is the second of these sensors and is situated in the tendon. The tendon is rigid which makes it impossible for the GTO to spot changes to the muscle length. However, what the muscle does is put pressure within the tendon when it pulls on the tendon that is connected to the bone.

The GTO is aptly situated in a place where it can quantify the pressure generated by a muscle. When stimulated, the GTO sends a sign to the spine. The spine then reacts to this by having a suppressive effect on that same muscle. This relaxed reaction triggered by the result of GTO firing is known as inverse stretch reflex.

The muscle spindles will continuously be stimulated as a person moves, because the muscles will be changing lengths at the same time as when movements are taking place. This process brings about a consistent supply of very important information to the CNS, regarding length of muscle and where body parts are in space. As well as this, the spindles also create muscular contractions which help with the movements being exhibited.

Just after the muscular contraction occurs, the GTO reacts by hindering the muscular contraction. This lets the opposing action to be executed.

So, in summary, the GTOs serve as muscle activity switches that turn on and off during exercise and when a person moves. It should be noted that when a muscle is undertaking its own action, the opposite muscles must be 'switched off' to let that movement occur. This prohibition of the opposing muscles is called 'reciprocal inhibition' or RI.

Reciprocal inhibition (RI)

This is a requirement for normal movement but RI can also be a reason for making muscles uneven and adversely affect muscular balance. Here, a closely-knit group of muscles send a constant message to the opposite muscle. This can result in them becoming constricted in the way they work.

Regular activity and training has been proven to boost the neural aspect of the muscular reaction. It has seen progress in the stretch reflex and the net reaction from the inverse stretch reflex. Training modalities like plyometrics have been formulated specially to advance the stretch shortening pattern, giving optimum results. Here, the muscle is taught to produce a higher degree of force with this form of training. The timing of the movement and the way in which the movement and speed works together is also enhanced, because the muscle spindles which assist muscle tissue are equipped to react better.

Many skeletal muscles are arranged as pairs or groups, working synergistically to perform movements. Other skeletal muscles work antagonistically, with one opposing the action of the other. The main working muscle is known as the **agonist** and sometimes for specific movements or activities such as exercising, other muscles may join in to help the agonist. These additional assisting muscles are called **synergists**. An example of muscles working in groups is when you do a leg curl. If the workload is heavy the gastrocnemius will assist the hamstring to perform knee flexion.

Muscular contraction types

Depending on how they contract, muscle contractions can be divided into:

- **Isotonic:** Isotonic contractions are those which cause the muscle to change length as it contracts and then causes movement of a body part. There are two types of isotonic contraction – concentric and eccentric.
- **Isometric:** Isometric contractions are those that do not change the length of the contracting muscle. During isometric contractions, the joints are not moving, however the muscles continuously contract.
- **Isokinetic:** Isokinetic contractions are those that produce movements at a constant speed. Isokinetic contractions are unlikely to occur during our day to day activities.

Several factors can affect muscle contractions such as:

- **Valsalva effects:** The impact of holding your breath at the wrong time during an exercise when the muscle in contracting.
- **Length of levers:** The longer a lever is during an exercise position the harder it is for the muscle to contract.
- **Gravity:** Depending on the position of the body during a movement, gravity may try and pull the body back.

Joints, muscles and movement types

It is important for a personal trainer to understand not only the movements possible at each joint type as seen in level 2, but also understand the muscles and muscle groups that are responsible for producing these movements. The table below shows the starting and ending point of muscles, the joints crossed and some of the exercise related to the contraction of these muscles.

Upper limb muscles	Start to finish	Joints crossed	Actions	Exercise examples
Biceps	Clavicle and scapula to radius	Elbow and shoulder	Flexion of elbow, supination of forearm, flexion of shoulder	Bicep curls
Triceps	Scapula and humerus to ulna	Elbow and shoulder	Extension of elbow, extension of shoulder	Tricep dips
Deltoids	Clavicle and scapula to humerus	Shoulder	Abduction, flexion and extension of shoulder and rotation	Dumbbell lateral raise
Pectoralis major	Clavicle and sternum to humerus	Shoulder	Adduction, inward rotation, horizontal flexion	Press up
Latissimus dorsi	Lumbar and sacral vertebrae, parts of thoracic vertebrae to humerus	Shoulder	Adduction, extension and inward rotation	Lat pulldowns
Trapezius	7th cervicle vertebra, thoracic vertebrae to clavicle and scapula	Shoulder girdle	Elevation, retraction and depression of shoulder girdle	Shoulder shrugs
Rhomboids	7th cervicle vertebra and thoracic vertebrae 1-5 to scapula	Shoulder girdle	Retraction of shoulder girdle	Pulling shoulder blades together

Lower limb muscles	Start to finish	Joints crossed	Actions	Exercise examples
Iliopsoas	Lumbar vertebrae and ilium to femur	Hip	Hip flexion	Kicks
Gluteus maximus	Ilium and sacrum to femur	Hip	Extension and outward rotation	Squats and kickbacks
Adductors	Pubis and ischium to femur	Hip	Adduction and outward rotation	Kicking across the body
Abductors	Ilium and sacrum to femur	Hip	Abduction and inward rotation	Side leg lifts
Quadriceps	Femur and ilium to tibia	Knee and hip	Knee extension	Leg extensions
Hamstrings	Ischium to tibia and fibula	Knee and hip	Hip extension and knee flexion	Hamstring curls
Gastrocnemius	Femur to calcaneus	Ankle and knee	Plantarflexion of ankle, flexion of knee	Heel raises
Soleus	Fibula and tibia to calcaneus	Ankle	Plantarflexion of ankle	Heel raises
Tibialis anterior	Tibia to first metatarsal	Ankle	Dorsiflexion of ankle	Heel digs

Trunk/core muscles	Start to finish	Joints crossed	Actions	Exercise examples
Rectus abdominis	Pubis to ribs	Thoracic and lumbar vertebrae	Flexion of spine	Curl ups
Erector spinae	Sacrum, ilium to thorax to ribs and vertebrae	Vertebrae	Extension and rotation of the thoracic spine	Side twists
Transverse abdominis	Iliac crest, lumbar fascia and cartilage of six interior ribs to xiphoid process, linea alba and pubis	Lumbar vertebrae	Support of internal organs, forced expiration	The plank
External obliques	Lower ribs to ilium	Vertebrae	Rotation and lateral flexion of spine	Oblique curls
Internal obliques	Ilium to lower limbs	Vertebrae	Rotation and lateral flexion of spine	Side bends lying down

Activity

Activity 1.2: What muscles have been used and joints have been crossed in these movements?

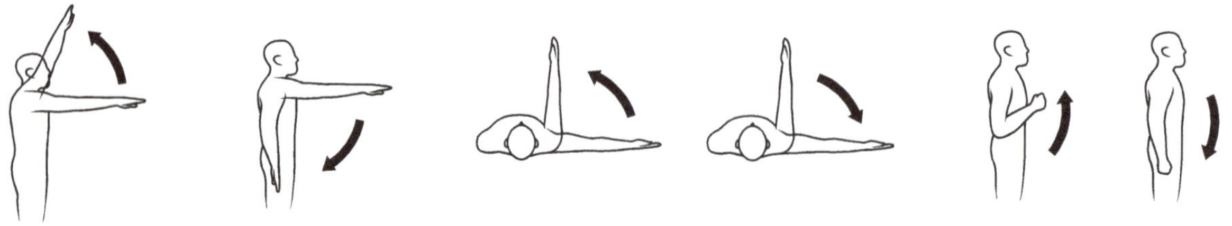

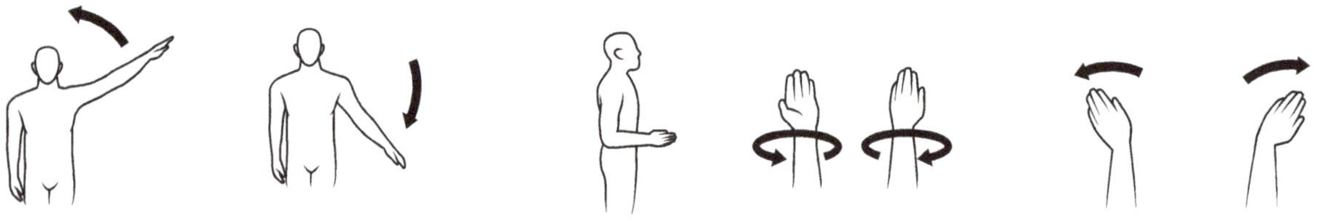

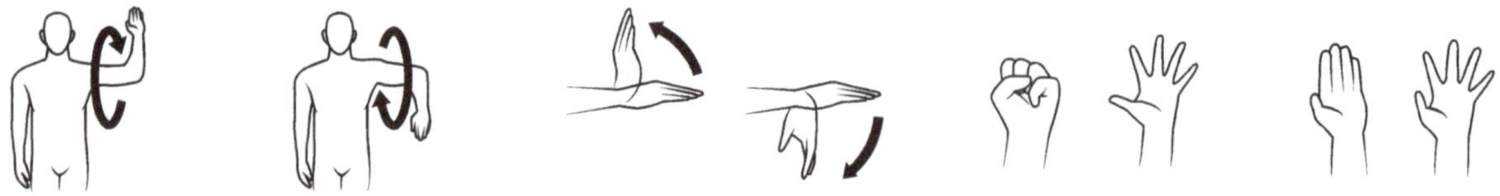

Anatomical terminologies

Body structures are often described by their position with respect to the center midline running from the head to between the feet of the body. It is important for a personal trainer to understand common anatomical terminologies.

Anatomical terminology	Description
Anterior	Front of the midline
Posterior	Behind the midline
Lateral	Away from the midline
Medial	Towards the midline
Superior	Upper part of the body
Inferior	Lower part of the body
Distal	Farthest away from the trunk
Proximal	Closest to the trunk
Superficial	Closer to the surface of the body
Deep	Farthest away from the surface
Sub	Underneath

These terminologies are often used to describe movements happening in different sections of the body known as the anatomical planes.

Anatomical planes

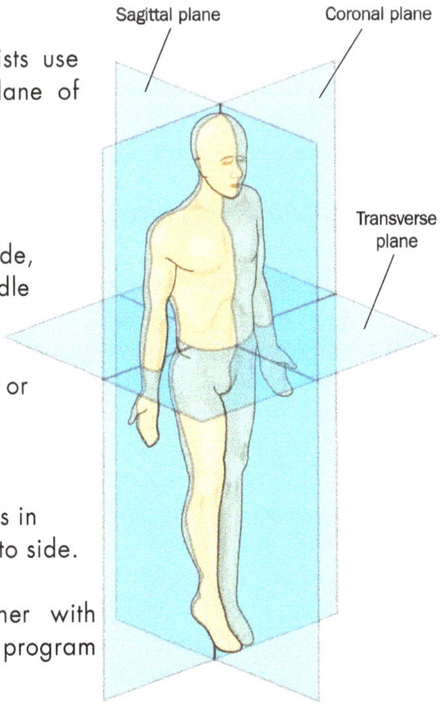

Scientifically, the human body is divided into sections and anatomists use a variety of terms to describe these sections depending on the plane of the dissection.

The main planes are:

- **The frontal / coronal plane:** Movements that go out to the side, away from the body (abduction) and then return towards the middle of the body (adduction) take place in the coronal plane.
- **The sagittal plane:** Movements that bring a body part in front or behind, such as swinging a limb, bicep curls and leg extensions take place in the sagittal plane.
- **The transverse:** Movements that rotates the body or part of it is in the transverse plane. An example is turning your head from side to side.

Understanding the movement planes can help a personal trainer with developing balance training program. A well co-ordinated program would include movements from all three planes.

The respiratory system

The respiratory system allows us to take in the required oxygen and supply it to the circulatory system. The oxygen we inhale is the oxygen that the circulatory system carries around our body. During oxygen transportation, waste substances are generated including carbon dioxide which is a potential threat if it is accumulated in high volume. Carbon dioxide therefore needs to be removed from the body, which we also do via the respiratory system when we exhale.

The close connection between respiratory system and the function of the heart in the circulatory system is referred to as the cardiorespiratory system.

The breathing process

The breathing process is in two parts. The first part is called **inspiration/inhalation** which is drawing air into the lungs (breathing in). The second part is called **expiration/exhalation** which means expelling air out of the lungs (breathing out).

Anatomical elements

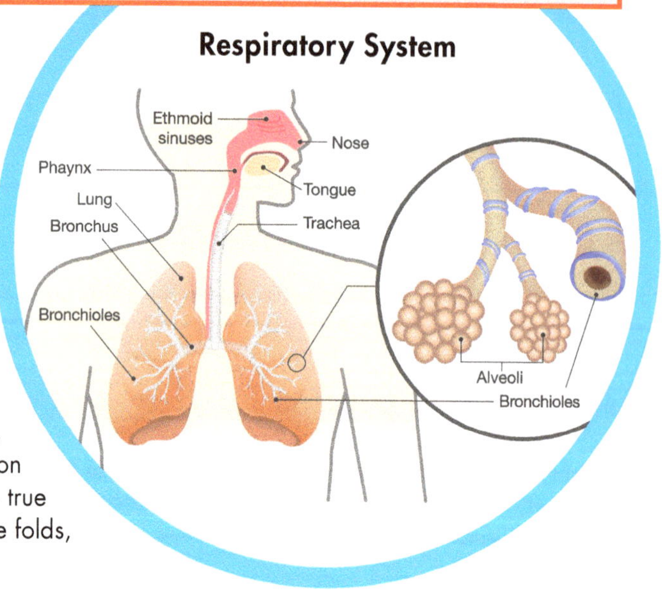

The main anatomical elements of the respiratory system are displayed in the opposite diagram. A small or nil amount of gas is exchanged in the many tubes that make up the upper portions of the system. At the top of the diagram, we can see that the nose and mouth warm and filter the air before it travels into the lungs. The pharynx is the back of the throat and starts from the region level with the nose and then to the larynx. The larynx, which is also known as a voice box, is a short section bordered with a number of cartilaginous folds. The true vocal chords, which are in the deep, inner part of the folds, produce speech and vibrate in order to do this.

Underneath the larynx, we have the trachea, which is situated just under the 'Adams apple'. They have specific ridges which can easily be identified when felt. These ridges are rings of hyaline cartilage which enable the trachea to be firm, stopping it from weakening when a person breathes in. The trachea branches out into two smaller sized bronchi at mid-chest level. These are organized into bronchioles. The smallest of these bronchioles are known as terminal bronchioles. This structure of vessels originating from the trachea can be best described as looking like tree branches.

The alveoli exist at the ends of the terminal bronchioles. These can be described as little formations that look like sacs. They signal the point at which the gases in the atmosphere join the supply of blood. There are around 300 million alveoli. Each one has extremely small blood vessels around them which enable the lungs to hold the title of having the greatest supply of blood from any other organs of the body. The alveoli have extremely thin membranes, which permit oxygen and carbon dioxide to circulate easily, in and out. A close-knit structure of capillaries cover the membrane of each alveolus. The blood from these capillaries convey the waste produced by respiration (carbon dioxide) through the alveoli. These are discharged when a person breathes out. While this is happening, oxygen spreads out of the alveoli into the bloodstream, and is taken back to the heart.

Controlling respiration

Breathing is regulated by the medulla and the pons, which are the respiratory control center of the CNS. This area of the body formulates the pattern for breathing and arranges the progression from inspiration (breathing in) to expiration (breathing out). During strenuous activity, movement receptors in the skeletal muscle send signals to the respiratory center. Chemoreceptors are sensors that identify chemical changes. Chemoreceptors that are in the medulla and arteries identify where levels of carbon dioxide have increased. The medulla reacts to this by raising the speed and depth of respiration. The cerebral cortex (area of brain linked with higher cognitive processes) also sends information to the medulla. This permits us to be in charge of our own breathing where needed.

At rest, our breathing rate is about 12-14 breaths per minute and the tidal volume is approximately 0.5 liters. As we exercise, our breathing rate increases because our need for oxygen increases. This means that the amount of oxygen we breathe in and pump around our bodies whilst exercising must change to maintain our body's required level of oxygen. To achieve this, we breathe faster and our heart pumps faster.

Activity

Activity 1.3: Summarize the respiratory process in your own words.

Inspiration

Expiration

The circulatory system

The circulatory system also known as the cardiovascular system is the process by which the heart pumps blood throughout the body as well as transports nutrients, hormones, oxygen and other gases to and from the cells.

The circulatory system is composed of:

- The heart
- Blood vessels
    - Veins
    - Arteries
    - Capillaries
- Blood

Although components of the circulatory system were covered in Level 2, it is worth having a closer look at them as strenuous activity places extra demands on the cardiovascular system. The muscles need for oxygen rises dramatically. Metabolic rates increase and more waste is produced. Use of nutrients increases along with the temperature of the body. The cardiovascular system has to balance these changes and accommodate the body's heightened demand in order to operate as smoothly as possible.

Components of the circulatory system

The heart

The main component of the cardiovascular system is the heart – a muscular pump and the organ which pushes blood into tissue through blood vessels. The heart muscles work continuously unlike any other muscle in the body. Each day the heart beats about 70 times per minute equating to about 100,000 times per day, pumping approximately 200 gallons of blood.

To allow blood circulation the heart has two chambers on each side, a number of valves, arteries and veins connected.

The heart chambers on each side are called the atria and the ventricles. The role of each atrium is to receive blood via the veins and then pump this blood down to the ventricle. The ventricles then generate the force to push the blood to the various destinations throughout the body.

The atria have relatively thick walls, whilst the ventricles have thick muscular walls to support the continuous function of circulating blood. The atriums are also smaller than the ventricles and do not have to strongly contract to pass blood to the ventricles. Even if they failed, blood will still passively flow to the ventricles.

Valves and arteries

There are four valves regulating blood flow through the heart via the chambers and the blood vessels (see next section).

1. The tricuspid valve in between the two chambers on the right regulates blood flow between the right atrium and the right ventricle.
2. The mitral valve in between the two chambers on the left allows oxygen-rich blood from the lungs to pass to the left ventricle from the left atrium.
3. The pulmonary valve controls blood flow from the right ventricle into the pulmonary arteries, which carry blood to your lungs to pick up oxygen.
4. The aortic valve clears the way for oxygen-rich blood to pass from the left ventricle into the body's largest artery called the aorta.

Anatomy of the heart

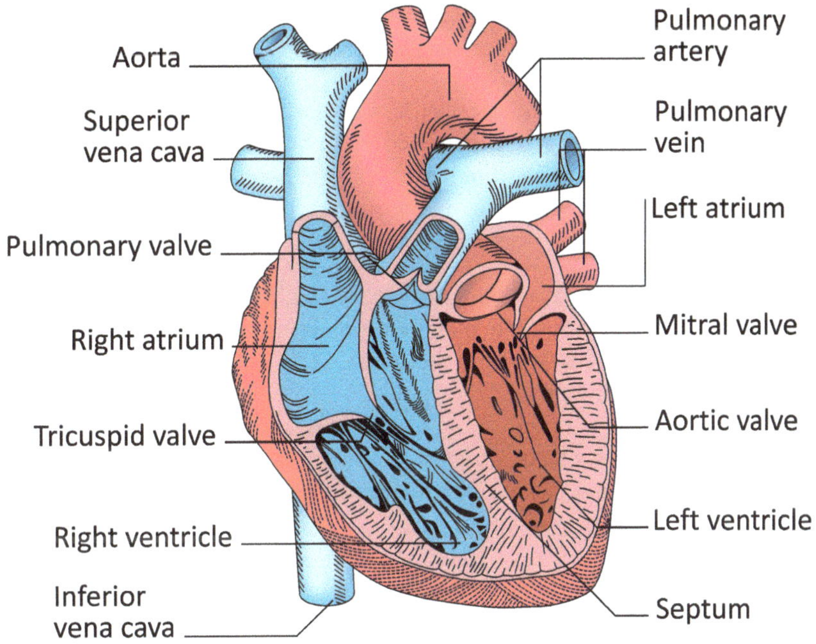

The blood vessels

Blood vessels are the transport system for the blood, from the heart to the rest of the body and back again. Blood vessels fall into different categories depending on their size and shape, but they are all connected in an ongoing loop. Blood vessels can be categorized into three groups:

Anterior	Arteries are blood vessels that can be described as muscular tubes, with thick walls that carry oxygenated blood away from the heart to the rest of the body. They are made of smooth muscles and elastic connective tissue which help maintain blood pressure at the required level. The elastic connective tissue is especially evident in arteries that are nearest to the heart. It has to cater for big waves of pressure amidst ventricular contraction. It then expedites the forthcoming flow of blood. Further down the circulation, the bigger elastic vessels make way for the medium sized arteries, where the larger share of soft muscle is apparent. These bigger numbers of soft muscle permit more vasoconstriction and vasodilatation. These alter the speed of blood flow to match the demands of the supplied structure. Arteries become smaller as they move away from the heart to the tissues. The smaller arteries are called **arterioles**. The aorta as seen above is the largest artery in the body, connected to the heart. The aorta is the main blood supplier to the heart itself. It has two main branches of blood vessels called **coronary arteries** and these arteries further branch into smaller arteries. Most major arteries branch from the aorta, except for the pulmonary artery which extends from the heart's right ventricle and branches into left and right pulmonary arteries to transport blood from the heart to the lungs.
Anterior	Veins are also blood vessels but tend to be smaller than arteries and structured to carry blood towards the heart. In other words, veins return blood to the heart whilst the arteries carry blood away from the heart. Veins come in various sizes and the smaller veins are called **venules**. The **inferior vena cava** is a large vein carrying de-oxygenated blood from the lower body to the heart and likewise the **superior vena cava** is a large vein carrying blood from the head, arms, and upper body. The walls of veins are made up of smooth muscle and connective tissue like arteries, but they differ in that they have thin fibrous walls and one-way valves to prevent backflow of blood.
Capillaries	Arteries continue to branch off and become thinner and finally become capillaries. These thinned out arteries have very thin walls and spread throughout the body, including the smallest area of tissue. The number of capillaries in the body outweigh any other types of blood vessels. Capillaries play an important role in the diffusion process of exchanging gases in the body.

More than one branch of the coronary arteries services most divisions of the heart. If the flow of blood is reduced through one vessel, (for example through heart disease), then the blood supply to the tissues can be preserved via collateral vessels.

Coronary arteries and heart disease

The coronary arteries are well known for their links with heart disease. Blood flow via these arteries and arterioles are vital to maintain the health of the heart. Many elements can result in harm to these arteries and loss of function. This results in limited blood flow to parts of the heart.

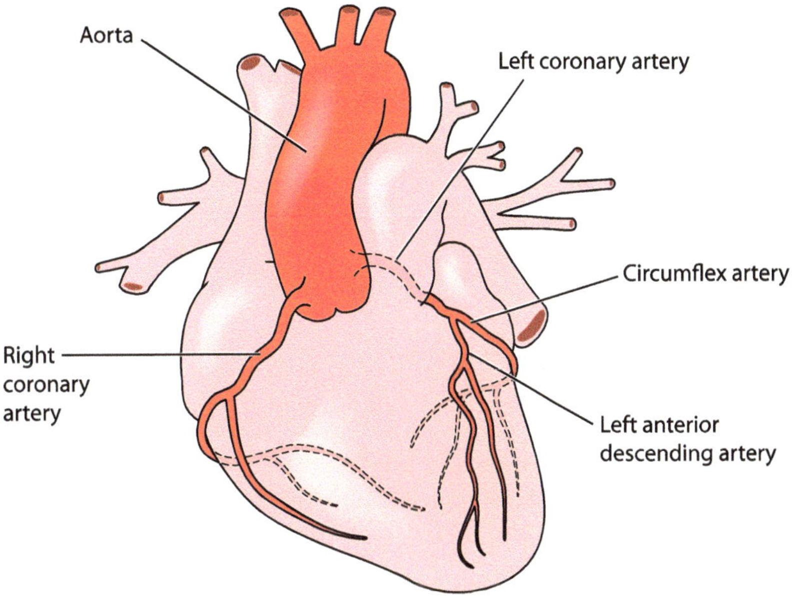

The thin epithelial membrane borders the inside of the arteries. When the internal structure of the heart permits damage to occur to these arteries, mineral, protein and fatty stores can increase in the walls of the arteries.

These hard, fatty stores decrease the plasticity of the arteries. Therefore, they are unable to stretch by reacting to blood flow and raised blood pressure may occur. If not reviewed, these fatty stores can become so big that they can dangerously limit blood flow by obstructing the inside of the artery. This could cause an unexpected heart attack from one of these stores bursting, with their components being released, starting a fast clotting action to halt blood loss from the artery. A clot that is forming may stop the flow of blood, resulting in a lack of oxygen to a division of the heart. The body reacts to this by immediately raising the heart rate to eject the blockage and restart blood flow. This extremely fast beating heart lacking oxygen is what is felt during a heart attack.

The blood vessels

Blood is circulated around the body during the cardiovascular process. It is a specialized body fluid with many different functions, including:

- Transporting oxygen and nutrients to the lungs and tissues
- Carrying cells and antibodies that fight infection
- Forming blood clots to prevent excess blood loss
- Regulating body temperature
- Assisting with the removal of waste products from the body

L2

Blood is composed of different components:

- **Plasma:** Liquid component
- **Erythrocytes:** Red blood cells
- **Leukocytes:** White blood cells
- **Thrombocytes:** Platelets

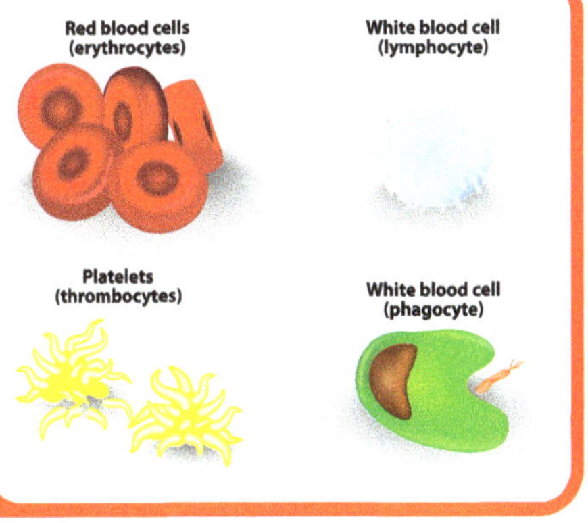

The cardiac conduction system

An efficiently working heart needs the contraction of the several chambers to work methodically and harmoniously. For this to happen, the heart has a smoothly operated 'conduction system'. This sends the action potential (electrical activity) through the heart tissues so that they can contract in a specific order.

This sequence is comprised of five components:

1. The sino-atrial (SA) node
2. The atrio-ventricular (AV) node
3. The bundle of His
4. The left and right bundle branches
5. The Purkinje fibers

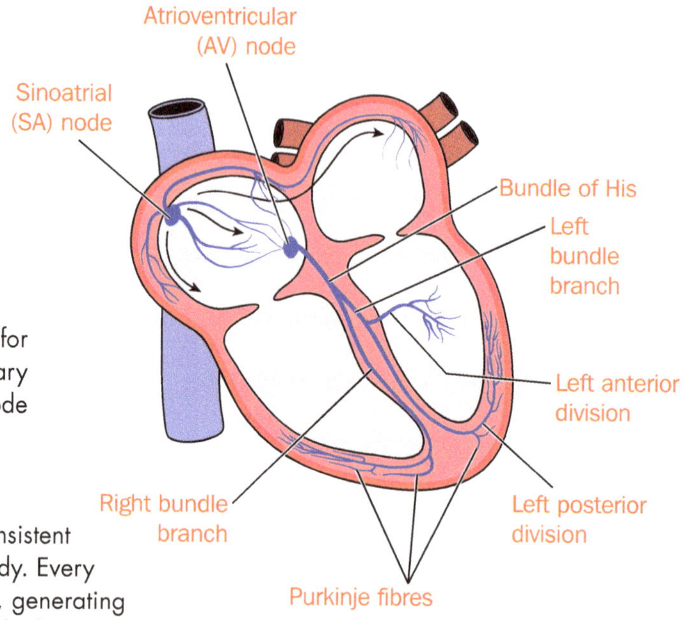

The SA node can be likened to a kind of pacemaker for the heart. Permanent Pacemakers (PPMs) and Temporary Pacing Wires (TPWs) are utilized when the SA node stops working properly.

The SA node discharges electrical impulses at a consistent speed. This rate is governed by the demands of the body. Every impulse goes through the myocardial cells of the atria, generating a surge of contractions which quickly advance through both atria.

ECG and electrical activity of the myocardium

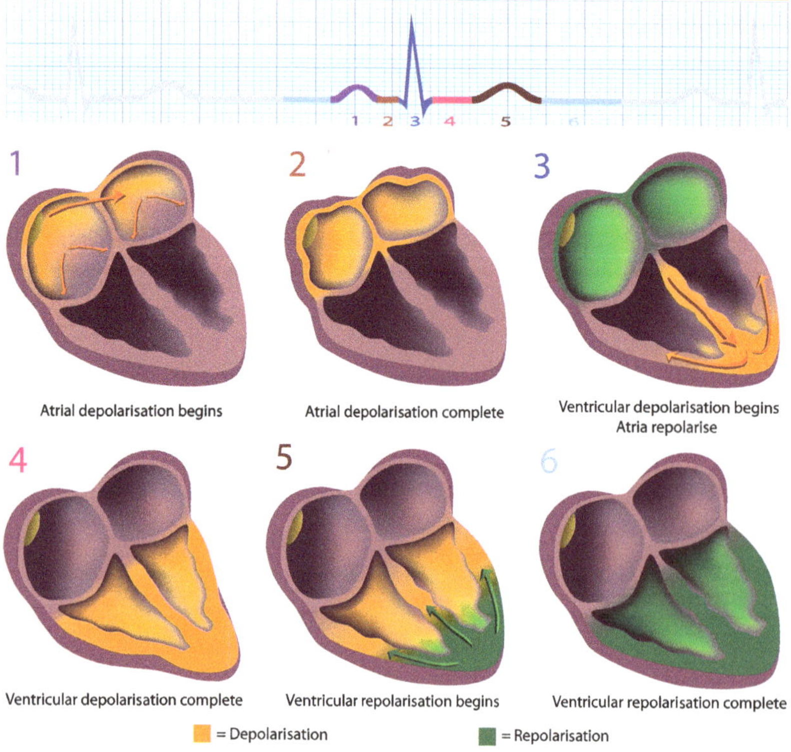

The electrical impulse from the SA node ultimately reaches the AV node. It is momentarily delayed, to allow the contracting atria sufficient time to send all the blood into the ventricles. Once the atria are vacated of blood, the valves between the atria and ventricles close. It is at this point that the atria start to refill and the electrical impulse goes through the AV node and Bundle of His into the Bundle branches and Purkinje fibers.

While the ventricles contract, the right ventricle sends blood to the lungs. Here, carbon dioxide is released and oxygen is absorbed. At the same time, the aorta receives blood from the left ventricle, where it travels into the coronary and arterial circulation.

At this stage, the atria are full and the ventricles are empty, with the valves in between them closed. The SA node is about to release another electrical impulse to repeat the process. However, the third section to the process means that it must first recharge before it can do this again. This is because the SA node and AV node share only one stimulus which can't be used at the same time. So, every time the nodes release an impulse, they must recharge before doing so again.

The SA node recharges at the same time as the atria are refilling. The AV node recharges when the ventricles are being filled again. This process enables the heart to function smoothly without any pauses. This system takes less than a third of a second.

The timings of the three various levels are formulated on a heart rate of 60 beats per minute (bpm) or one beat per second.

The cardiac cycle

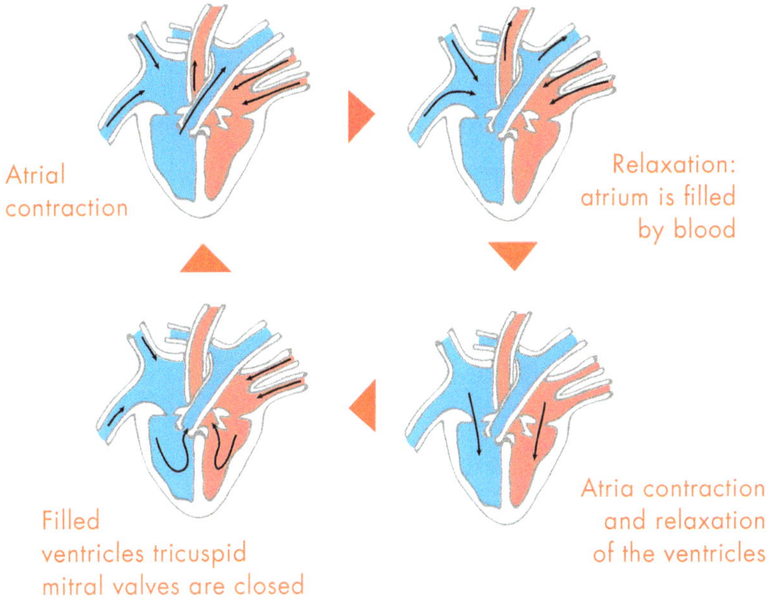

This is used to describe the chain of events which occur when the heart beats. As it beats, the heart spreads blood via the pulmonary and systemic circuits of the body. This cycle has two parts to it. The first is the diastole phase where the ventricles of the heart are placid and the heart is filled with blood. The second phase is known as the systole phase where the ventricles contract and send blood to the arteries.

Once the heart is filled with blood and this blood is pumped to the body, one cycle is completed. The descriptions outlined below detail the route of the blood once it goes into the heart, is pumped to the lungs, travels back to the lungs and is sent out to the rest of the body. It must be noted that the first and second diastole stages occur concurrently and this is also the case for the events of the first and second systole stages.

Cardiac cycle: 1st diastole phase

- Atria and ventricles are placid and the atrioventricular valves are open
- De-oxygenated blood from the superior and inferior vena cava travel into the right atrium
- Open atrioventricular valves permit blood to go through the ventricles
- SA node contracts, prompting the atria to also contract
- The right atrium vacates its contents into the right ventricle
- The tricuspid valve stops the blood from traveling back into the right atrium

Cardiac cycle: 1st systole phase

- The Purkinje fibers send signals to the right ventricle, prompting it to contract
- Atrioventricular valves close and semilunar valves open
- De-oxygenated blood is sent into the pulmonary artery
- Pulmonary valve stops the blood from being pumped back into the right ventricle
- Pulmonary artery conveys the blood to the lungs
- Blood picks up oxygen and is sent back to the left atrium of the heart by the pulmonary veins

Cardiac cycle: 2nd diastole phase

- Semilunar valves close and the atrioventricular valves open
- Left atrium is filled by blood from the pulmonary veins. At the same time, blood from the venae cavae fills the right atrium
- The SA node contracts again, prompting the atria to contract
- Left atrium is emptied into the left ventricle
- The mitral valve stops the oxygenated blood from being pumped back into the left atrium

Cardiac cycle: 2nd systole phase

- Atrioventricular valves close and the semilunar valves open
- Purkinje fiber sends signals to left ventricle, making it contract
- Aorta receives oxygenated blood
- The aortic valve stops the oxygenated blood from being pumped back into the left ventricle

The aorta subdivides out to spread oxygenated blood throughout the body. Deoxygenated blood is sent back to the heart through the venae cavae.

Cardiac output and stroke volume

The heart beats on average about 70 times per minute, pumping blood with each beat. When the heart beats, the heart's chambers (atria and ventricles) alternately contract and relax in a sequence (the cardiac cycle as described above).

The amount of blood pumped out by the ventricle in one minute is known as the cardiac output and the amount of blood pumped by a heart per beat is known as the stroke volume.

Cardiac output = stroke volume x heart rate

The heart's pacemaker

The cardiac muscle unlike other muscles does not require signals from the nervous system to contract. The heart has its own pacemaker - a cluster of cells called sinoatrial node, located near the top part of the atrium. The pacemaker is genetically programmed to produce electrical cells to cause heartbeats. When the pacemaker is stimulated, the cardiac cycle described above is triggered.

Controlling the heart

The autonomic nervous system controls the heart. The workings of the autonomic system can be categorized into two – the sympathetic system, which gets the body ready for activity, and the parasympathetic system, which gets the body to rest again. The sympathetic system increases the productivity of the heart whereas the parasympathetic system reduces output. The autonomic system is covered in more detail in the next section.

As per demand, (for example, when one starts to walk briskly) the autonomic system can boost the amount of work done by the heart, through two cardiac accelerator nerves, operating from the medulla of the brain. These prompt the SA node to bring about action potentials more speedily. It does this while also making the myocardium contract more powerfully (i.e. the heart beats faster and with more force).

In comparison, whilst in a resting position, the vagus nerve (also operating from the medulla) makes the SA node produce action potentials more slowly. This subsequently reduces the heart rate. The SA node normally produces 90-100 beats per minute. The effect of the vagus nerve normally lowers this to about 60-85 beats per minute. However, a trained athlete may see a drop to below 30 beats per minute (Wilmore and Costill, 2004).

L2

Dual circuits of blood

The cardiovascular system is composed of two circulatory paths:

- **Pulmonary circulation:** The circuit beginning from the right side
- **Systemic circulation:** The circuit beginning from the left side

The circuits are interlinked and operate as a whole rather than separate circuits to ensure we have a seamless flow of blood throughout the body at all times.

As blood circulates, its pressure drops. Pressure is at its highest point in the aorta when it receives blood from the left ventricle, but then the pressure drops steeply and by the time the veins are reached, the bold pressure is only a fraction of its starting point.

Blood pressure is covered in more detail in *Chapter 3B,* including classifications of blood pressure measurements and associated health risk. The autonomic system is covered in the sections to follow.

The nervous system

As exercise activity represents one of the biggest challenges to the internal environment of the human body, it is important to understand the role of the nervous system and endocrine system at the start of this course, as these systems contribute to how movements are performed and how the body responds to actions, internal and external.

Homeostasis is the maintenance of a balanced internal environment. The body preserves homeostasis via the nervous and endocrine systems. The nervous system does this by using a network of nerves. Conversely, the endocrine system maintains homeostasis via a number of glands and hormones, also known as chemical messengers. The human body's senses constantly react when it takes part in an activity with regards to the position of the limb, force generation and the outcome. In other words, it can relay whether the movement was successful, or poorly executed. Other senses can be used and a new movement can then be attempted. Training and practicing regularly result in changes in the central nervous system. This increases the control over movements, resulting in more swift and precise movement and an improved performance overall.

Even though the systems are different, they work in tandem with one another, with one instigating a response from the other. Each will be explained below.

As human beings, we have complicated nervous systems made up of a complexly wired brain, spinal cord and nerves. The purpose of the nervous system is to make sure there is communication between all parts of the body. It also acts on external information received and responds appropriately by controlling bodily actions.

Below is a diagram detailing the many nerves from the brain which make up the nervous system.

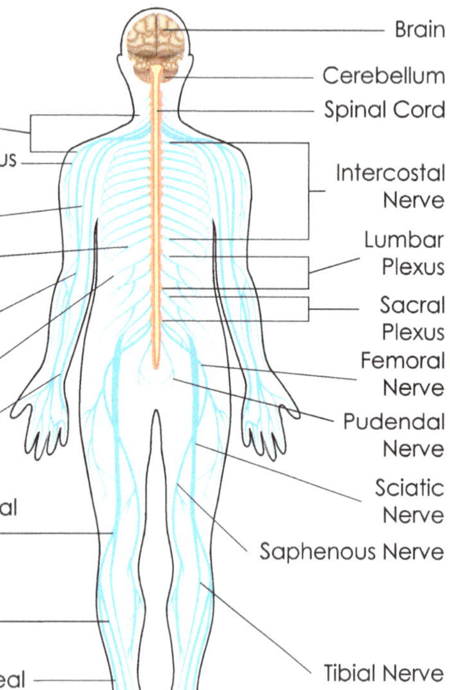

A simplified way of explaining the nervous system is to see it as a communication network, made up of three main components; sensation, analysis and response (Tortora and Grabowski, 1996):

1. **Sensation:** This is where a huge number of sensors are spread across the body. These constantly collect information about the internal environment, for example blood CO_2 levels and the external environment, for example air temperature.
2. **Analysis:** Sensory input reflects a huge amount of information. The nervous system analyses this information, interprets it and gives the relevant response. Many of these reactions are automatic, with no voluntary control over them.
3. **Response:** The correct and most relevant response must be initiated. For example, a muscular contraction or a glandular secretion.

The nervous system consists of two parts: **the central nervous system (CNS) and the peripheral nervous system (PNS)**

The central nervous system (CNS) is the main processing center of the human body. It receives information from and sends information to the peripheral nervous system. The two main organs of the CNS are the brain and spinal cord. The brain processes and interprets sensory information sent from the spinal cord.

A system of hollow cavities known as ventricles can be found inside the CNS. Cerebral cavities found in the brain are continued into the central canal of the spinal cord. A cerebrospinal fluid, produced by the choroid exus, fills the ventricles. The fluid helps to protect the spinal cord from trauma by cushioning around them, as well as assisting with the circulation of nutrients going to the brain.

The peripheral nervous system (PNS) consists of all the nerves and nerve cells located on the outside of the central nervous system. It is responsible for relaying information from the brain and spinal cord to the rest of the body and in reverse from the rest of the body to the brain and spinal cord.

Peripheral nerves help us perform voluntary and involuntary actions. Actions such as picking up a plate, clicking your fingers or lifting shopping bags are all considered voluntary actions as we are aware of what we are doing. Involuntary actions on the other hand, are carried out without our control, such as our heart beating and our intestines digesting.

The autonomic nervous system (ANS)

In addition to the central nervous system and the peripheral nervous system, there is also the autonomic nervous system which controls some mechanisms within the body, like heart rate and blood pressure. The ANS is made up of two parts, the sympathetic and parasympathetic. Both parts do the same job of supplying organs like eyes, heart, lungs, stomach, intestines, liver, kidneys, bladder and glands. However, they have opposing effects on these organs due to differences in their activating chemicals. Exercise wise, the sympathetic part seeks to increase activation levels in preparation for activity, whereas the parasympathetic part seeks to reduce levels of activation during rest and recovery periods. This is relevant to the workings of the heart during exercise because the sympathetic system increases the hearts productivity.

The following figure explains the role of each part of the autonomic system.

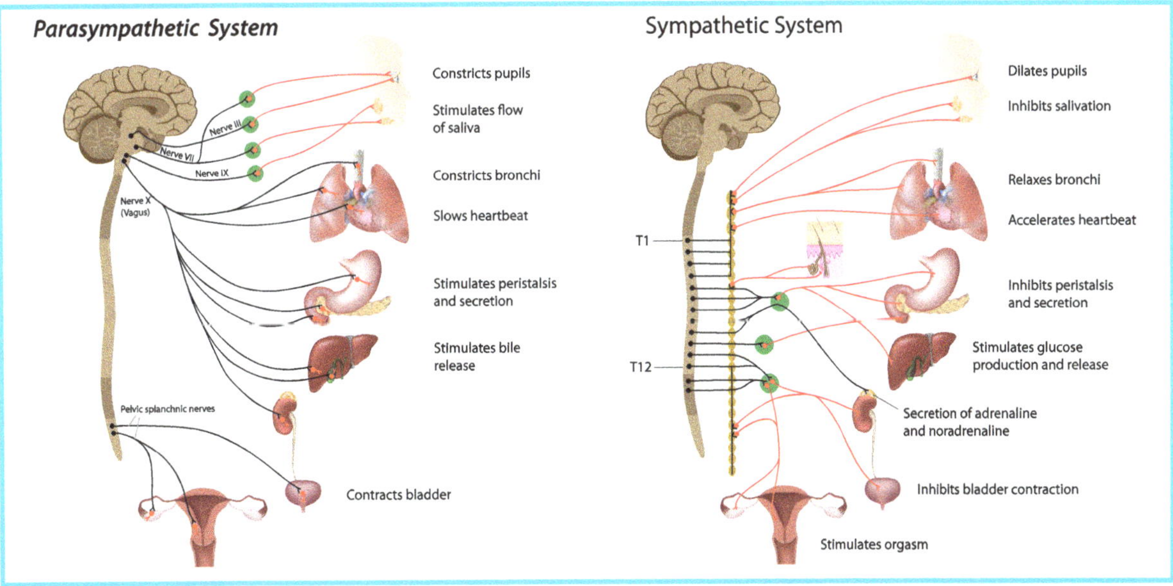

Neurons

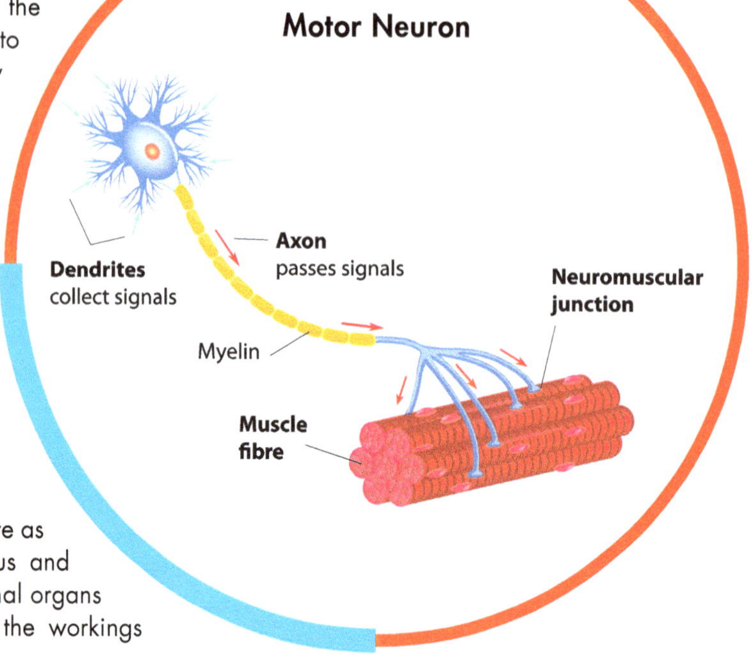

The human body contains millions of sensory receptors that send information to the Central Nervous System to allow it to control and co-ordinate all bodily functions. To understand this better, it is best to look more closely at one of its most core units – the neuron. A neuron or nerve acts like a virtual wire, letting impulses move from one area of the body to another. Distances traveled could be short, for example from the one end of the CNS to another, or long, e.g. from the feet to the lumbar area of the body. Whatever the case, all neurons contain the same key anatomical features.

A neuron is made up of the same structure as most other cells in the body, a nucleus and some organelles (the latter are the internal organs of each cell and play a key role in the workings of a cell).

Neurons have within them systems which consist of **axons** and **dendrites**. Axons send signals away from the cell body and appear to be long and cylindrical. The nerve impulses are conducted along this. The axon has a unique covering which is a protein compound and known as a **myelin sheath**. Its role is to act as a form of insulation and it is essential for speedy conduction of impulses. **The axon terminal** lies at the end of the axon. This acts as a boundary between the neuron and other cells like the muscle cells.

Dendrites allow signals to be carried towards the cell body and are spread out. They are likened to branches of a tree ('dendro' relates to tree). These 'feel' or sense the stimulus, for example heat or pain.

Neurons are classified as either **motor, sensory or interneurons**. Motoneurons transmit information from the CNS to the organs, muscles and glands. Sensory neurons however, convey information from the internal organs and outer stimuli to the CNS. The job of the interneuron is to conduct signals between the motor and sensory neurons.

There are various kinds of proprioceptor which give different sensory data for the nervous system to react to. Muscle spindles measure muscle length and golgi tendon organs measure more the muscle tension. Muscle spindles are located further in the muscle fiber. These spindles can perceive shifts in muscle length as well as the speed in which this change happens. Their response is to generate muscular contractions. Essentially, the stretch reflex has a protecting feature which helps stop tearing of the muscles which often occurs by excessive stretching of a muscle. The spindle can be described as a small component which is encased securely around separate muscle fibers, comparable to a coiled spring. When the muscle's length changes, the 'coils' of the muscle spindle are taken apart or pushed towards each other, according to whether the muscle is being shortened or being extended in length. Neural firing is instigated when a muscle is quickly extended in length. Consequently, an action potential is transmitted from the spindle to an excitable interneuron in the spinal cord. This sends a signal to a motor neuron, which transmits an action potential to the muscle. This results in the muscle contracting quickly and shortening back up to avoid damage. This reaction is called the 'stretch reflex'. It is necessary to acknowledge that the muscle spindles activate in proportion to the pace of stretch. They also fire at a greater rate the quicker the lengthening of the muscle.

It is useful to know that when a muscle is taken to a stretch position during a static stretch, a firing of the muscle spindles is unavoidable and the muscle subsequently contracts against the stretch. The purpose of holding the stretch for a short period is for it to have an effect on the muscle spindle so that the target muscle is relaxed. Where there is progressive stretching, the stretch can be progressed further.

The golgi tendon organ (GTO), is the second proprioceptor to have an effect on the muscle. The GTO is situated in the tendon, which lacks flexibility. It therefore cannot spot changes in muscle length. However, a muscle has a pulling effect on the tendon when it contracts, causing a strain on the muscle. When the GTO is activated, it transmits a signal to the brain. This has a restraining influence in the same muscle. Autogenic inhibition is the name given to this relaxing reaction created by GTO 'firing'. It is also known as the 'inverse stretch reflex'.

Autogenic inhibition is manipulated in Proprioceptive Neuromuscular Facilitation (PNF) techniques where the muscle has to contract against any opposition to activate the GTO's and cause relaxation of the muscle. The muscle is then more prone to stretching and can be increased in length further. If practiced for lengthy periods, PNF techniques decrease the strain in muscles which are created by hypertonicity or hyperactivity. This results in less rigidity, a wider area of motion, enhanced posture and increased productive movement.

Muscle spindle

The muscle spindles are continuously triggered in the course of movement, as the muscles length changes whilst movements occur. The spindles are also responsible for causing muscular contraction that helps with the movements which are occurring. The GTO reacts soon after muscular contraction commences, by hindering the muscular contraction. It does this to permit the opposing action to occur. It can therefore be said that muscle spindles and GTO's act rather like 'on' and 'off' switches for muscle activity during exercise and movement. The part that muscle spindles play is reinforced within responsive plyometric exercise methods. During these explosive movements, the quick increase in muscle length triggers the muscle spindles. This results in a reflex contraction by the muscle, which synchronizes and joins with the flexible recoil of adjoining tissue to make an even more violent contraction. If this type of training is conducted consistently, then the firing capacity of the muscle spindles increases and the motor units become more synchronized in their contractions. This results in more effective and forceful movements (for example, jumping).

Reciprocal inhibition

Reciprocal inhibition (RI), explains the restriction in reflex of an antagonist muscle when the agonist contracts. Muscles all over the body perform in tandem during periods of movement and activity. To regulate these movement patterns effectively, conflicting and linked muscle groups are triggered in many different patterns and in different orders. In order for an agonist to contract, the antagonist has to be in a relaxed and calm state when looking at opposing muscle groups. The appropriate motor components have to hinder any contraction that may happen in the antagonist, so that this corresponding occurrence between the opposing muscle groups can happen. This whole process is RI and is a vital part of normal movement. In the course of exercise, this reflex occurs to make sure that swift, smoothly operated and explosive movements can be started by an agonist in the absence of undesirable resistance from antagonist muscles.

Muscle fibers and neurons

One motor neuron is comprised of muscle fiber and can provide activation to up to 1000 of these muscle fibers, according to its location and purpose. These muscle fibers are not all equal though and can be divided into Type 1, Type 11a, or Type 11b. This fiber is spread throughout the muscle. The amount of each fiber type within the muscle helps to define the properties of that specific muscle.

Muscle fibers are formed in groups known as 'motor units'. These are small bundles of fibers that are always used together. The more motor units that are 'fired' at once, the more power you will exert. Exercise is a way of making neuromuscular messengers which result in improved fitness.

The endocrine system

The endocrine system encompasses all glands in the human body, as well as the hormones that are triggered by those glands. The endocrine system explains the detailed workings between the glands, hormones and other organs.

Certain cells make a hormone, which is a chemical. It is normally made inside an endocrine gland. To send a message to a different part of the body, the hormone is let out into the bloodstream. Hormones are commonly known as 'chemical messengers' and provide a means of communication between cells which are situated far apart within the human body.

Within a human body, there are two kinds of communication that use hormones. The first is to communicate between two endocrine glands. This is where one gland discharges a hormone which provokes another target gland to vary the levels of hormones that it is releasing. The second kind of communication is between an endocrine gland and a target organ. An example of this taking place is when insulin is released by the pancreas, causing muscle and fat cells to absorb the glucose from the bloodstream.

The endocrine system works in conjunction with the nervous system to formulate the human body's control systems. It is however, comparatively slower than the extremely fast nervous system, which has a narrow-minded target system. The endocrine system is slower but its reactions do have a wider effect. It also has a more lasting impact. Hormones are sent out to the whole body by the glands. This is done via the bloodstream and it affects all cells which have a receptor for a specific hormone. Most hormones impact cells in various organs, or even throughout the whole body. This results in a range of strong reactions.

The nervous system, chemical receptors and hormones (made by other glands) all regulate the glands when they are stimulated. By regulating the workings of organs in the body, these glands assist in helping to preserve homeostasis of the body as well as cellular metabolism, reproduction, sexual development, sugar, digestion, heart rate and mineral homeostasis. On their journey through the body, the hormones go past cells or alongside the plasma membranes of cells. They continue to do this till they meet a receptor for that specific hormone.

The endocrine system makes a lot of hormones called tropic hormones. A tropic hormone is one that can cause a hormone in a completely different gland to be released. Tropic hormones allow a route of control for hormone creation and they also allow for glands to be regulated in different areas of the body.

http://www.innerbody.com/image/endoov.html#full-description

Glands in the endocrine system

The main glands in the body are shown in the figure below.

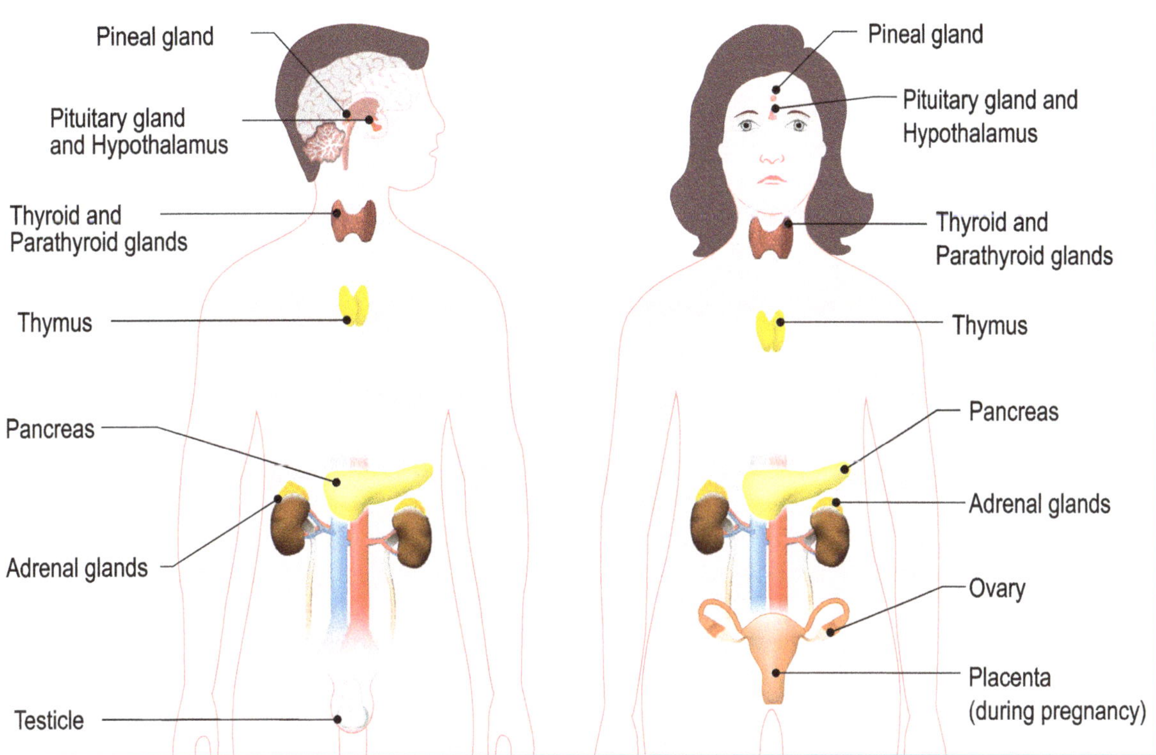

Some of these glands are more specialized, as listed below:

- **Hypothalamus:** Often called the 'master gland', it controls the pituitary gland that lies underneath it. It provides a vital link between the endocrine and nervous systems.
- **Pituitary gland:** Hormones released from this gland control our growth, blood pressure, some workings of the sex organs, thyroid gland and metabolism.
- **Thyroid gland:** Situated in the neck and produces hormones which influence the metabolism of the body.
- **Parathyroid gland:** Sits behind the thyroid gland and controls blood levels of calcium.
- **Adrenal glands:** We have two of these glands and they are absolutely essential for our well-being. Adrenal glands sit just above each of our kidneys. These glands produce hormones that aid the body in regulating blood sugar, burning protein and reacting to stress such as illness and blood pressure.
- **Pancreas:** This sits near the stomach and controls blood sugar levels throughout the course of each day.
- **Testes:** This reproductive organ also acts as an endocrine gland. It releases the hormone testosterone, which is essential to the normal growth and progression of male physical features.
- **Ovaries:** These produce the reproductive hormones oestrogen and progesterone which are vital to female fertility.

The hormones

There are many hormones found in the human body or released by the body when they are required. It is not within the scope of this course to cover all the hormones but some of the major ones are detailed below. Further information on hormones can be obtained from: http://www.yourhormones.info/default.aspx

Growth hormone and thyroid hormones

The pituitary gland discharges a growth hormone straight into the bloodstream. This hormone is mainly an anabolic hormone which encourages growth in all regions of the body, especially bone growth during the puberty years. It also stimulates protein synthesis within muscle tissue and assists in the breaking down and discharge of fat tissue from storage areas around the body for oxidation.

The hypothalamus situated above the pituitary gland is often referred to as the 'master gland' because many hormonal secretions emanate from here.

The thyroid and parathyroid hormones are released from the thyroid and parathyroid glands (situated in the neck). The main function of these hormones is to regulate our metabolism and a number of different systems, like usage of oxygen to create cellular energy, muscle contraction, preservation of body temperature and metabolic rate in general. It is imperative that the correct level of hormone is maintained as growth and thyroid hormones have a huge impact on the way the human body functions to preserve optimal health. Decreased thyroid ability is now a common disorder, resulting in slow metabolism, fatigue, depression, increase in weight and being more sensitive to the cold.

Insulin and glucagon

The pancreas releases two hormones called insulin and glucagon. The main job of the pancreas is to control glucose levels. After eating a carbohydrate based meal, the digestive system breaks down food, and glucose is taken into the bloodstream. Increasing blood glucose tells the body that the pancreas needs to release insulin. The insulin journeys to tissues such as muscle, bone and adipose tissues. When there, it transmits a signal to enable the cellular channels to open, in order to let the glucose travel from the blood into the cells for it to be used. This lowers the blood glucose to a regular level.

Conversely, after a long time without any food, glucose levels can drop under their ideal level. When this happens, the pancreas discharges glucagon which encourages the liver to break down glycogen. Glycogen is an enlarged molecule which also acts as a store for glucose. The release of glycogen helps to return dwindling blood glucose back to a more satisfactory level.

The result of exercise assists in reinforcing the correlation between insulin and glucagon. Whilst activity levels rise, the body's uptake of glucose also rises. This is a reflection of the cells' heightened sensitivity to insulin. As a result, insulin levels are reduced during exercise. Parallel to this occurrence, the pancreas boosts its secretion of glucagon, which assists in preserving a stable supply of blood glucose.

Catecholamines and corticosteroids

The adrenal glands are small in size and are situated on top of the kidneys. They are sectioned into an inner and outer layer. The inner layer, also known as adrenal medulla, creates a group of hormones known as the catecholamines. The outer layer, called the 'adrenal cortex' generates a group of hormones called corticosteroids.

Being positioned on top of the kidneys gives the adrenals a clearer connection to the main blood vessels of the body. This enables their hormones to be released into the bloodstream, thus having an immediate influence. The most common hormone in the catecholamine group is adrenaline. The medulla discharges adrenaline and noradrenaline when there is a need for a vigorous or sudden response. These hormones take action because they boost the heart rate, flow of blood, one's level of awareness and breathing levels, quickly getting the body ready for action.

Cortisol is the main corticosteroid discharged from the adrenal cortex. It helps to administer stores in the body to regulate types of stress, including mental, physical and emotional stress. Cortisol is mainly catabolic, and it helps to diminish carbohydrates and fats to supply energy for the body during stressful times. It provides help during short bursts of stress. Prolonged periods of stress result in extra cortisol being produced. This may have the effect of a decline in health by destabilizing the endocrine system. Another corticosteroid discharged by the adrenal cortex is aldosterone. It assists in the control of equilibrium of the minerals sodium and potassium in the blood, and it plays a big part in preserving the balance of water in the bloodstream.

Adrenaline and noradrenaline

Although adrenaline and noradrenaline are independent of each other, they are linked by hormones and neurotransmitters. The medulla of the adrenal glands and some of the neurons of the central nervous system are the regions where these hormones are formed. They serve as chemical 'mediators' once discharged into the bloodstream, and transmit the nerve impulses to several organs. Adrenaline behaves differently depending on the kinds of cells it is reacting to. The overall result of the adrenaline is to get the body ready for the vigorous reaction during stressful times. The main things adrenaline does is boost the heart rate, raise blood pressure, broaden the lungs air passage, increase the pupil in the eye, reassign blood to the muscles and changing the body's metabolism to increase blood glucose levels as much as possible (mainly for the brain). A closely linked hormone, noradrenaline, is discharged primarily from the endings of the nerve of the sympathetic nervous system (in addition to small amounts from the adrenal medulla). There is consistently less activity of the nervous system. This has the effect of a release of noradrenaline into the bloodstream. The release of adrenaline however, is only increased in times of intense stress.

Just like noradrenaline, adrenaline acts like a tool for some nerve cells to communicate with other cells (a neurotransmitter). Not much adrenaline is used like this.

Oxytocin

The hypothalamus generates oxytocin and the posterior pituitary gland releases it into the bloodstream. Secretion is dependent on the electrical activity of neurons in the hypothalamus – when the cells are stimulated it is released into the bloodstream.

Oxytocin does mainly two things – contract the womb, or uterus, during childbirth and whilst breastfeeding. The uterine muscles are triggered by oxytocin, causing it to contract and to boost prostaglandin production. This further increases the contractions. Sometimes, artificial oxytocin is given to a pregnant woman to bring on labor. This is an option when labor will not start naturally or when contractions are required to be strengthened during labor itself.

Oxytocin helps to trigger movement of milk within the breast, resulting in it being more easily discharged by the nipple. Oxytocin can even be found in men, assisting in the movement of sperm and the creation of testosterone by the testes.

Testosterone and oestrogen

Important hormones that help form the physical changes usually seen in puberty are released by the sexual glands found in males and females. The ovaries discharge oestrogen in females and in males, testosterone is released by the testes. These hormones also encourage good health when adulthood is reached. They regulate necessary processes relating to growth, repair and storage in the body. Testosterone in male and females helps to support muscle tissue growth. Oestrogen influences fat stores around the hips, buttocks and thighs. Males have ten times the amount of testosterone as compared to women. Testosterone is the main cause of male sexual features such as facial hair, body hair and larger muscle mass. Women who are at an age where they can reproduce, have higher levels of oestrogen than men, resulting in breast growth and regular periods. Both hormones play a part in dictating growth of bones during puberty and as an adult. The right amount of sex hormones is vital for teenager and adult health.

Relaxin

Relaxin is a hormone which originates in the ovary and the placenta. It has important repercussions in the female reproductive system and during pregnancy. Relaxin, as the name suggests, relaxes the tissues which connect the bones and makes the cervix softer and wider, to get it ready for labor.

The part of the ovary called corpus luteum is responsible for releasing relaxin into the bloodstream. Whilst a woman is pregnant, it is released from the placenta, the membranes around the foetus, and the uterus or womb lining. In men, relaxin is discharged from the prostate gland and can be found in the semen. However, it is not usually in the circulation of the blood.

Relaxin's effects can be seen during the female reproductive cycle and pregnancy. After ovulation, relaxin content in the bloodstream increases. This happens in the second half of the menstrual cycle. Here, it relaxes the uterus or womb wall by restraining contractions. It also equips the lining of the womb or uterus for pregnancy.

The role of relaxin in men is uncertain. However, there is evidence that it may increase the movement of sperm cells in the semen. (http://www.yourhormones.info/hormones/relaxin.aspx)

The digestive system

The digestive system is a group of organs working together to convert food into energy and nutrients to nourish the entire body. Food passes through a long tube inside the body known as the gastrointestinal tract (GI tract). The GI tract is made up of the oral cavity, pharynx, oesophagus, stomach, small intestines, and large intestines. In addition to the GI tract, there are several important accessory organs that help your body to digest food but food does not have to pass through them. These organs include the teeth, tongue, salivary glands, liver, gallbladder and pancreas.

To provide the body with energy and nutrients, six major functions take place in the digestive system.

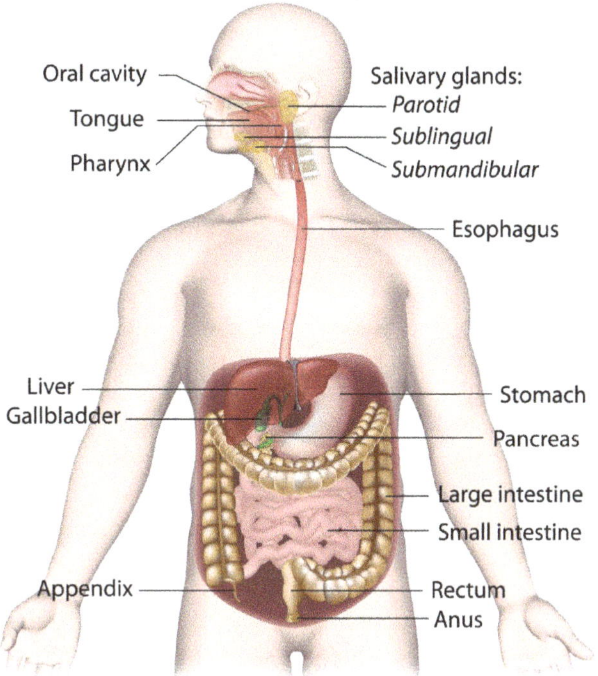

Ingestion

Ingestion is the intake of food by the mouth. The stomach serves as a storage for the food while it waits to be digested. The stomach's large capacity means that humans can ingest more food than the body can process at one time.

Secretion

The digestive system secretes around seven liters of fluids in a day. These fluids include saliva, mucus, hydrochloric acid, enzymes and bile. These fluids begin the digestive process, helping to digest food chemically and protecting the body by killing bacteria present in our food.

Mixing and movement

The digestive system uses three main processes to move and mix food. Swallowing of food is the first process, followed by peristalsis which is a muscular wave pushing down partially digested and food mixture through the oesophagus to the stomach. Thirdly, segmentation occurs in the small intestine which helps to increase the absorption of nutrients by mixing food and increasing its contact with the walls of the intestine.

Digestion

Digestion is the process of turning large pieces of food into its component chemicals. Digestion actually begins with the chewing of food by the teeth and is continued through the mixing and movement stage described above. The liver produces bile to mechanically break fats into smaller drops and at the same time other secretions like enzymes continue to be chemically digested with molecules being broken down into smaller molecules to make absorption easier. The bulk of chemical digestion takes place in the small intestine due to the release of pancreatic juice, which is capable of digesting lipids, proteins and nucleic acids.

Absorption

Once food has been broken down, it is ready for the body to absorb. Water and alcohol is absorbed directly into the bloodstream but most absorption takes place in the walls of the small intestine, which are densely folded to maximize the surface area in contact with digested food. The intestinal wall includes small blood and lymphatic vessels that take up the molecules and carry them to the rest of the body. The large intestine also participates in this process. It helps the body to absorb water and certain vitamins before waste is removed from the body.

Excretion

The final function of the digestive system is excretion, which is the removal of waste in a process known as defecation. Indigestible substances are removed by this process from the body to prevent a build-up of indigestible materials which can be harmful to the body.

Connection to the energy systems

The digestive system is closely linked to the energy systems and the production of **adenosine triphosphate (ATP)**, an energy rich compound. Energy in this context refers to the conversion of food into usable fuel which the human body uses to function on a day-to-day basis. Human beings need energy for almost everything they do, even sleeping. Some activities require less energy than others, some require a contact level of energy whilst some activities require quick energy bursts. Energy is generated by the body from the food consumed by breaking down carbohydrate, fat and protein. Some food once digested are good sources of energy, whilst others do not give as much energy. Energy is stored in our body for it to be used of as required. All the processes in the human body require and consume energy. When you start exercising the body needs to produce energy at a much faster rate. This is because as the muscle contracts frequently during the movements, the heart beats faster pumping blood around the body. The reactions of the energy systems in response to exercise is detailed in *Chapter 1B*.

L2

Different types of energy system

1. Phosphocreatine energy system
2. Lactic acid energy system
3. Aerobic energy system

The energy systems and how they are impacted by exercise will be covered in *Chapter 1B*.

End of Chapter activities

Activity 1.4: **Write down the biological systems these organs contribute to.**

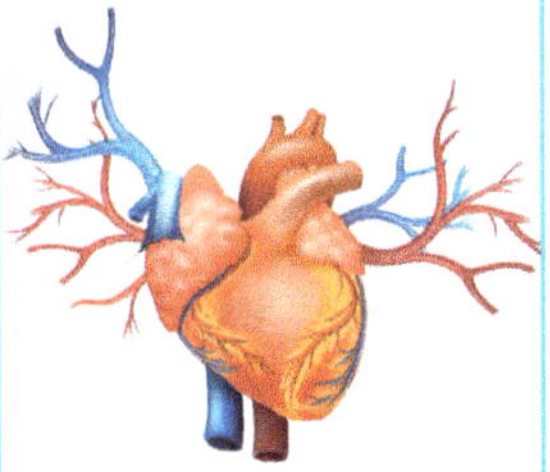
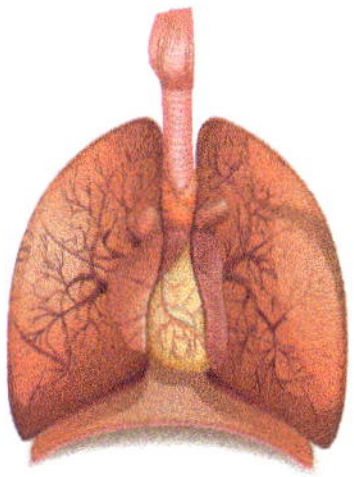
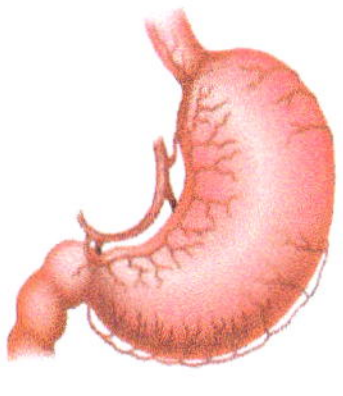
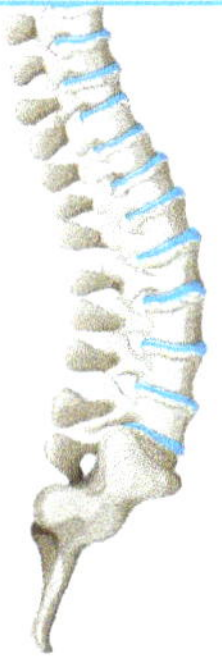
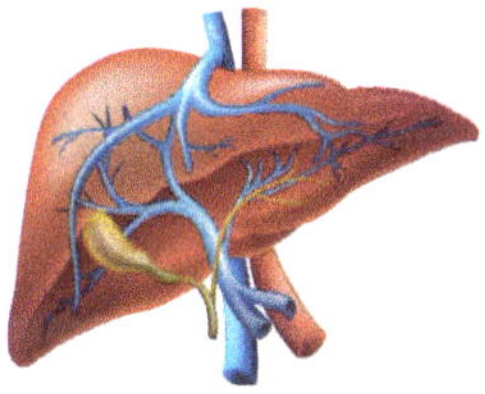
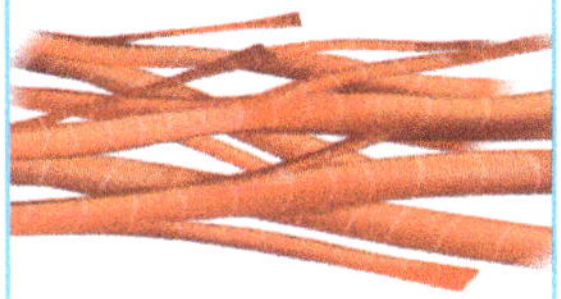
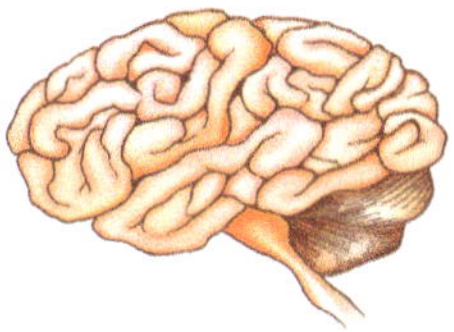
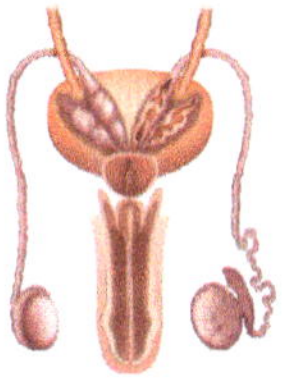

Activity 1.5: **Match up each part of the cycle to show the order of activities in the cardiac cycle.**

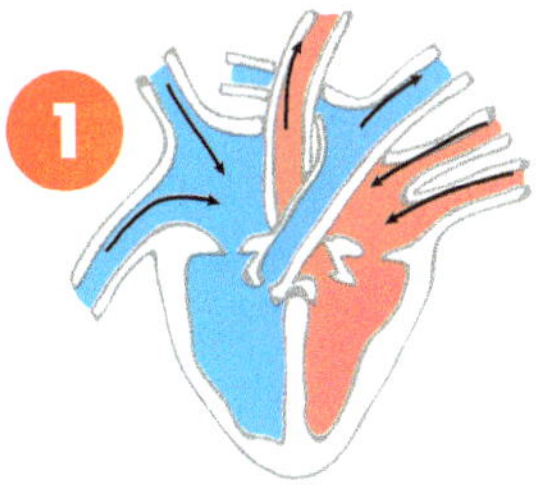

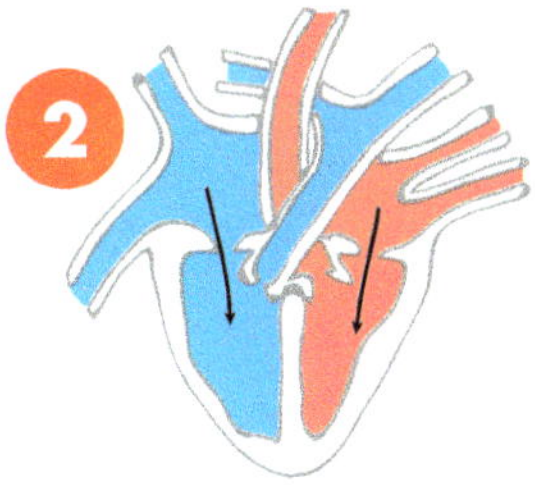

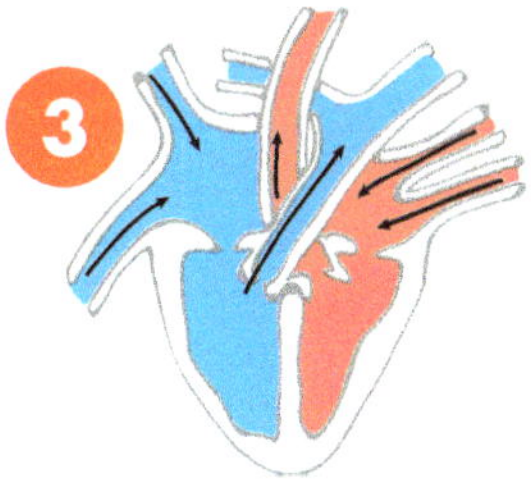

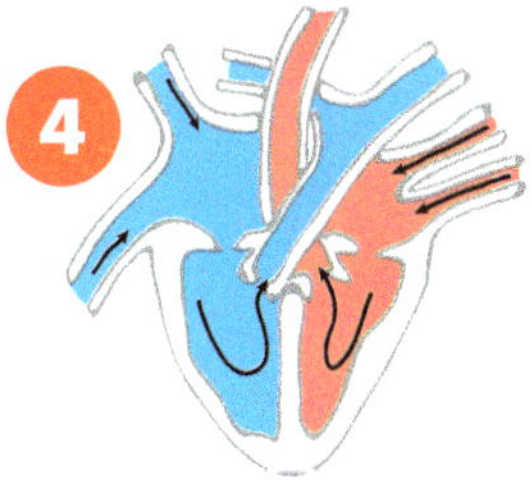

A Relaxation: atrium is filled by blood

B Filled ventricles tricuspid mitral valves are closed

C Atrial contraction

D Atria contraction and relaxation of the ventricles

THE CORRECT MATCHED PAIRS ARE...

Activity 1.6: Complete the equation.

Cardiac output = ... x heart rate

Activity 1.7: The figure below shows parasympathetic or sympathetic system?

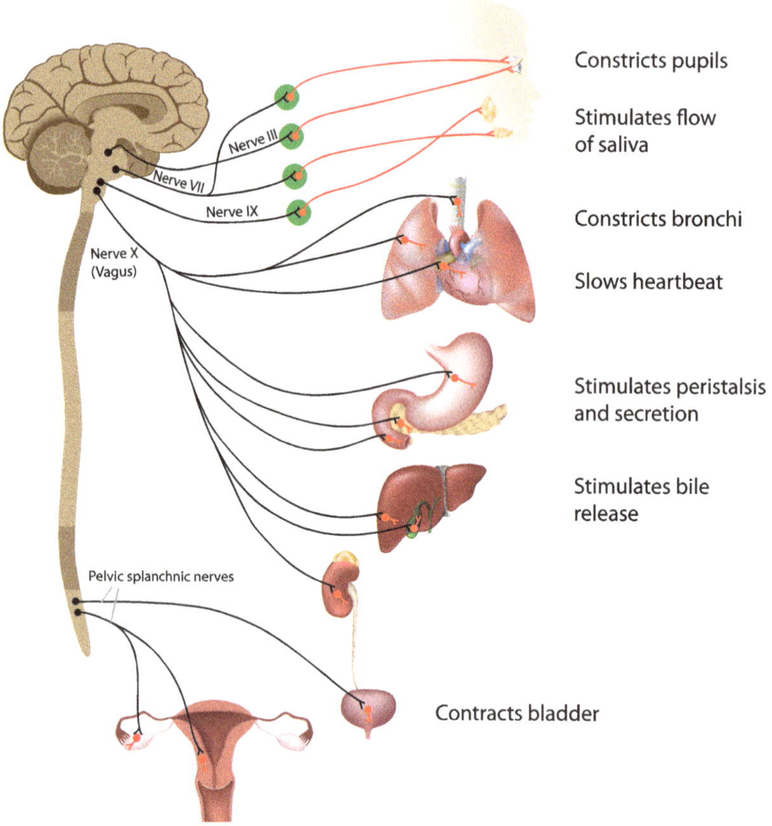

Activity 1.8: List three types of hormones and glands.

HORMONES	GLANDS

Activity 1.9: **Put the steps in the digestive system in the correct order by writing a number 1-6 next to each step.**

Activity 1.10: **Label the interior of the heart.**

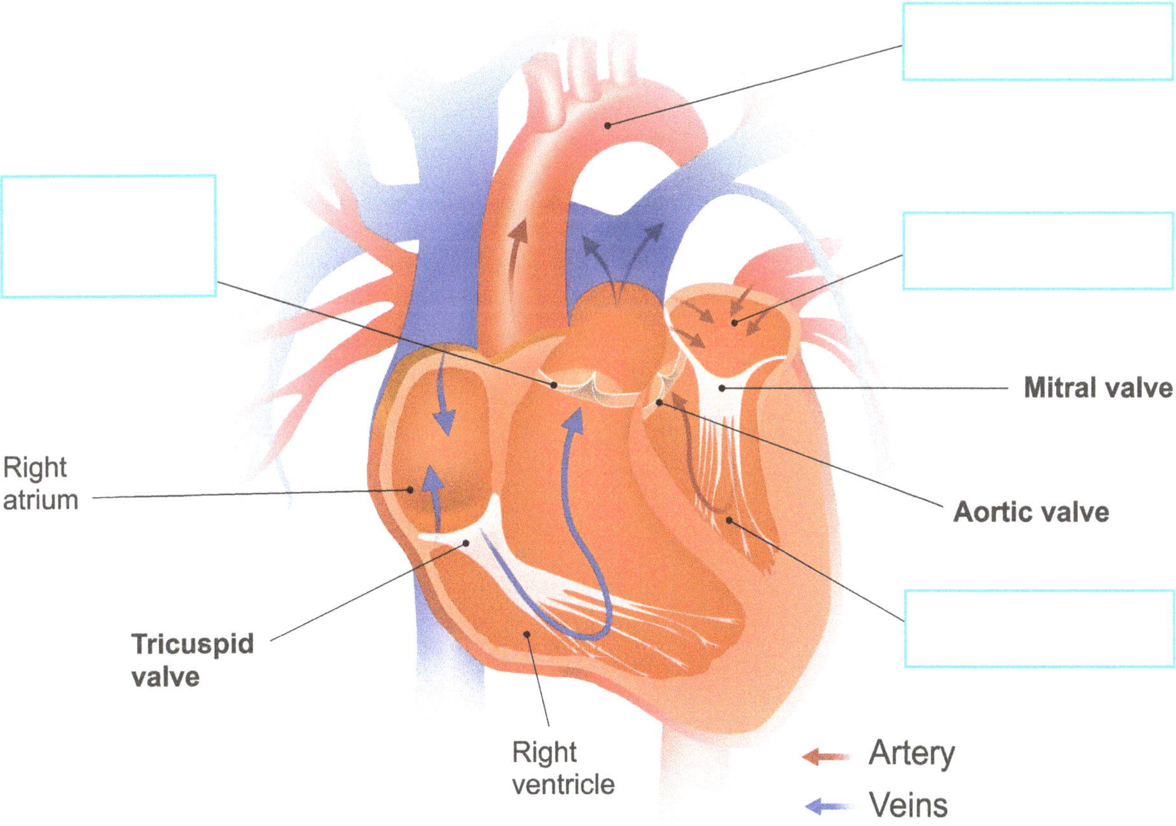

End of Chapter checklist

1. What are the main functions of the nervous system?
2. What are the two main divisions of the nervous system?
3. What is a neuron and what is its role in the nervous system?
4. What is an axon?
5. What are dendrites?
6. What are proprioceptors?
7. How can muscular force be controlled with regards to motor units?
8. What are the divisions of the autonomic system? Describe the function of each division.
9. What is the role of a golgi tendon organ (GTO)?
10. What information do muscle spindles provide?
11. What are fascicles?
12. How do hormones work within the body?
13. What is insulin and what is its function?
14. Which hormone is released from the pancreas when blood glucose rises?
15. Why is glucagon released?
16. What is the role of oxytocin?
17. Where are the adrenal glands located and what do they do?
18. What is the 'core' and why is it important?
19. How many bones in the human skeletal system?
20. What are the different types of bones in the body? Give one example of each type.
21. What is the pelvic girdle and its function?
22. What is the shoulder joint called?
23. What is an agonist?
24. What are the five segments of the spine?
25. Why is a healthy spinal cord important?
26. What are the different types of spinal curves that can occur?
27. What are the features of Panjabi's model of core stability?
28. What fractures can affect posture?
29. Why is it important to ensure the body is not deficient of calcium?
30. What is the difference between fast twitch and slow twitch muscles?
31. How is force generated by muscles?
32. What is a myosin head and what is its role?
33. What are the different muscle contraction types?
34. What is the definition of the terminologies anterior and posterior?
35. What are the three anatomical planes called?
36. What organs are used in the circulatory system?
37. What are the functions of the heart valves?
38. What are the valves between the atria and ventricles called?
39. What is the name or the largest artery in the body?
40. The right coronary artery supplies blood to which part of the heart?
41. What can cause coronary heart disease?
42. What is the cardiac conduction system?
43. What is the digestive system's connection to the energy systems?
44. What is the role of the alveoli?
45. How is breathing regulated by the medulla and the pons?
46. What are synovial joints?
47. What are the six types of synovial joints and where are they found?
48. Why do you think a personal trainer needs to understand anatomy and physiology?

Chapter 1B: Impact of exercise on the body

Chapter summary

This Chapter will elaborate on the working of the biological systems. It will highlight how the systems respond to exercise and create and process energy.

Aim

The aim of this Chapter is to allow personal trainers to discuss with confidence the impact of exercise on the main biological systems and how they react to the changes that occur during exercise and post exercise.

Learning objectives

After completing this Chapter, personal trainers will be able to:

1. Explain the long-term and short-term impact of exercise on the skeletal system.
2. Discuss the impact of exercise on different muscle types (slow twitch and fast twitch).
3. Discuss the role of the cardiovascular system during exercise and how the system can be improved through exercise.
4. Summarize the long-term and short-term impact of exercise on the respiratory system and how it can be improved through exercise.
5. Summarize how the nervous system responds to exercise and its contribution to neuromuscular fitness.
6. Discuss the reaction of the energy system to exercise, including ATP generation and consumption.
7. Summarize how improved results in exercise can be achieved if the many variations within the different energy systems are used.

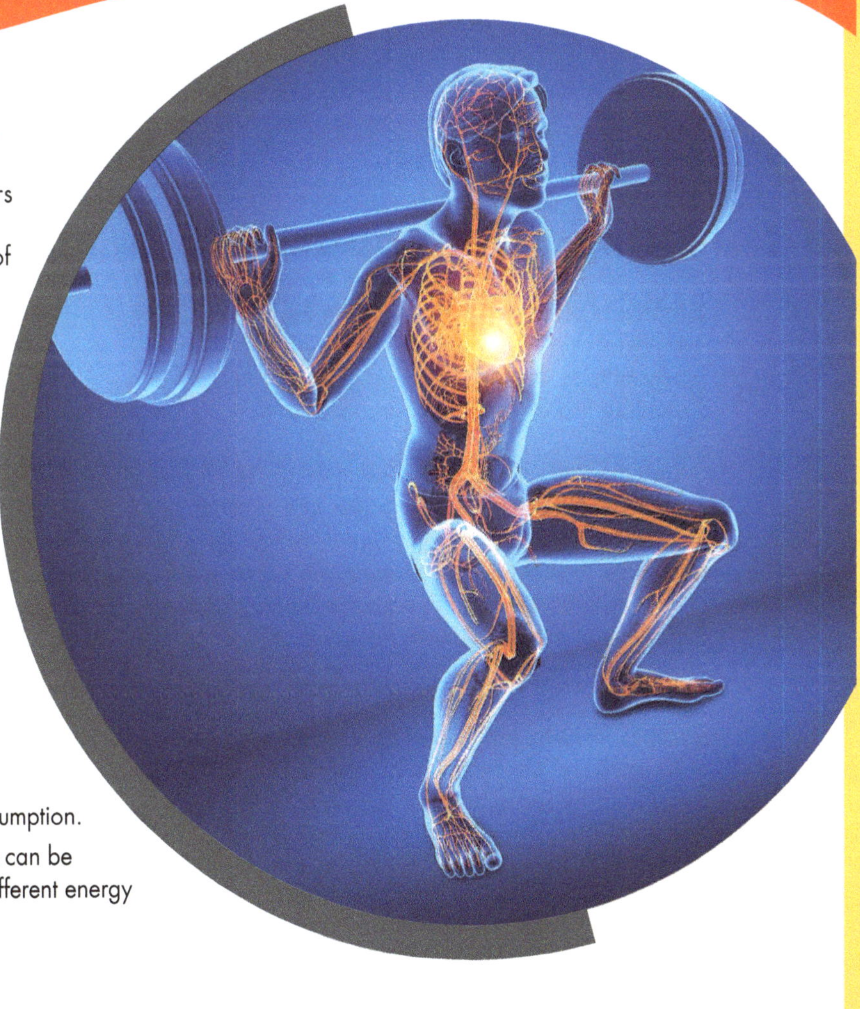

Impact of exercise on the human body

It is important for a personal trainer to understand the short-term and long-term effects of exercising on the human body and biological systems in the body. This is to prescribe exercises that are suitable for each client, monitor intensity progress and prevent injuries whilst exercising.

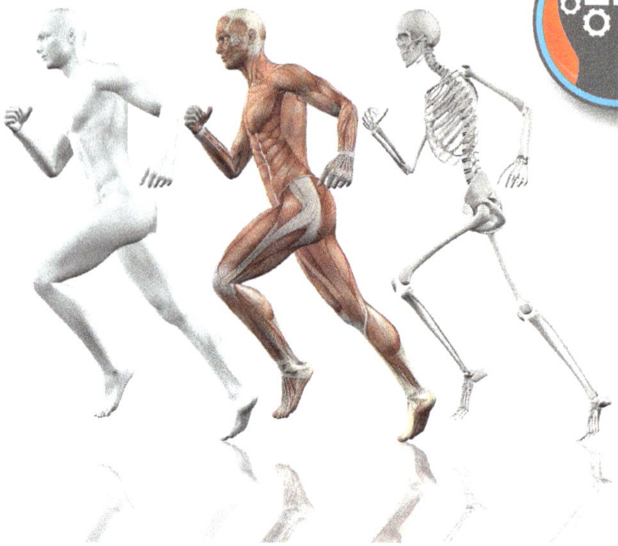

L2

According to the UK NHS, the overall health benefits of exercise include:

- Up to a 35% lower risk of coronary heart disease (CHD) and stroke
- Up to a 50% lower risk of type 2 diabetes
- Up to a 50% lower risk of colon cancer
- Up to a 20% lower risk of breast cancer
- A 30% lower risk of early death
- Up to an 83% lower risk of osteoarthritis
- Up to a 68% lower risk of hip fracture
- A 30% lower risk of falls (among older adults)
- Up to a 30% lower risk of depression
- Up to a 30% lower risk of dementia

Impact on the skeletal system

Exercise has a number of effects on the skeletal system (bones and ligaments) both in the short and the long-term as detailed below.

Short-term impact

Short-term refers to the impact on the body during exercises and long-term refers to the effect on the body after a period of training, for example after completing a six week training program.

Short-term effects tend to result in an increase in synovial fluid production. The synovial joints produce the lubricating synovial fluids in response to movements, making the joints move more easily and freely. This avoids damage to the body joints and surrounding muscles.

The bones and joints have little or no blood supply. To keep joints healthy and the cartilages nourished and lubricated, synovial fluid is produced by the synovial membrane in response to short-term or acute exercises. Regular exercise increases the production of synovial fluid, subsequently increasing the range of movements possible at a joint.

Synovial joint

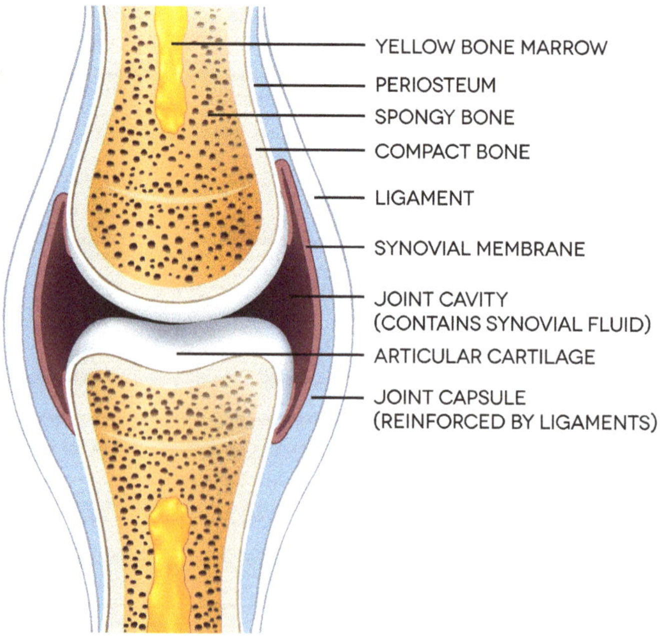

Long-term impact

Many exercise types such as strength training and running put stress through your bones. The body responds to this stress by producing osteoblasts which make bones stronger and denser as well as building new bone. Increased bone density can prevent the bone thinning disease osteoporosis.

Exercise also makes the bones stronger and more resistant to injury. The bones are held together with non-elastic avascular strap or cord-like structures called ligaments. Without ligaments, the joints would be very unstable and would probably bend the wrong way! When exposed to regular exercise, ligaments become stronger and more resistant to injury.

As ligaments have no or little blood supply, any adaptations are very slow to develop and therefore only happens through long-term exercise adherence.

Osteoporosis

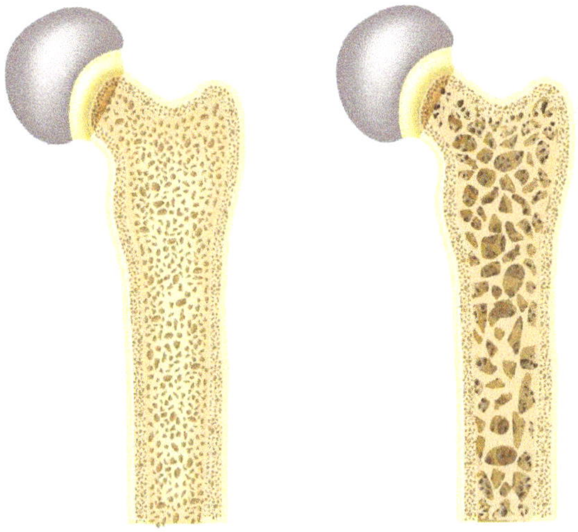

Normal bone | **Bone with osteoporosis**

The skeletal system is an important part of fitness and it is important to exercise to keep the skeletal system strong, without which your bones may easily break from a simple fall. A strong skeletal system reduces the chances of injury and if you are injured, bones will repair faster if the skeletal system is healthy and strong.

Impact on the muscles

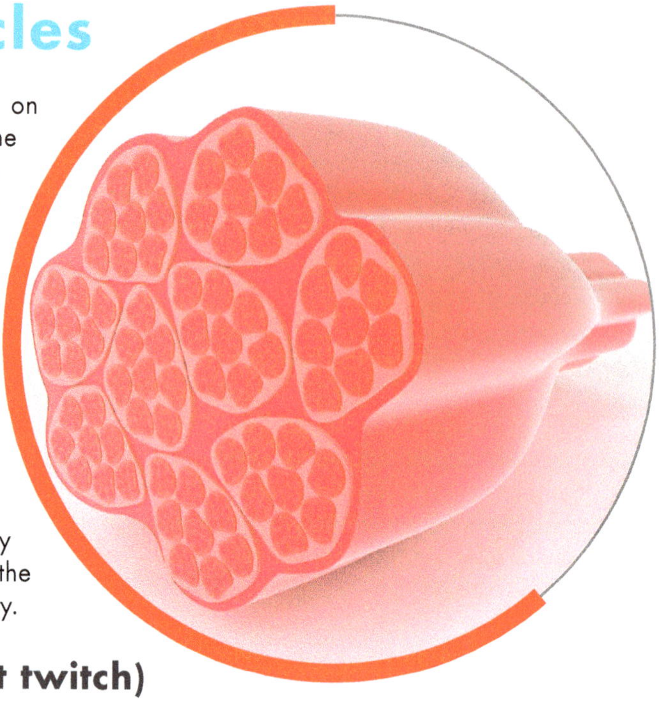

In general, exercise has a beneficial effect on the advancement of muscle tissue. However, some activities have an impact on different types of muscle fibers. As seen earlier, muscles can be divided into different types of muscle tissue (fast twitch and slow twitch).

The slow twitch muscle is also known as Type 1, and the fast twitch muscles are divided into Type IIa, and Type IIb.

Type 1 fibers (slow twitch)

These are the most aerobic and have the most supply of blood. They have more mitochondria and this has the effect of reacting well during low to moderate activity.

Type IIa and Type IIb fibers (fast twitch)

Type II fibers react best to exercise which has a high intensity force and high production of power. Type IIa fibers contain all the components found in alternative types of fast twitch types of fiber, with the capacity to accommodate some of the characteristics of the Type 1 fiber.

Type IIa fibers react to changing degrees of exercise intensity towards the direction of the stimulus which has been applied.

Type IIb muscle fibers are extremely anaerobic with a lesser supply of blood compared to the Type 1 and also has reduced mitochondria.

Muscle fatigue, soreness and oxygen debt

All people, at some point in their lives, suffer from muscular fatigue. This is where the muscle is less able to generate force. As explored earlier, there are various stages to a muscular contraction, and so the reasons for muscle fatigue may differ. McArdle et al. (2001) noted that a disruption in some of the chain of events between the CNS and the muscle fibers may be a cause of fatigue. With regards to the nervous system, decreasing stages of neurotransmitter may lessen the volume of action potentials joining the muscle fibers. More complicated neural communications linked with pain recognition and uneasiness may help to lower performance. Fatigue can come about from a number of origins. Deficiency of glycogen storage will restrict the pace at which ATP can be synthesized, while inadequate oxygen will end up causing variations to the internal chemistry. This disrupts the sliding filament system. The type of activity will also affect how the fatigue is caused.

Delayed onset muscle soreness (DOMS)

Unlike pain or uneasiness experienced during exercise, DOMS usually happens 24 to 72 hours after a reasonably substantial session of exercise. The exact process responsible for DOMS is widely not agreed upon. Some say the soreness is connected to damage in the structure, whilst another argument suggests that it is caused by an inflammatory reaction.

Minimizing DOMS

Several ways to keep DOMS to a minimum has been recommended.

The first would be to lessen as much as possible any unusual muscle activity during the initial levels of training. This however, may be hard to apply, especially in sports.

The second way would be to begin an extremely low exercise program, slowly building up the intensity to a higher level. It is arguable that this is the best way to begin training a new client.

The third and last way is completely different to the second, in that training begins at a high intensity. The idea behind this is that even though DOMS will be high at first, any exercise after this will only reduce sore muscles.

Impact on the cardiovascular system

Five key roles of the cardiovascular system during exercise are listed below:

1. It brings oxygen to muscles.
2. Removes carbon dioxide from the body.
3. Conveys heat (a result of exercise) from the core to the skin.
4. Supplies nutrients and energy to active tissues.
5. Carries hormones.

Strenuous activity places extra demands on the cardiovascular system. The muscle's need for oxygen rises dramatically. Metabolic rates increase and more waste is produced. Use of nutrients increases along with the temperature of the body. The cardiovascular system must balance these changes and accommodate the body's heightened demand to operate as smoothly as possible.

During exercise sessions, the heartbeat increases and therefore a healthy heart may pump up to 34 liters of blood per minute! An average person's stroke volume amounts to about 70-80ml per beat, but during exercise the amount increases.

In well trained athletes stroke volume at rest can be 100 - 110ml per beat, and even higher whilst exercising.

Athletes such as sprinters and cyclists often tend to have heart rates around 60 beats per minute. This is known as bradycardia and is due to the fact that the heart muscles have enlarged from exercise and therefore the heart can pump more blood during each cardiac cycle. An average person's stroke volume amounts to about 70-80ml per beat, but during exercise the amount increases.

Regular activity has been proven to improve the overall function of the cardiovascular system. A healthy person who regularly engages in an exercise regime which includes aerobic and endurance based resistance training can expect to enjoy the following results:

- A rise in the growth of cardiac muscle
- Greater stroke volume
- Decreased heart rate for the same relative pre-trained intensity exercise
- Flexible arteries with more strength than previously
- Enhanced blood cholesterol markers
- Higher network mass of capillary beds
- More haemoglobin in blood
- A long-term decrease in blood pressure

Blood flow and exercise

The blood flow is also impacted during exercise. The smooth muscle found in the walls of blood vessels allow the vessels to either narrow (known as vasoconstriction) or widen (known as vasodilation), causing the amount of blood flow through them to increase or decrease. This allows the body to send the blood flow to various tissues according to the condition of the body and where the nutrients and oxygen are needed.

Once food has been consumed, the blood vessels that supply the digestive system become vasodilated thus increasing the blood flow. Likewise, the blood vessels that supply the muscles become narrow which is known as vasoconstriction, causing the blood flow to reduce. However, during exercise the opposite occurs and the blood flow to the muscles increases and blood flow supplied to the digestive system decreases. Eating large meals too close to an exercise session will not give sufficient time for the food to be digested in the stomach and can lead to stomach cramps and vomiting.

As blood circulates within the body via the bloodstream, its pressure drops. Pressure is at its highest point in the aorta when it receives blood from the left ventricle, but then the pressure drops steeply and by the time the veins are reached, the blood pressure is only a fraction of its starting point. Blood pressure can therefore be described as "a measure of the force that the blood applies to the walls of the arteries as it flows through them." (Bupa, 2002).

Blood pressure varies according to what we are doing. Anything which makes the heart beat faster or makes the arteries narrower can affect blood pressure. Short-term increase in blood pressure can be due to various factors such as anger, fear, excitement and exercise. However, long term increase or decrease in blood pressure can be due to health issues such as heart problems. The exact reasons for increase in blood pressure are hard to identify although sometimes lifestyle choices such as poor eating habits, smoking and excessive drinking can be connected. High blood pressure or unusually low blood pressure could be signs of clinical significance and should be investigated by a health professional. Hypertension is the clinical term for high blood pressure.

The illustration below summarizes how blood pressure is measured.

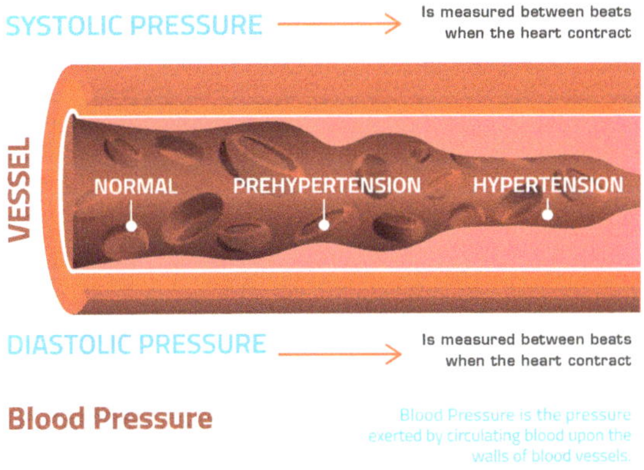

For someone with high blood pressure, it is recommended to focus on doing aerobic activities to help the heart and blood vessels become stronger. These types of activities involve movements which are rhythmic and repetitive and that use large groups of muscles, for example those found in the legs, shoulders and arms. Aerobic activities include swimming, dancing, walking, digging and jogging.

Activities which are intensive for short amounts of time, such as sprinting, should be avoided as they can cause blood pressure to rise quickly and can cause strain on the heart and blood vessels.

Good for your blood pressure	Not good for your blood pressure
Cycling, swimming, brisk walking, jogging, dancing, mowing the lawn and tennis	Weight lifting, squash, skydiving, sprinting and scuba diving - get approval from your doctor

WARNING

Activities such as scuba diving or parachuting can be dangerous if your blood pressure is not under control. As a personal trainer, if your clients suffer from high or low blood pressure it is vital that you advise them to seek professional help. It is outside a personal trainer's expertise to advise on such health and dietary issues.

Impact on the respiratory system

Breathing is regulated by the medulla and the pons, which are the respiratory control center of the CNS. This area of the body formulates the pattern for breathing and arranges the progression from inspiration (breathing in) to expiration (breathing out). During strenuous activity, movement receptors in the skeletal muscle send signals to the respiratory center. Chemoreceptors are sensors that identify chemical changes. Chemoreceptors that are in the medulla and arteries identify where the levels of carbon dioxide have increased. The medulla reacts to this by raising the speed and depth of respiration. The cerebral cortex (area of brain linked with higher cognitive processes) also sends information to the medulla. This permits us to be in charge of our own breathing where needed.

At rest, our breathing rate is about 12-14 breaths per minute and the tidal volume is approximately 0.5 liters. As we exercise, our breathing rate increases because our need for oxygen increases. This means that the amount of oxygen we breathe in and pump around our bodies whilst exercising must change to maintain our body's required level of oxygen. To achieve this, we breathe faster and our heart pumps faster. This increased oxygen uptake is measured by your VO_2 max, or the amount of oxygen your body uses in a minute. This VO_2 max can be used as a prediction of your fitness level - the higher the figure, the more effective your body is at taking in and using oxygen.

Short-term

- The respiratory center identifies changes in the concentration of CO_2 and O_2 in the blood. This raises the rate of breathing.
- In order to draw in more air, the intercostal muscles, diaphragm and other muscles which help to expand the thoracic cavity, work more solidly so that expansion during inhalation can be increased, so that more air can be drawn.

Long-term impact

- The respiratory muscles (diaphragm/intercostals) are enhanced in strength.
- This results in bigger respiratory amounts, which permits more oxygen to be delivered into the blood flow and used (VO_2 max).
- The efficiency of gaseous exchange is vastly improved by an increase in the number and diameter of capillaries around the alveoli.

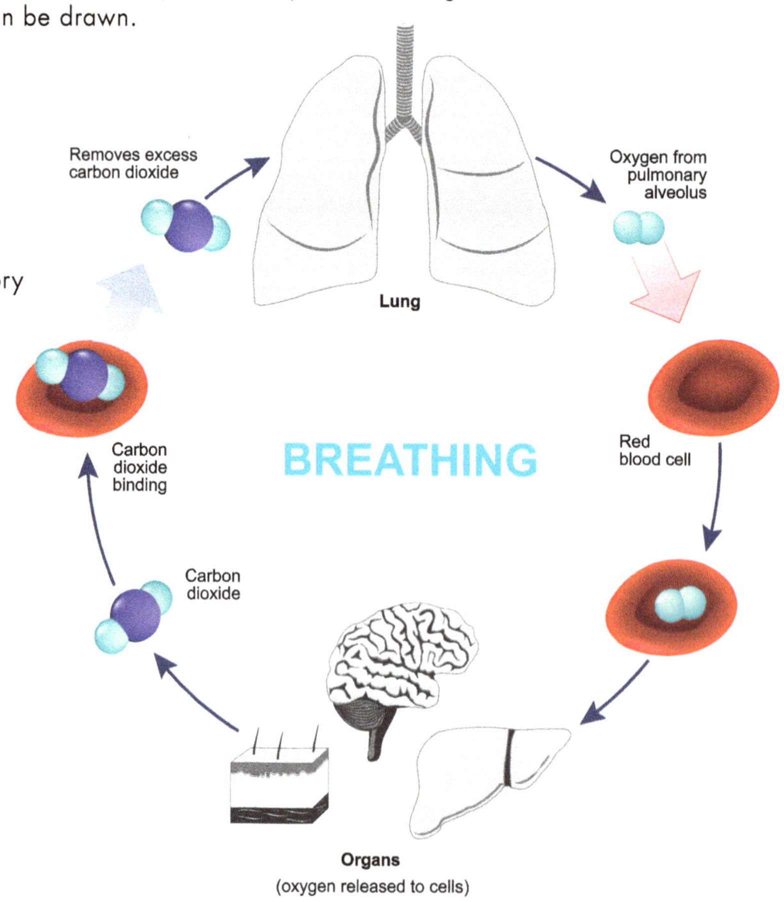

Impact on the nervous system

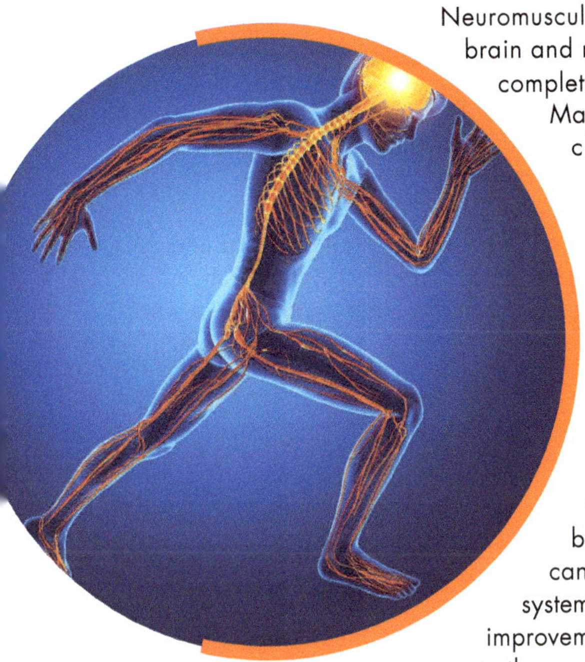

Neuromuscular fitness or motor skills can be described as the ability of the brain and nervous system to control the movements of the body in order to complete a set of prescribed tasks such as an exercise program. Many sports exercise types such as yoga for balance and studio classes for co-ordination require a high level of motor skills to be used to perform them correctly.

The nervous system is affected by most types of training because of its central role in control communication throughout the body. If the nervous system can be developed, the muscular system will follow this trend and overall performance will automatically improve.

This is because when we perform a movement, our senses provide feedback regarding limb position, force generation and the performance outcome. Unsuccessful or poor performances can be linked with other sensory inputs and so a new movement strategy can then be tried. Regular training and practice will adapt the nervous system to give clients greater control of movement as well as lead to improvements in speed, acceleration, co-ordination, strength, endurance and most other aspects of fitness.

The direct impact on the body include:

- Muscle size increases due to increased numbers and thickness of actin and myosin filaments, an increase in myofibrils and an increase in intracellular sarco plasm.
- Contractions of anaerobic fast twitch fibers can increase strength, speed, power and size of muscles.
- Increases in supporting synergistic muscle activity provide improved strength, power, speed and muscle mass growth.
- Faster reaction times with improved muscle neural pathway efficiency.
- Increased co-ordination of muscle action across multiple muscles and body segments.
- Greater resistance to fatigue.
- The number of capillaries in the muscle increase enabling more O_2 to be delivered to working muscles.
- Muscles and more CO_2 to be absorbed back into the blood.
- Muscles and liver increase their ability to store carbohydrate and fat ready for energy production.
- The number of mitochondria increases with aerobic exercise raising the threshold between aerobic and less efficient anaerobic energy production.

Reaction of the energy systems to exercise

When you start exercising the body needs to produce energy at a much faster rate. This is because as the muscle contracts frequently during the movements, the heart beats faster pumping blood around the body.

Fats, protein and carbohydrates are broken down by the body to produce **adenosine triphosphate (ATP).**

The process of breaking down large molecules to smaller ones, generally leads to the release of energy and the process is known as **catabolic**. The energy released from the catabolic reactions can result in the production of smaller molecules from larger molecules, for example the formation of proteins from amino acids. This process is termed as **anabolic**.

The human body is constantly in the state of anabolism and catabolism and together this is known as **metabolism**. Energy released from catabolic reactions is used to drive anabolic reactions and through ATP.

ATP must be present for muscles to contract. If ATP is exhausted, it must be replenished immediately for further muscle contractions to occur.

ATP composition and generation

ATP composition

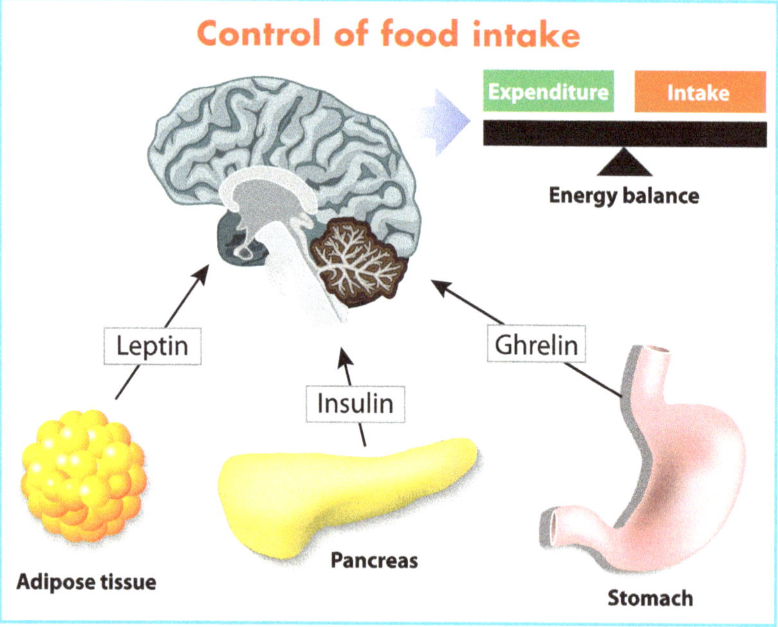

ATP is made up of one adenosine molecule, which is tied together with three phosphate molecules. The adenosine molecule is composed of adenine (nitrogen based) and ribose (carbon sugar based). Adenine and ribose together is known as adenosine.

ATP is classified as a high-energy molecule because the two phosphate groups store large amounts of energy. When one of its two high energy group is destroyed by the enzyme myosin called ATPase, the ATP triggers its energy. When one phosphate group is removed, this results in the release of adenosine diphosphate (ADP) and removal of the second phosphate group results in adenosine monophosphate (AMP).

The ATP is stored on the myosin head and it catalyses the breakdown of ATP to form ADP. When the ADP is discharged, it results in the myosin head moving. This shifts the actin over the myosin. After this, the myosin head joins with another ATP molecule, making it break away from the binding area. It then joins itself up to the next binding area and the same process is repeated. This continues to happen, for as long as ATP is accessible, when nervous stimulation is apparent, and when other tiring factors do not disrupt.

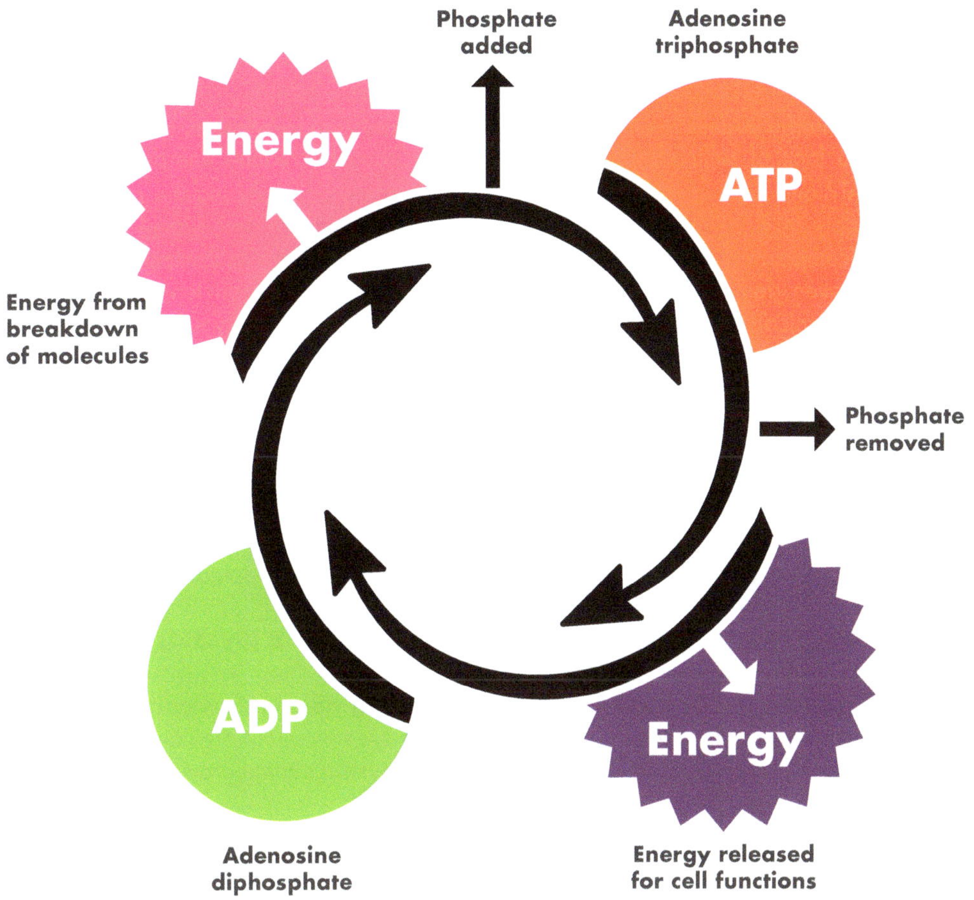

ATP generation

The regeneration of ATP is done by the energy systems shown below.

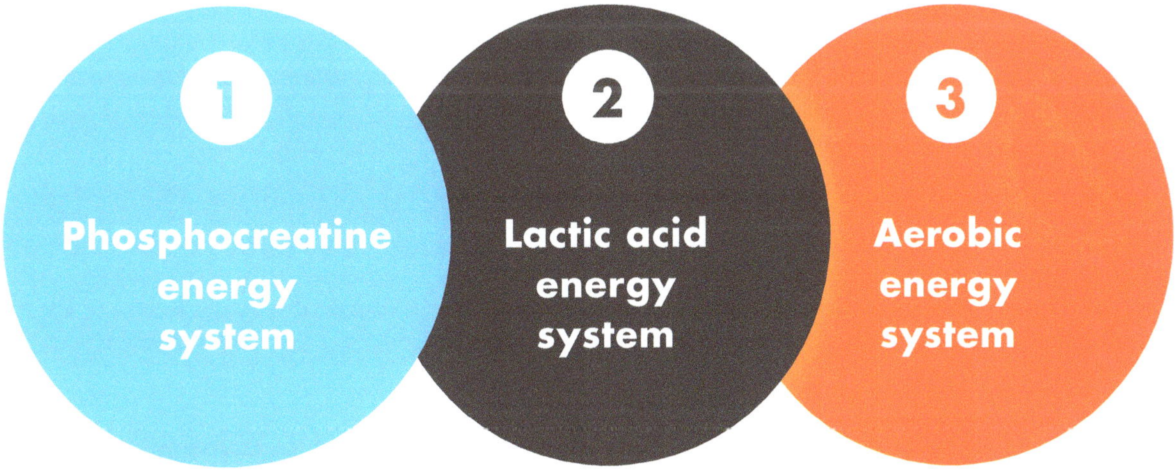

There is substantial overlap between the three systems, even though they have been explained. All three processes can supply the body with energy at any one time. How much each type produces depends largely on the exercise intensity.

Phosphocreatine energy system

The phosphocreatine energy system is utilized by the body when a muscle needs to generate a lot of force quickly but there is a lack of sufficient O_2 (anaerobic). The phosphocreatine energy system uses chemical energy to produce ATP and does not require oxygen, carbohydrate or fat during the production process. As soon as the ATP supply in a muscle has been exhausted, it can almost immediately be regenerated by a chemical substance (compound) called creatine phosphate. Similar to ATP, this compound has a high energy bond which when broken down by the enzyme creatine kinase, releases sufficient energy to yield an ATP molecule. The entire chemical reaction is very rapid and will only last for a very short period of time because of the limited storage of creatine phosphate within muscles. Once the creatine phosphate is used, it must be replenished which means that other fuel such as fat and glycogen must then be used to continue supplying energy for the regeneration of ATP and therefore other energy systems then take over the job.

Lactic acid energy system

Lactic acid is waste product produced during exercise. It is a water-soluble liquid produced during anaerobic glucose metabolism in muscles. It is a by-product of breaking down glycogen to release ATP during periods of reduced oxygen. The breakdown of glycogen is known as **glycolosis**.

The lactic acid system (also referred to as lactate energy system) provides energy for quick high bursts of high intensity activities. It comes into play when the phosphocreatine system cannot provide sufficient ATP during an activity, or if during intense aerobic training, the aerobic energy system cannot provide sufficient energy.

The lactate system's fundamental role is to fill the gap between the aerobic and phosphocreatine processes. The system lets ATP be produced continuously at great speed, much more than the several seconds allowed by the phosphocreatine system. It also does this at a higher rate than the aerobic system. It can maintain between 60 and 180 seconds of activity of high intensity such as jogging. It administers a rapid energy supply, which is made by the insufficient breaking down of glycogen. Glucose goes through several phases to a substrate, which is called pyruvate. Subsequently, the pyruvate goes in either of two directions. The direction in which it takes depends on the presence of oxygen. If there is enough oxygen, the pyruvate will go into the aerobic energy system. If the supply of oxygen is inadequate, then it is very quickly changed to lactate. This action generates three ATP per glucose molecule and does not happen where there is oxygen (anaerobic).

The body in actual fact is constantly producing lactic acids by converting glucose and at the same time it is also removing lactic acid from the body to force you to terminate the activity. This is because a build-up of lactic acid leads to symptoms like breathlessness, pain in the limbs and other sensations. Well planned training will improve the body's ability to withstand the accumulation of lactic acid and make the body more able to remove lactic acid at the same rate that it is produced or quicker delaying or preventing an accumulation.

TIP

If lactic acid accumulation is occurring frequently, then exercise intensity should be reduced so that firstly the muscles have access to more oxygen and secondly so that the bloodstream can carry away the acid to the liver to convert back to glucose or for other cells to make usage.

It is widely believed that lactic acid make muscles stiff and hinders achievement in running contests. It is also believed that when lactic acid or its crystals are collected, it results in a feeling of stiffness often experienced after a long run. These theories however, are not true. Stiffness is actually most often caused by muscle damage. Lactic acid briefly occurs and so lactic acid and lactic acid crystals cannot build up in the body. The lactate which is discharged from the muscle is transformed into glucose. This takes place in the liver. It is then recycled as a source of energy by the muscles, during the course of an extended exercise session. This makes it more likely to impede the occurrence of hypoglycaemia, which is a reduction in blood glucose level, causing a runner to feel exhausted and weak (New Studies in Athletics, no. 2/2008).

Aerobic energy system

Aerobic simply means 'with oxygen' and refers to the energy system that produces ATP by breaking down carbohydrate and fat in the presence of oxygen. The aerobic energy system is dominant when there is sufficient oxygen in the cell to meet the energy production requirements. The aerobic energy system is used for activities lasting more than 90 seconds such as running, cycling and swimming.

Carbohydrate (glucose) and fat (fatty acids) are the two macronutrients that are required to supply the body with ATP during aerobic metabolism. Whether the body is resting or participating in physical activities, to produce ATP, a mixture of glucose and fatty acid is required, but in different proportions. At rest, approximately 70% of ATP is derived from fats and 30% from carbohydrate, but when physical activity commences there is a shift to derive more ATP from carbohydrate, with the shift increasing as the exercise intensity increases. During high intensity activity, almost 100% of the ATP is derived from carbohydrate. (Earle and Baechle, 2004).

Fat is often said to 'burn in a carbohydrate flame'. This effectively means that carbohydrate must be present for fat to break down. The strength of the exercise and nutritional value will affect the relative amounts. Whilst resting or during low intensity exercise, fat supplies more aerobic energy.

When the aerobic system produces ATP in the presence of oxygen using glycogen, it also forms other by-products such as carbon dioxide and water, rather than forming lactic acid like the lactic energy system. This cycle (often referred to as aerobic glycolysis) of producing ATP is far more efficient than the other systems. However, there are some limitations to the aerobic system in that it is slow to engage due to the complex series of chemical reactions involved and because it takes a good few minutes for the heart to circulate oxygen rich blood to the required muscles.

As intensity rises, the ATP is needed more rapidly. This is where carbohydrates start to give more to this process. Even though protein has the same number of calories as glucose, it will not produce sufficient energy, because carbohydrates are accessible. Regular aerobic training makes the body more efficient at transporting and oxidizing fatty acids because the body develops a greater number of mitochondria and fat-burning enzymes as it adapts to exercise. As a result, the body becomes increasingly efficient at burning fat and weight loss occurs.The process of generating energy via the aerobic system occurs within a specialized structure in the muscle cell called mitochondria. When glycolysis takes place in the presence of oxygen, the waste product is not lactic acid but instead the pyruvate is transferred to the mitochondria. When pyruvate enters this specialized muscle structure, it is converted to acetyl-CoA (coenzyme A) and can enter the Krebs cycle for further ATP production.

Krebs cycle according to en.wikipedia is "the citric acid cycle (CAC) – also known as the tricarboxylic acid (TCA) cycle" and "is a series of chemical reactions used by all aerobic organisms to release stored energy through the oxidation of acetyl-CoA derived from carbohydrates, fats and proteins into carbon dioxide and chemical energy in the form of adenosine triphosphate, (ATP.)"

Exercise intensity and energy system used

Duration	Intensity	Primary energy system
0 - 6 seconds	Very intense	Phosphocreatine
6 - 30 seconds	Intense	Phosphocreatine and Lactic
30 seconds - 2 minutes	Heavy	Lactic
2 - 3 minutes	Moderate	Lactic and Aerobic
> 3 minutes	Light	Aerobic

Source: Adapted from Earle and Baechle, 2004

Adaptations of energy system to training

Improved results in exercise can be achieved if there is sufficient motivation and if the many variations within the different energy systems are used.

Phosphocreatine energy system adaptation

Exercises like heavy weight lifting and sprinting have a substantial effect on training, mainly resulting in a rise in muscle mass and a superiority of fast twitch muscle fibers. It has also been seen that this type of training can substantially increase muscular storage of anaerobic fuel suppliers i.e. ATP, creatine phosphate and glycogen (McArdle et al., 2001). However, what is not agreed upon is if this type of training increases the ability of enzymes within these muscles to produce larger amounts of ATP. There is insufficient research to suggest that this may be true.

Aerobic system adaptation

It was examined earlier how the principle restriction on the production of aerobic energy is the function of breathing in, transfer and use of oxygen (these will now be referred to as pulmonary, cardiovascular, and muscular changes). Aerobic training has been demonstrated to improve three of these areas (McArdle et al, 2001):

- Pulmonary changes. The main changes linked with the pulmonary system are that the respiratory muscles work more efficiently. This is shown when a person breathes more rapidly and more deeply when working at the highest level of intensity. It has also been indicated that respiratory muscles that work more efficiently use less oxygen. Subsequently, it reduces waste products. This in turn allows a potential boost of oxygen supply to other working muscles.

- Cardiovascular changes. There are several training adaptations linked with the cardiovascular system. First of all, a trained person's heart displays substantial hypertrophy and increased coronary flow of blood, resulting in a higher capability for work.

  The most marked adaptation related to the coronary adaptation seems to be a higher stroke volume. This is displayed by a reduced resting heart rate and an increased cardiac yield at maximum heart rates. In addition, the blood plasma volume is boosted and these may also add to the raised stroke volume and transferring of oxygen.

  The increased cardiac production of the heart enables more blood to flow to the working tissues. However, it should be noted that increased blood flow to the muscles may also be a result of a change in blood distribution, a higher arterial diameter, or an increased capillary density.

- Muscular changes. A better supply of blood to the active muscles is paired by an increased capability of the muscles to obtain and use oxygen from the blood. With regards to this, one of the main adaptations within the muscles is a boost in the number and size of mitochondria. Mitochondria are the networks which make up the muscle cells. This is where ATP is produced, therefore where there are larger and more mitochondria, there is more ATP production. Also, there are substantial increases in the volume of aerobic enzymes within the mitochondria. This increases the metabolic rate of the muscle, making it more able to break down fat and carbohydrate.

Lastly, McArdle et al (2001) point out that even though aerobic training might not replace one type of fibers with another (fast twitch into slow twitch), it will maximize muscle fiber's aerobic capacity. A person who has trained aerobically will display mostly slower twitch muscle fibers. McArdle et al (2001) even go as far as saying that '...highly trained endurance athletes have larger slow twitch fibers than fast twitch fibers in the same muscle'.

Lactate system adaptation

Adaptations of the lactate system is difficult to elaborate on. It seems that changes in this process are linked to developments in the cardiorespiratory system. Muscles that are given and use more oxygen, make less lactic acid at a certain exercise intensity. It also seems that consistent anaerobic exercise enhances resistance to the accumulation of fatiguing waste products. Up until now, research cannot show whether the cause of this is because of physiological adaptations or a result of changes in motivation.

End of Chapter activities

Activity 1.11: True or false?

Statement	T/F
Exercise reduces the risks of cancer.	
Exercise increases the risks of coronary heart diseases.	
Exercise can help you grow taller.	
Synovial fluid is produced by the synovial membrane in response to short term or acute exercises.	
The body responds to this stress by producing osteoblasts.	

Activity 1.12: Which activity will place more demands on the cardiovascular system? *Indicate by ticking a box*

☐

☐

Activity 1.13: Tick the activities that are good for controlling blood pressure.

Scuba diving	
Swimming	
Mowing the lawn	
Weight lifting	

End of Chapter checklist

1. What is hypertension?
2. During blood circulation, when is pressure at its highest point?
3. What happens to the cardiovascular system when you exercise?
4. What is delayed onset muscle soreness (DOMS) and why does it happen?
5. Why may someone experience muscle fatigue?
6. What are ligaments and how do they help joints?
7. What is osteoporosis?
8. What type of joint is the knee joint and how is this joint type impacted by exercise?
9. What is the long-term impact of exercise?
10. Why does our breathing rate increase when we exercise?
11. What is the long-term impact of exercise on the nervous system?
12. What are the three energy systems called?
13. What is ATP?
14. How is ATP produced?
15. What is the composition of ATP?
16. What does aerobic mean?
17. When is the aerobic energy system used?
18. What is lactic acid and why is it produced?
19. When is the phosphocreatine system utilized by the body?
20. What energy system is used for activities like running and cycling lasting approximately 90 seconds or more?

THE KINETIC PULSE COLLECTIVE KPC

Chapter 2
NUTRITION

Chapter 2A: Nutrition and healthy eating

Chapter 2B: Applying the principles of nutrition to training programs

Chapter 2A: Nutrition and healthy eating

Chapter summary

This Chapter will summarize the importance of healthy eating and the main nutrients required by the body as part of a healthy well-balanced diet.

Aim

The aim of this Chapter is to allow personal trainers to identify the important nutrients required by the body and the amount that should be consumed to maintain a healthy diet in line with the FSA's Eatwell Guide.

Learning objectives

After completing this Chapter, personal trainers will be able to:

1. Describe macro nutrients (protein, fat and carbohydrate), their structure, types, sources and function.
2. List common micro nutrients and their function.
3. Discuss the importance of a balanced diet and some of the common health issues resulting from poor nutritional intake.
4. List the main nutritional recommendations for adults, including calories and reference intakes.
5. Summarize the FSA's Eatwell Guide, its components and healthy eating tips.
6. Interpret labels on food products.
7. List the benefits of organic food.
8. Summarize healthy and unhealthy food preparation methods.

Nutritional basics

Importance of healthy eating

A well-balanced diet alongside a well thought out physical activity schedule is fundamental to improving and maintaining your fitness and overall health.

At its most basic, nutrition is a simple concept: the body needs a range of compounds in various quantities in order to function, which must be ingested. Too much or too little of any of these nutrient compounds has the potential to cause negative effects.

Problems associated with and exacerbated by getting the balance of nutrients incorrect include:

- Obesity & diabetes
- Dementia
- Hypertension
- Stroke
- Heart disease
- Cancers

Of course, the question of how much of each nutrient should be ingested becomes very much more complex when physiological variations across the population are considered. The fact is that we each vary what functionality we ask of our bodies from day to day, and that measuring each nutrient level both within our bodies and our food is not easily achieved. This section will strive to provide guidelines which personal trainers can take on board to support their clients with diets that may need to be incorporated within a fitness training program. Diet is of course a sizeable and complex topic. However, a personal trainer should be able to provide dietary advice to promote well-being and training performance but also recognize when an expert should be sought.

L2

The body requires many nutrients to function healthily. These include:

Macro nutrients:

- Protein
- Carbohydrate
- Fat

Micro nutrients:

- Vitamins
- Minerals

In addition, whilst water is not strictly a nutrient, it is an essential dietary component. Water is found in most fresh foods as it is contained within all cells. Many animals can gain sufficient water from eating fresh foods. However, humans cannot and so water must be taken in separately to support its many and varied functions in the body. Typically, the body will make clear demands for water when it is required, in the form of thirst. It is not usually necessary to force oneself to drink if not to quench a thirst. That said, if a client overtrains it may be necessary to encourage re-hydration as normal brain function may temporarily be impaired.

Overhydration can be a serious condition. Symptoms of overhydration can include:

- **Nausea and vomiting**
- **Headache**
- **Changes in mental state such as confusion or disorientation**
- **Muscle weakness, spasms or cramps**
- **Seizures**
- **Unconsciousness**
- **Coma**

Macro nutrients

Protein

Protein is a nutrient found in food that is made up of blocks of amino acids. Proteins are found in every cell in the body as well as bodily fluid (except bile and urine). It is considered a fundamental dietary requirement.

Trillions of cells exist in our body and protein is in each one of these cells. Without protein, there can be no life. 18-20% - almost a fifth - of our total body weight consists of protein. Water is the only other element that exceeds this amount.

Structure

Most proteins are relatively large molecules comprised of at least 100 amino acids, but there are others that are small structures of amino acids and referred to as peptides. Proteins will differ according to the number and sequence of the amino acids that form it.

Functions of protein

Protein is required for growth, repair of cells and a wide range of metabolic processes. This essential nutrient is also important for the body to function healthily during a pregnancy.

- Protein acts as a stimulant for enzymes.
- They carry molecules around the body and are also used to store molecules (haemoglobin transmits oxygen).
- The liver stocks iron as a complex with the protein called ferritin.
- Protein is utilized whenever we move (most muscle is made up of protein).
- It provides structural help for cells. Collagen is a protein made of fiber. It is also a major ingredient of skin and bone.
- Protein settles the reaction that cells give. The protein in the eye which is necessary to see is called rhodopsin.
- Proteins with antibody properties are vital for our immune system.

Amino acids

Proteins are broken down by the digestive system into amino acids. Amino acids are organic components made up of a minimum of one amino group (-NH2) and a carboxy (-COOH) group. When protein is fragmented down to amino acids, it can be used to construct the proteins required for each of their functions in the body. In addition, protein can be used to provide a source of energy providing four calories per gram.

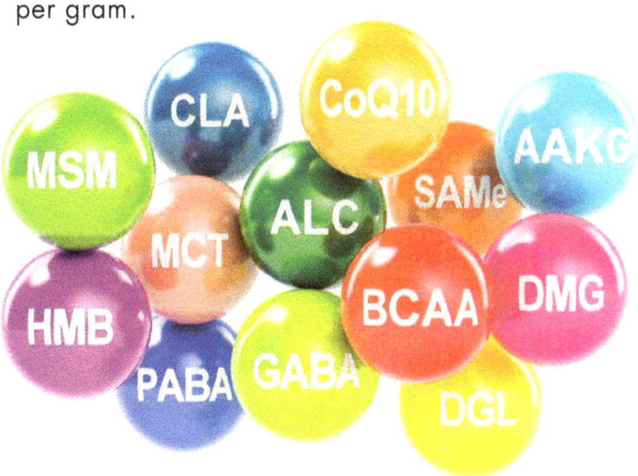

Our body uses amino acids for the breaking up of our food. Amino acids must be eaten in big enough portions to maintain prime health. They are in many animal based foods such as fish, meat, eggs, plants such as legumes, soy beans and nut butters and grains like wheat germ. The required amount of protein that our bodies need can be obtained wholly from non-meat products.

The three groups of amino acids

Within the human body, 20 amino acids are produced to make protein. These are called proteinogens or standard amino acids and can be further split into three categories: essential, semi-essential and non-essential.

Essential

A total of eight amino acids are vital for human beings. These must be sourced from outside the body as the body is unable to make them itself. These eight amino acids are called isoleucine, valine, tryptophan, threonine, methionine, leucine, phenylalanine and lysine.

Semi-essential

These are known as arginine and histidine, and must be incorporated into the diet in limited circumstances.

Non-essential

There are 10 of these - alanine, aspartic acid, asparagine cysteine glutamic acid, glycine, glutamine proline, serine and tyrosine. They can be made in the body.

One point to be noted is that apart from the ones just mentioned, there are around 250 amino acids which are not made up of protein. They can be used to produce sugar.

Another important point is that categorizing the acids into 'essential' and 'non-essential' doesn't indicate one is more significant than the other. Dividing them into groups doesn't reflect the supply level of the amino acids. Our bodies have different protein needs. Variants such as stress levels (mental and physical), age, and being in stressful situations affect the production level of essential and non-essential amino acids. These regulate the many amino acid levels needed to stay in prime health and fitness.

Sources of protein

Most foods contain protein and foods vary in the amount of protein they provide. The main sources from animals include eggs, chicken, meat, fish, milk and cheese. Non-animal sources are cereals, nuts and pulses (beans and lentils).

Proteins from animal foods are generally considered to be of higher biological value as they generally are closer to those required in human bodies. However, as most animal sources also contain higher saturated fat content than plant sources, advice does not dictate animal fats to be better. Protein-rich foods tend to make people feel fuller than foods rich in carbohydrates or fat. Thus, including a lean source of protein with a meal can help to minimize feelings of hunger and decrease overall energy intake. However, too much protein can lead to high cholesterol as well as reduced liver and brain function and weight gain.

Complete and incomplete proteins

All the protein which we consume goes towards meeting our daily protein consumption targets. However, some protein is more efficiently used by our body compared to other proteins. So, whilst eating complete protein as part of our diet benefits us, it's not vital. Understanding how to opt for the correct proteins in the diet will make sure that the body's demands are met.

The most significant difference between complete and incomplete proteins is that complete proteins have all the necessary amino acids that our body needs every day. Incomplete proteins on the other hand, include only some of these amino acids. The body transforms the protein we consume into amino acids. These acids construct and restore tissues in the body, assist in food digestion, provide energy and carry out many other functions of the body. Normal growth of children is heavily reliant on essential amino acids. They are commonly known as 'high-quality' proteins and are used up easily by the body.

Origins of complete protein

Animal protein can be found in eggs, milk, yogurt, cheese, poultry, meat, fish, seafood and eggs. On the other hand, soy protein comes from a plant and is of high quality.

Origins of incomplete proteins

Other than the complete plant originated protein already stated, most other plant based proteins are incomplete. This is because they contribute a limited number of essential amino acids but not all of them. These incomplete proteins are provided in most types of grains, seeds, nut butters, nuts, green peas and varieties of legumes, for example lentils, chickpeas, black, pinto and navy beans.

It is easier to receive all essential amino acids from complete proteins. However, it is still possible to get the essential amino acids the body needs from plant sources, if one's diet is prepared in advance.

Additional proteins

Commonly in diets, various proteins work well together, completing any gaps in their amino acid pattern. For example, in a meal, where there are two types of vegetable protein on a plate, like bread and pulses (e.g. lentils), the amino acids of one protein may make up for the deficiencies in the other. This increases its biological worth. This process is called the 'complementary action of proteins'. So, the protein quality of an animal protein diet consisting of meat, milk, fish, eggs or other animal protein foods is not compromised for those following a vegan and vegetarian diet containing plant based protein from nuts, seeds, pulses, mycoprotein and soya products. Grains also contain small amounts of protein.

Most people in the USA include sufficient amounts of protein in their daily diets, supplying plenty of amino acids. For some countries though, protein consumption is insufficient and so the complementary action of proteins is crucial in allowing people to meet their daily protein requirements. A good example of this is shown by the popular dish of rice and lentils in the subcontinent.

Protein intake recommendations

Guidelines suggest that adults and children should eat two to three servings of protein daily or 0.8 grams per kilogram of body weight for an average sedentary adult. Where most proteins are plant based, a variety of these types of proteins should be eaten.

One typical portion size equates to:

- Two medium eggs
- 100g of lean boneless red meat
- 100g of lean boneless poultry
- 140g of fish
- 3 tablespoons of seeds or nuts

Protein and metabolic processes

Metabolic processes, either at the cellular, organ or organism state, can be classified as anabolic or as catabolic.

Anabolism

These are a group of metabolic routes that build molecules from smaller ones. The reactions that these produce need energy (for example protein synthesis and photosynthesis). The process is sometimes described as a construction process in the body and usually happens when we are resting. As proteins make up such a major part of most cells, sufficient protein consumption is vital to preserve physical well-being and productivity.

Catabolism

These are a group of metabolic routes that factor down molecules into smaller ones while releasing energy. Amid processes like respiration and digestion, larger sized molecules like polysaccharides, fatty acids, nucleic acids and proteins are fragmented into smaller sized elements such as monosaccharides, nucleotides and amino acids.

It can be said that to a degree, such protein catabolism happens all the time, because current proteins emanating from fractured cells are broken down into their amino acids and reprocessed to construct fresh proteins somewhere else. Muscle catabolism which happens during rigorous exercise, is a consequence of micro-tear fracture and the limited use of main amino acids as fuel.

Carbohydrate

Carbohydrates are also known as saccharides. They are atomic compounds composed of only three constituents: carbon, hydrogen and oxygen.

Carbohydrates are the most important source of energy for the body providing four calories per gram. Once broken down in the digestive system, carbohydrates become glucose, which is the simplest of sugars, which in turn is transported in the blood to wherever energy is required.

Carbohydrates have six fundamental roles to play in the body as listed below:

1. To give energy and maintain blood glucose levels
2. Reserving utilization of proteins for energy
3. To break down fatty acids and avoid ketosis
4. To recognize biological processes
5. To be used for flavor and to sweeten
6. To act as dietary fiber

Some glucose is stored in the liver and muscles ready for exertion. Although glucose can be digested to produce glucose, carbohydrate digestion is a far more efficient process and so is of importance in training. In general however, the amount of simple carbohydrates ingested needs to be limited to the amount required as too much glucose in the blood can cause dizziness, nausea and more serious conditions such as Type 2 diabetes.

Carbohydrate types and their sources

- Simple carbohydrates (sugars)
- Complex carbohydrates (starches)
- Fibrous non-starch carbohydrates

Simple carbohydrates

These have a more basic molecular make-up and consist of one or two sugar molecules. The most basic type of carbohydrate is glucose. Sucrose is one type of basic sugar found in food. Fructose is in fruit and lactose is a form of sugar found in milk. Not all basic carbohydrates are 'bad' though. The natural sugars found in fruit and milk are good for us. Low or non-fat dairy products like yogurt, milk and cottage cheese are good options to maintain good health, providing a quality supply of calcium. Even though fruit and fresh fruit juices are good for our health, containing vitamins and minerals, they should be consumed with limitations. This is because complex carbohydrates like vegetables hold more value if a person's main aim is to lose weight, more so if they are sensitive to carbohydrates. The optimum time to eat fruit is before and after a workout.

Complex starchy carbohydrates

These also consist of sugars; however, the molecules are held together to make longer, more complicated chains. Complex carbohydrates containing starch could be wholegrains, beans and peas (full of vitamins), fiber and minerals. The only issue with complex starchy carbohydrates is that they are usually refined.

Refined carbohydrates are where machines are utilized to get rid of parts that are high in fiber (the bran and the germ) from the grain. Refining the complex carbohydrate strips its complex make-up, together with all its properties that make it healthy. It instead assumes the features of a simple carbohydrate and the body processes it in a similar manner. Examples of refined carbohydrates are white rice, white flour, white bread and sugar-rich cereals. White pasta and noodles are also refined. Basically, anything made from white flour is classed as refined carbohydrate. These refined carbohydrates should be avoided as much as possible just as much as avoiding sugar in its purest form.

The body takes more time to fragment down complex carbohydrates. Complex carbohydrates expend energy progressively over a prolonged time period compared to simple carbohydrates. Simple carbohydrates are fragmented down quicker and create a brief increase in blood.

Fibrous non-starch carbohydrate

Fibrous carbohydrates are enriched with vitamins, minerals, phytochemicals and additional nutrients. These are more likely to come in the form of green vegetables and be rich in fiber. fiber is the part of the plant which cannot be digested, meaning that a lot of the food goes directly to the gut and is not absorbed. They are therefore often referred to as 'colon cleansers', vital in keeping the digestive system functioning with optimum health. fiber rich carbohydrates also have low calorific value so there is no such thing as overeating green vegetables! Foods high in fiber include fruits, vegetables, beans, peas, nuts, seeds and wholegrain foods (such as wholewheat bread, oatmeal and brown rice).

There are two kinds of non-starch carbohydrate:

- **Soluble:** Normally feature on the outer layer of plants. Soluble fiber make up foods like unrefined wheat, bran, rye, rice and many other grains just like fruit and the skins of vegetables.
- **Insoluble:** These are normally found in the inner parts of plants. Beans, barley, broccoli, prunes, apples, citrus fruits and oats are all good suppliers of this. It has been suggested that soluble carbohydrates assist in decreasing cholesterol by joining with fats in the digestive canal and transporting them out into the stools.

All carbohydrates provide energy, but their real dietary benefit is measured by whether they are refined or unrefined.

Refined and unrefined carbohydrate

Refined

- Contain excess sugar
- Processed, poor quality fats
- Possess high energy density
- Lack vitamins and minerals
- Negatively affect insulin reactions

Examples of refined carbohydrate include white bread and pasta, cakes, biscuits and white rice.

Unrefined

- Contain fructose and glucose in different amounts
- Comprised of antioxidants and phytochemicals
- High in fiber, vitamins and minerals and elements of amino acids

Examples include wholemeal and wholegrain foods, wholegrain rice, frozen or fresh vegetables, pulses and quinoa.

The primary difference between the two is that unrefined carbohydrates have more natural nutrients whereas refined carbohydrates are processed and are stripped of important vitamins and minerals. Natural sources of unrefined carbohydrates include wholegrains, legumes, fruits and raw vegetables. Eating the correct amount of these are advantageous to health.

Glycaemic index

To expend energy, carbohydrate (CHO) from diet must be transformed into glucose. The varying types of CHO have differing layouts of molecules; some are changed more rapidly than others and thus are prone to increase blood glucose more quickly also. The glycaemic index (GI) is a good indicator of how fast food is converted into glucose and immersed into the bloodstream. The purest form of glucose is utilized as a reference point to measure and is given a GI of 100. The remainder CHO is then indexed based on this measure. For example, roast parsnips have quite a high level of GI at 97, compared to kidney beans, which have a comparably low GI of 27. An understanding of the GI will equip people to choose the foods they eat according to their precise circumstances. For example, someone with diabetes can aim to consume low GI foods, as these hinder the radical changes in their blood sugar levels. Another example could be the athlete who chooses the high GI option to assist in their performance and their subsequent recovery stage. Reactions to GI will differ depending on the person and it can show higher than it should in diabetes sufferers. So, consistent and routine monitoring of the responses of different carbohydrate food on blood sugar level can be beneficial.

Fats

Fats are another important part of healthy living. Oils and fats are commonly known as lipids. When liquids are lipids at room temperature, they are called oils whilst solid lipids are known as fats.

The majority of dietary lipids are made up of links or rings of carbon atoms, chained together with other atoms, mostly hydrogen and oxygen.

Types of fats

There are three main types of fat:

- Saturated fat is found in fatty meats such as bacon and sausages, butter, eggs and dairy foods.
- Monounsaturated fat is found in meat, olive oil and nuts.
- Polyunsaturated fat is found in fish, nuts and leafy greens.

Fat is a concentrated source of energy (nine calories per gram) which the body can use to produce glucose although this is a far more complex process than for even complex carbohydrates and so will only occur when usable protein or carbohydrate supplies are exhausted.

In addition, fat:

- Provides a cushion to help protect our vital organs from damage.
- Acts as an insulator, helping us to maintain the correct body temperature.
- Enables our bodies to process vitamins A, D, E and K, which are all fat soluble and vital to good health.
- Contains essential fatty acids which help the heart and immune system.

However, too much fat is not good as:

- Too much fat storage means more bulk and weight which in turn increases the workload of the heart and other organs.
- With a high fat diet, the liver produces more cholesterol, a waxy substance that in low levels is vital for keeping blood vessels flowing freely, but has the opposite effect in high quantities making the heart work harder and risking development of, for example, coronary heart disease.

In addition, some fats are worse than others. Unsaturated fats are generally considered better for us than saturated fats. Saturated fat molecules clump together more easily and subsequently stick to the sides of arteries and allow other saturated fat molecules to build up; this can gradually clog the arteries leading to higher blood pressure and making it more difficult for the heart to pump oxygen-rich blood around the body. Fats are not soluble in water and therefore blood. Unless saturated fats are limited in the diet to what is actually needed, they can lead to serious health problems.

Sources of fat

Type	Animal sources examples	Non-animal sources examples
Saturated	Meat: beef, lamb, pork, venison Poultry: chicken, duck, quail Dairy: butter, cheese, cream, milk, yoghurt Eggs	Palm kernel oil Cocoa butter Palm oil Coconut oil
Monounsaturated	Lard	Avocado Canola oil Nuts Olives Rapeseed oil Peanut oil Sesame oil Seeds
Polyunsaturated fat	Fish	Seeds Soybean Sunflower and canola oil Pine nuts, walnuts and brazil nuts

The breaking down of fats triggers the production of fatty acids. Fatty acids are 'good fats' and are not easily dissolvable in water. They can be utilized for energy by most kinds of cell. They arise as triglycerides. This is where three fatty acids secure themselves onto a carbohydrate 'support' called glycerol. In the digestion process, the fatty acids are fragmented and the body uses them as needed. Fatty acids contribute to keeping skin healthy and the anti-ageing process. These acids may even help with losing weight by assisting the body in processing cholesterol. Crucially, they allow the arteries to prevent the development of cholesterol. Another function of fatty acids is to support the adrenal and thyroid glands, which could help to monitor weight.

The role and conduct of a fat is dependent on the make-up of fatty acid chains, which may be of various sizes and shapes. Fatty acids are mainly either saturated, monounsaturated or polyunsaturated, and are organic i.e. they possess molecules that are both carbo and hydrogen.

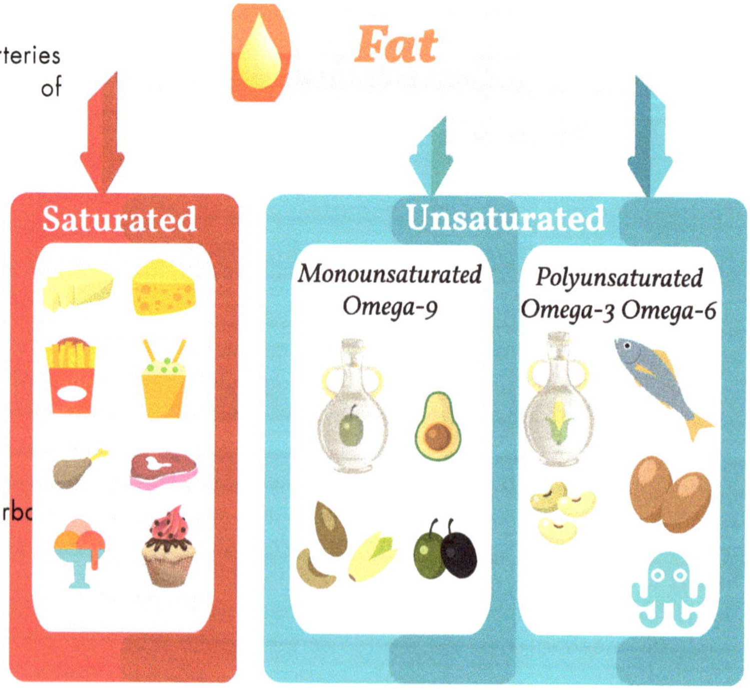

Saturated fat

Within fatty acid groups are a framework of carbon atoms. Each of these atoms are joined with either a single or two hydrogen atoms. The number of hydrogen atoms decide the shape and the role that the chain plays. Saturated fat chains are occupied with hydrogen (commonly called 'saturated'); this awards them significant features. Saturated fatty acids are straight and are prone to present themselves more evenly. This explains why saturated fats are more likely to be in a solid state whilst at room temperature. They are also more prone to be chemically balanced and not susceptible to change when warm or subjected to oxygen.

Unsaturated fat

These are classed as unsaturated because sections of the carbon chains lack hydrogen atoms. The point where there are no carbons in the fatty acid chain commonly has a curve or a fold. This results in a less even and more watery setting and this is the reason why these fats are normally liquid at room temperature (oils). Unbalanced double bonds are set between adjacent carbons where the hydrogen is lacking; this makes these chains more insecure and responsive.

There are two key types of unsaturated fats: monounsaturated and polyunsaturated.

Monounsaturated: Mono means one, so it follows that monounsaturated oils contain fatty acids with just one double bond. The molecule therefore has only one bend in it. The body identifies the unique shape and size of the different monounsaturated fatty acids and uses them appropriately. Dietary habits which include a lot of monounsaturated fats have been proven to decrease LDL (low-density lipoproteins), cholesterol (bad cholesterol) and plasma triglycerides (fat within the blood). As a result, they are believed to lower the chances of contracting coronary heart disease (NHS). The body can incorporate monounsaturated fatty acids from saturated fatty acids where needed.

Polyunsaturated: These types of fatty acids are lengthy chains of carbon atoms. Commonly, they are lacking hydrogen at more than one stage, so they have over one double bend (hence the word 'poly'. Every double bond features a bend or a twist in the chain. Like with the monounsaturated fatty acids, there is a unique bend at the location of each double bond. This leads to a different shape and usage.

The differing conditions of the double bonds make way to unique forms of polyunsaturates. Two of these are believed to be crucial to core health – omega 3 fatty acids and omega 6 fatty acids. These are also known as Essential Fatty Acids or EFA's, because the body is not able to manufacture them itself.

These crucial omega fatty acids play a vital part in many metabolic actions and are significant in the working of the cell. They have to be consumed in the necessary amounts in order to achieve a good standard of health.

Oily fish contains omega 3 fatty acids which are advantageous to health. They have been proven to decrease the blood's habit of clotting, lowering rates of triglyceride, cholesterol and in some instances, increases HDL (high-density lipoproteins) cholesterol. All of this is believed to reduce the chances of contracting coronary heart diseases (NHS). Much of the processed food available today contains vegetable oil. The widespread advice for people to avoid saturates has meant that our diet tips the balance towards more omega 6 fatty acids. This may present an issue, because the omega 6 oils trigger inflammatory passageways in the body.

Sources of omega 3:

- Cod liver oil
- Flax oil
- Oily fish
- Pasture-reared eggs
- Walnut oil

Sources of omega 6:

- Corn oil
- Evening primrose oil
- Grapeseed oil
- Pumpkin seeds
- Sesame seeds
- Soybean oil
- Sunflower oil

Functions of fat

There are definitive reasons why there is a need to include saturated fat into our daily diet. Some of these reasons are:

- To improve the immune system
- To improve the workings of the liver
- To provide energy and framework to the cells
- To offer limited safeguarding from the dangerous effects of alcohol and some medicines
- Lipids (oil) have a variety of roles including:
  - The creation of cell membranes
  - Storing energy in the adipose tissue
  - The creation of myelin sheath in the nervous system
  - Supplying energy during periods that require lower-intensity tasks
  - Helping to control enzymes
  - Cushioning via subcutaneous adipose tissue (tissues that lie under the skin)
  - Guarding the internal organs
  - Synthesizing steroid hormones
  - Making up most of the central nervous system (CNS) and spinal cord
  - Transmitting, storing and using vitamins A, D, E and K, which are able to dissolve fats

Micro nutrients

Minerals

Minerals are not organic but the body needs them in little amounts for a range of uses. One example is for the development of bones and teeth. Minerals are also used by the body as vital components of bodily liquids and tissues, and they make up the enzyme process. They are also needed for every day nerve function.

The body needs some minerals in higher amounts and some in lower amounts. Some examples of minerals needed in high amounts are magnesium, phosphorus, sodium, potassium, calcium and chloride. Minerals only needed in small amounts – often referred to as 'trace' minerals – include copper, fluoride, iron, chromium, cobalt, iodine, selenium and zinc. It should be noted that these trace minerals are just as important as the minerals needed in larger amounts.

The body uses minerals supplied in food more effectively than minerals consumed as supplements. Eating patterns that lack one type of mineral are often low in others. It is therefore advisable to evaluate and adjust a diet if this is the case. Including a variety of foods will assist in making sure a sufficient number of most minerals are being consumed regularly.

Mineral sources and function

The macrominerals that are required in greater amounts by the body are detailed below.

Mineral	Main functions	Source
Sodium	• Counterbalances liquid • Distribution of cell liquids	• Pure, unrefined seasalt • Meat soup • Zucchini
Phosphorus	• Development of bones • Kidney utilization • Cell development • Important role in protein, fat and carbohydrate utilization	• Fish • Eggs • Meat and poultry • Dairy products • Grains and nuts
Calcium	• Development of bones • Muscle tightening • Controls the balancing of acid and alkali	• Milk and milk products • Green vegetables which are leafy • Fish which includes soft bones
Magnesium	• Nerve transportation • Forming of bones • Key in metabolizing carbohydrates, minerals and sugar • Helps to absorb other minerals • Teeth enamel	• Pure, unrefined seasalt • Fish • Dairy products • Nuts • Green vegetables • Wholegrains
Sulphur	• Safeguards against infection • Part of the muscle cell structure • Makes up cartilage and skin • Safeguards against radiation and pollutants	• Vegetables from mustard plants • Dairy produce • Eggs
Chloride	• Controls the counterbalancing of acid and alkali • Controls the balancing of liquid • Helps to digest proteins and carbohydrates	• Pure, unrefined seasalt • Coconut

It should be noted that even though a person may not visibly show they are lacking minerals, they could still be consuming insufficient mineral amounts. For example, teenage girls, women who can bear children, and some vegan/vegetarians are prone to have low iron levels. They are subsequently at an increased risk of anaemia. Current trends suggest a worrying number of adolescents with low calcium intake. The impact this can have for both young and older women's future bone and teeth health is of concern.

Vitamins

Vitamins are a body of carbon filled organic compounds. These are essential for us to grow and for metabolism. All vitamins are synthesized by plants, so can be consumed by either eating the relevant plant or by eating animal products, whose vitamin content originates from plants.

Vitamin types

Vitamins can be categorized into two types:

- Fat soluble
- Water soluble

Fat soluble vitamins

Vitamin	Functions	Sources
Vitamin A	• Encourages gastric liquids to aid the digesting of protein • Needed for good eyesight • Development of bones • Immune system • Safeguards against pollution and progressive damage	• Cod liver oil • Liver • Seafood • Sweet potatoes • Carrots • Green leafy vegetables • Fortified food like cereal
Vitamin D	• Processes calcium • Preserves healthy bones and teeth. • Claimed to be able to safeguard against cancer and multiple sclerosis.	• Fortified milk • Butter originating from cows fed by grass • Cod liver oil • Cheese • Cereals • Egg yolks • Salmon • Sunlight • Seafood
Vitamin E	• Works as an antioxidant • Helps to circulate blood • Preserves structural quality of the cells, for example skin, nails and hair • Assists in repairing of tissue and the healing process • Decreases rate of ageing • Strong antioxidant • Alongside some other trace minerals, it helps safeguard against cancer and CHD	• Pure unprocessed vegetable oils • Butter • Meats originating from organs • Wholegrains, nuts such as almonds and hazelnuts • Seeds • Leafy vegetables which are dark in color • Vegetable oils such as sunflower, canola and soybean
Vitamin K	• Vital in blood clotting function • Helps to form and preserve the health of the bones	• Leafy green veg e.g. parsley, chard & kale • Oils such as olive, canola and soybean • Broccoli

The above vitamins fall in the fat-soluble category because they can only be absorbed, transported and utilized in the presence of fat. Therefore, a low-fat diet can negatively impact one's health because of deficiency in the fat-soluble vitamins.

Water soluble vitamins

Vitamin	Functions	Sources
Vitamin B	• Encourages nerves, the skin, hair, liver, muscle tone and eyes to stay healthy • Stops extreme tiredness • Plays major part in aiding metabolism • Assists in the production of cholesterol • Creation of red blood cells and preserves iron rates in the blood • Preserves fertility and development	• Pure, unprocessed grains • Fresh fruit and vegetables • Nuts which are raw • Legumes • Seafood and meats originating from bodily organs
Vitamin C	• Assists in the development of immune system • Needed to form collagen which binds the cells together • Helps transmit chemical messages to the brain • Makes the capillary walls stronger • Assists in breastfeeding process • Helpful to the working of the adrenal gland • Strong antioxidant	• Fresh fruit such as citrus fruits, red berries and tomatoes • Fresh vegetables such as potatoes, broccoli, cauliflower, sprouts, red/green bell peppers, cabbage and spinach • Some meats originating from bodily organs

The B and C group of vitamins are all water-soluble, which means that they are absorbed, transported and utilized within water. Water soluble vitamins cannot be stored within the body in large quantity, so they need to be included in the diet daily to avoid their deficiency. A diet high in refined simple carbohydrates containing an excess of sucrose can lead to deficiency of vitamin B and C.

Vitamin intake recommendations

A healthy balanced diet (see *Eatwell Guide* section) will provide most people with the amounts of vitamins and minerals required by the body, eliminating the need to take vitamin supplements.

The Department of Health however, recommends certain supplements for some groups of people (e.g. children, pregnant women) who are at risk of deficiency. These are described in the *Supporting clients* section.

Antioxidants

With the passage of time, and as the human body progressed to use oxygen, it also developed ways to restrict the potential erosion that can happen as a consequence of oxygen-fueled responses (like ageing and structural erosion). The body does this by using the antioxidant enzymes which are made by the body within cells. Food that we regularly eat are also a source of dietary antioxidants. Those who are deficient in nutrients may be more sensitive because the antioxidant enzymes within the body need nutrients, like vitamins A, C and E and minerals like zinc, manganese, copper and selenium. As we age, we begin to lose the fight against radiation, pollution and poor diet induced environmental damage.

Taking part in exercise pushes up the oxidative pressure because of the increase in oxygen that is consumed. It is therefore imperative that people participating in regular, especially intensive exercise should make sure their diet is of a higher than average quality, to ensure maximum nutritional benefit. A mixture of vitamins from a variety of sources will make sure the body is working at its maximum potential. This will in turn assist in limiting the damage and injuries caused by exercise and encourage the recovery process.

Sources of antioxidants

Antioxidant	Source
Vitamin C	• Citrus fruit (lemon, lime and oranges), green vegetables, peppers and tomatoes
Vitamin E	• Almonds, egg yolks, green leafy vegetables, wholegrains
Selenium	• Eggs, peas and oysters
Zinc	• Dairy, fish, meat and shellfish

Activity

Activity 2.1: List some sources of the following macro and micro nutrients.

Carbohydrate	Fat	Protein	Vitamin A	Vitamin C

Digesting and absorbing nutrients

A functioning digestive system is a pre-requisite for any benefits of healthy eating to take effect. Failure of part or parts of this system will compromise the amount of nutrition entering the body.

Because the body cannot absorb big amounts of food, it utilizes the digestion process to break down food into smaller constituents which are both easier to be absorbed and travel around the body. Carbohydrates are absorbed as sugars, fats are absorbed as free fatty acids and proteins are digested as amino acids.

The small intestine is where most of the nutrients are absorbed. The walls within the small intestine are presented in many folds, coated with microscopic hairs known as microvilli. This gives a platform where nutrients can be immersed into the bloodstream. Water and a few vitamins are immersed in the large intestine.

A number of materials, like water, can be absorbed without being digested. Human beings can't digest other materials, like dietary fiber and so these are unable to be absorbed. Such material travels straight through the digestive area and are ejected by the body via the faeces.

The digestive process is detailed in *Chapter 1A*.

Importance of a balanced diet

A balanced diet is one that gives your body the nutrients it needs to function correctly. To ensure your body gets proper nutrition, a healthy diet should contain food from the main food groups including:

- Potatoes, bread, rice, pasta and other starchy carbohydrates
- Fruit and vegetables
- Dairy and alternatives
- Beans, pulses, fish, eggs, meat and other proteins
- Oils and spreads

In addition, it is essential to remain hydrated. It is important to drink six to eight cups/glasses of fluid each day.

A proportional diet is essential as our bodily organs require the right nutrition to function properly. Poor nutrition increases the risk of disease, infection, tiredness and unsatisfactory performance. Children who have a poor diet often experience issues with development, growth and lack academic success. Such negative eating habits can continue into adulthood and the remainder of their lives.

It has been well evidenced through scientific research, that eating well with proper nutrition has many benefits, which are:

- Helps to regulate a good weight
- Lowers body fat
- Supplies body with energy
- Encourages adequate sleep
- Reduces chances of developing modern day diseases

Health problems related to poor nutrition

There are many health conditions related to poor diets and lifestyle choices (including lack of exercise). Some of these conditions are listed below, however, note that this list is not exhaustive and as a personal trainer you may come across other conditions that are related to getting nutritional intakes wrong which require referral to specialists such as dietitians.

- **Being obese:** Lack of adequate nutrition can result in a person being overweight or obese. One way to combat this is to lower salt consumption and also reduce the number of calories that are obtained from solid fats and hidden sugars. This can lead to a significant decline in people classed as overweight or obese.

- **Malnutrition:** Being under-nourished is just as much an issue as eating too much.

- **Cardiovascular disease:** The likelihood of developing heart disease increases if a person has a diet which includes lots of fats, in particular saturated and trans fats. Foods such as cheese, sausages bacon, burgers and whole milk contain saturated fats. This type of fat, which is also contained in other animal-originated food, raises low-density lipoprotein in the blood. Cholesterol builds up and begins to thicken the arteries. This in turn makes the heart perform harder to drive blood through. The additional burden on the heart progressively reduces its strength and makes the chances of having a heart attack more likely. Both kinds of trans fats – artificial or natural – are just as damaging as each other. Trans fats are responsible for increasing harmful low-density lipoprotein (LPL), but at the same time they decrease 'good' high-density lipoprotein (HDL). Lots of animal-originated food contain tiny amounts of trans fats which occur naturally and cannot be fully avoided. Foods which are processed, like some margarine, cakes, biscuits, sweets and chips have added artificial trans fats which are avoidable, as the foods just mentioned don't necessarily form part of a balanced diet.

- **Bowel issues:** The digestive tract is adversely affected by a bad diet. This is due to the probable lack of fiber in the diet. Lack of the recommended daily fiber allowance presents itself with signs in the body such as too much gas, diarrhea or constipation that doesn't allow bowel movements for days or discomfort when using the toilet. Excess fat in some fatty food only further irritates the digestive tract. All of these symptoms can be avoided by simply incorporating wholewheat bread, wraps or rolls into the diet as much as possible. Adding vegetables onto a burger or choosing a salad increases fiber consumption. It is recommended to have condiments or dressing at hand so that there is greater control over how much you add to your plate, thus avoiding eating excessive fat.

- **Hypertension:** Eating too much salt and not having enough potassium in the diet can cause hypertension. Too much alcohol can also result in hypertension.

- **Diabetes:** Occurs where there is a metabolic imbalance in the body. It can happen when the body is unable to produce enough insulin to break down glucose. This is known as Type 1 diabetes. There is also something known as Type 2 diabetes, where the insulin that is present cannot be utilized. Type 1 diabetes is inherited. However, Type 2 diabetes is caused by obesity, which is linked to bad food choices. Because weight gain is more likely to happen to people who eat unhealthy food, it therefore follows that the chances of developing Type 2 diabetes for people who have poor nutrition also increases. For any Type 2 diabetes sufferer who takes medication to balance out their sugar levels, losing weight can keep down the adverse effects of the illness.

- **Osteoporosis:** None or little physical activity and poor nutrition are both causes of osteoporosis-linked fractures. A proportional diet together with exercise can manage the condition.

- **Mental disorders:** Lack of good nutrition can aggravate some mental disorders. Our emotions and brain performance rely on what foods we eat. One example of this are omega 3 fatty acids, which have a positive impact on brain function.

Nutritional recommendations

Calories

Calories are a Chapter of measurement. A calorie is a Chapter of energy contained in the food and drink which we all eat. The amount of energy that we need is determined by how old we are. For example, developing children and teenagers may require more energy than other groups. Secondly, our way of life is also a factor which has an effect on required energy levels. For example, if our daily life requires us to be more active than others then we will need more calories. Finally, our own stature is a factor so our height and weight may affect the speed at which we use up energy.

Additional elements can also influence how much energy is used. Thyroid hormones as well as other hormones can have an effect. Some medicines are another of these elements. For example, the steroid called glucocorticoids, which heals inflammation, has such an effect. Being ill is also another factor which may influence how much energy is burned.

A man with an average, proportional and good diet requires approximately 10,500kj (2,500 calories) daily in order to preserve his weight. For women, the required figure is approximately 8,400kj (2,000kcal) a day. These figures may change and are dependent on one's age, metabolism and activity levels, amongst other things.

To preserve a good weight, the number of calories eaten and drunk need to be in proportion to the amount of calories expended via exercise and activity.

The best and healthiest method of losing weight is to use up more calories than what is consumed. This is to be achieved by eating healthily within a balanced diet and at the same time taking part in more exercise.

Reference intakes

Reference intakes (RIs) are a form of guidance which are printed on food labels. They provide helpful information about the amount of energy a typical person may need, as well as provide helpful advice on how well a specific nutrient adjusts to a daily eating plan. Reference intakes have been worked out using the estimated level of daily nutrition and energy required for a healthy and proportionate diet. Reference intakes are not goals, because the energy and nutritional needs differ from person to person. Reference intakes replaced the former system of Guideline Daily Amounts (GDAs) which were on all food labels before the RI system was introduced. Both shared the same aims.

Adult reference intakes

The RIs for a typical adult's healthy and proportional daily diet are 2000 calories of energy; 70g of total fat; 20g of saturates; 260g Carbohydrates; 90g total sugars; 50g protein and 6g of salt.

The RIs for all sugars could be sugar contained in milk, fruit and also added sugar. Multiple food companies place food labels on their products that share information on the levels of every nutrient like fat, sugars and sodium.

The information can be relayed in the form of percentages of the reference intake for that particular nutrient by weight (per 100g), volume (per 100ml) and/or by serving.

Food companies are obliged to add the statement 'Reference intake of an average adult (8400kj/2000kcal)' when percentage RI's are written with 'per 100g/ml'. RI advice and nutrient percentages are normally located on the back or side of food packets. For some nutrients, the percentages are also featured at the front of the packet.

Dietary reference values

Dietary reference values (DRVs) – are a group of approximate calculations detailing the amount of energy and nutrients required for different types of healthy people. These were formulated by the Committee on Medical Aspects of Food and Nutrition Policy (COMA) in 1991.

They are not intended to be goals for people to meet. COMA set four types of dietary reference values:

1. **Reference Nutrient Intakes (RNIs):** These are utilized for protein, vitamins and minerals and are a rough calculation of the amounts that should satisfy the requirements of the type of people to which they apply to. These are not minimum goals of any kind.
2. **Estimated Average Requirements (EARs):** This is used specifically for energy.
3. **Lower Reference Nutrient Intakes (LRNIs):** Any consumption below this number are almost always insufficient for most people.
4. **Safe Intake (SI):** This is used where there isn't enough proof to set an RNI, EAR or LRNI. The Safe Index is an amount deemed to be sufficient for nearly every individual, but also beneath a level that can have unwanted effects.

The DRVs have been incorporated into the UK's food advisory guidelines. For example, the Eatwell plate is a visual description of the types and amounts of foods that contribute to a healthy and proportional diet.

Scientific Advisory Committee on Nutrition (SACN)

COMA now no longer exists. The Scientific Advisory Committee on Nutrition (SACN) is now the advisory body for the government on diet and health. SACN were responsible for:

- Re-evaluating the population advice for estimated energy needs in 2011.
- A report entitled 'Carbohydrates and Health 2015' in which they issued new advice for free sugars and fiber nutrients.
- A report entitled 'Vitamin D and Health 2016' in which it issued new advice on vitamin D.

The Eatwell Guide

The Foods Standards Agency (FSA)

In order that advice can be given to the public, various organizations including the UK Food Standards Agency (FSA) have developed generic information that can be used when a 'normal' diet is required. The 'Eatwell Guide' produced by the FSA gives graphical representation of the proportions of food that should be taken to meet a basic level of nutritional health amongst most of the population.

Food category	Nutrients supplied
Green: Vegetables and fruit	Vegetables and fruit both provide: • A generous amount of minerals • Vitamins that dissolve quickly in the body • fiber • Water In addition, vegetables provide complex carbohydrate whilst fruit supplies sugar.
Yellow: Foods containing plenty of starch	Mainly complex carbohydrates. Wholefood and wholegrain choices also supply: • fiber • Vitamins and minerals which dissolve quickly in the body
Pink: Meat, fish and substitutes	Protein is the main nutrient here. Fat also comes under this category. Vitamins and minerals which dissolve quickly in the body, like iron and sulphur, can also be present.
Blue: Milk and dairy products	Protein, milk, sugar and fat all come under this group. Also present are vitamins and minerals which are stored in the body when not in use – for example, calcium and magnesium.
Purple: High added fat and sugar content	The majority of foods in this category are mostly processed and are of poor nutritional benefit. They can also have a high content of refined sugar and vegetable oils.

The Eatwell Guide is a visual aid designed to help people achieve a healthy and balanced diet. The method has been comprehensively trialed in Northern Ireland amongst medical experts and customers alike.

The size of each portion tallies with government advice for a diet that gives all the nutrients needed for a healthy child (aged two or over). The guide shows how much of what you eat overall should come from each food group.

The Eatwell Guide is based on the main food groups that together provide a healthy, balanced diet:

- Potatoes, bread, rice, pasta and other starchy carbohydrates
- Fruit and vegetables
- Dairy and alternatives
- Beans, pulses, fish, eggs, meat and other proteins
- Oils and spreads
- Drink six to eight cups / glasses of fluid each day

The Eatwell Guide can be followed by most individuals including:

- People from all ethnic origins
- Those who are deemed underweight and overweight
- Vegetarians
- Any person under medical care or with specific dietary needs, although both these groups are advised to check their suitability to the Eatwell Guide with a doctor or regulated dietitian

It should be noted that the Eatwell Guide is wholly unsuitable for infants under the age of two as their nutritional needs are vastly different to others.

Healthy eating tips

The Eatwell Guide is also supported by eight specific healthy eating tips provided by the Food Standards Agency:

1. Base your meals on starchy foods
2. Eat plenty of fruit and vegetables
3. Eat more fish – including a portion of oily fish each week
4. Cut down on saturated fat and sugar
5. Eat less salt
6. Get active and be a healthy weight
7. Stay hydrated by drinking plenty of water
8. Don't skip breakfast

Portion sizes

The table below provides some guidelines on typical portion size that would form one serving of the required nutrient.

Food category	One portion amount example
Fruit 	• Small fruit: 15 cherries, 6-8 strawberries, 2 kiwis, 2 plums • Moderate fruit: one whole apple, pear, banana or an orange • Large fruit: half a grapefruit, one slice of melon, half a mango
Vegetables 	• Green vegetables – 2 x broccoli heads, 4 x spinach or green beans • Salad vegetables – 3 x celery or sticks 7-8 cherry tomatoes • Cooked vegetables – 3 x full tablespoons of cauliflower, carrot, cabbage or peas
Pasta, potatoes, bread and rice 	• A single slice of bread • Handful of rice, pasta or couscous • Small to moderate sized potatoe
Fish, meat, beans and eggs 	• A piece of fish about 15cm • Lean meat 10cm by 5cm • 1 large boiled egg
Milk and dairy 	• 1 medium cup of milk • 150ml yogurt portion
Food and drink containing a high amount of sugar or fat 	Consumption of such products should not exceed 8% of overall daily intake

Recommended intakes

Fat, carbohydrate and fiber recommendations

	Population average % of food energy
Saturated fatty acids	Not more than 11
Polyunsaturated fatty acids	6.5
Monounsaturated fatty acids	13
Trans fatty acids	Not more than 2
Total fat	Not more than 35
Non-milk extrinsic sugars	Not more than 11
Intrinsic and milk sugars, and starch	39
Total carbohydrate	50
Fiber as non-starch polysaccharide (g/day)	18*

*Only applicable to children over five years

Source: FSA nutrient and food based guidelines for UK institutions, 2007

Salt

Age	Target average salt intake (g/d)
0-6 mths	Less than 1
7-12 mths	1
1-3 yrs	2
4-6 yrs	3
7-10 yrs	5
11yrs+	6

Protein, vitamins and nutrients

Nutrient	1-3yrs	4-6yrs	7-10yrs	11-14yrs	11-14yrs
Protein	15g	20g	28g	42g	55g
Iron	7mg	6mg	9mg	14.8mg	14.8mg
Zinc	5mg	6.5mg	7mg	9mg	9.5mg
Vitamin A (retinol equivalents)	400mcg	400mcg	500mcg	600mcg	700mcg
Folate	70mcg	100mcg	150mcg	200mcg	200mcg
Vitamin C	30mg	30mg	30mg	35mg	40mg
Salt	2g	3g	5g	6g	6g

Nutrient	Adults 19-50 yrs	Adults 50 yrs and above
Protein	55g	53g
Iron	14.8mg	9mg
Zinc	9.5mg	9.5mg
Vitamin A (retinol equivalents)	700mcg	700mcg
Folate	200mcg	200mcg
Vitamin C	40mg	40mg
Salt	6g	6g

The U.S. Food & Drugs Administration (FDA) https://www.fda.gov/food/ and FSA in the UK https://www.food.gov.uk/

The Food Standards Agency (FSA):

- **Is accountable for the safety and cleanliness of food in the whole of the UK.**
- **Co-operates with local authorities to implement food safety rules.**
- **Undertakes compliance work to ensure that food safety regulations are being met by meat plants in the UK.**
- **Authorizes research linked with food safety.**
- **Has ceased being answerable for nutrition or healthy eating procedures, including the Eatwell plate and reducing salt. However, it still has responsibility for nutritional policy in Scotland and Northern Ireland.**
- **Maintains responsibility for safety and labeling matters – for example, 'use by' labels and labels relating to allergies.**

Vitamin D guidelines

The main source of vitamin D is sunlight on the skin. Some adults may not be exposed to such sunlight often enough, especially if they spend most of their time inside. Such individuals may need to take Vitamin D as a supplement. Government guidelines suggest for this particular group, a 10 microgram (mcg) supplement be taken daily. This guidance is applicable to pregnant or breastfeeding females, elderly individuals, people of Asian origin, people who tend to cover up all of their body when they go out, those who prefer not to go outdoors and people who don't eat meat or fish.

Guidelines for special populations

Ideally, all of us should be able to obtain all the nutrients we need from the food and drink that we consume. However, this is not always possible for all groups of people and so they are advised to take supplements. Such groups include:

- Females who may become pregnant.
- Females hoping to conceive are advised to take an extra 400 micrograms (mcg) folic acid daily before conception and until the 12th week of pregnancy. It is also recommended that this group eat foods high in folate. For example, green vegetables, brown rice and fortified cereals (this would total up to 600mcg of folate daily from folate heavy foods and supplements).
- Females who are already pregnant and breastfeeding are advised to take a daily 10mcg dose of vitamin D.
- Children under the age of 5 who are bad eaters may need to take vitamins A, C and D.

Children who have a good appetite and eat a wide variety of foods including fruit and vegetables may not need vitamins at all.

Food labels

Anyone who is serious about bettering their nutrition should learn how to interpret or 'decode' labels on food products. Food companies are legally required to put on a lot of information on their labels and such information is of great assistance when an individual is out shopping; reading labels correctly will allow the individual to make informed choices about what they eat.

The fundamentals of food nutrition

The information table printed on food packaging gives an average amount of each type of nutrient within a product. Ingredients are usually listed on food labels in descending order of weight. Presently, loose foods sold or food that is cooked 'in-house' do not have to be as stringently regulated as pre-packed foods.

Food labels are normally stated separately from the total carbohydrate content. Some food companies like to conceal the true amount of sugar by not further dividing this figure. Fat content is another nutrient which is not always further broken down, despite the need for consumers to know how much saturated fat is in their food product. Salt content is about two and a half times of sodium. GDAs are advice of the number of calories and nutrients individuals should eat daily for a healthy, well-proportioned diet.

Food companies are duty-bound to list a high number of permissible food additives. They do this by stating the E-number or the actual full name of it. Companies tend to use 'wordy' names so that the average member of public will be unlikely to question further rather than stating the actual E-numbers. Companies rely on the consumers ignorance of such terms as those conscious of their health are more likely to be put off by E-numbers. It is therefore imperative that we equip ourselves with knowledge of the more familiar terms so we can make informed choices about the food that we eat.

Traffic light labeling

The government, together with food manufacturing companies and food stores have agreed to universal labeling at the front of food packages. These correspond with a traffic light method (I.e. red, amber and green). Therefore, a brief glance at the product should equip the consumer with information on how high, medium and low the contents are with regards to fat, saturated fat, sugars and salt. **The more green on a label, the healthier it is!**

Food marketing terminology

Food companies deploy various strategies in order to merchandise their goods. Terms such as 'fresh', 'natural' and 'traditional' are deployed. There is evidence to suggest that some companies abuse some terms to bolster sales. The Food Advisory Committee (FSA) has evidence to suggest some language used is significantly far from the actual description of the goods on sale, thus potentially misleading consumers. Taking into account this evidence, the FSA has issued guidance to companies and stores, reminding them of the right way in which to describe certain details on food labels. This will prevent consumers from being misled. All the current words have been reviewed and replaced except for 'homemade', as detailed in the table on the next page.

Revised Existing Terms	New Terms
Original	Farmhouse (Pate)
Homemade*	Hand-made
Traditional	Selected#
Authentic	Quality#
Real	Premium#
Fresh**	Finest#
Pure**	Best#
Natural**	Seasonal#
Farmhouse**	Style#
	Wild#
	Type#

*This word has not been replaced, but the consultation recommended that a change should be made.

** The guidance on these words was not judged as needing any consumer research. However, they have been changed due to the recent issues and enquiries brought about my consumers, enforcement agencies, and the industry prior to, and during the consultation.

Broad advice only is given on these words.

Criteria for the usage of these terminologies is summarized below.

Word	Summary
Fresh	• Can assist the consumer where the word sets apart goods that are sold shortly after being produced or harvested. However, the latest ways of storing and distributing goods makes it hard to tell when the word is used deservedly so. • The use of this word should be avoided where it has no real significance to the description (e.g. 'garden fresh', 'ocean fresh'). • When making statements like 'freshly prepared', 'freshly picked', it is best to also state a time (e.g. 'freshly picked this morning'). • Term should not be used to describe meat that has been frozen but sold in a thawed state.
Original	• This word should only be included in descriptions where a food has been made to a formula, and where its origin can be traced back. It should have stayed unaltered over the course of time. • It should not include substitutes for main ingredients. • It may be used to outline a procedure, only if the procedure was used first in the production of the food and that it has stayed unaltered over time. • To be given 'original' status, a product cannot have been altered to any significant degree. It should stay accessible as the 'standard' product when new ingredients are brought in.

Word	Summary
Natural	• A product should stay true to its description when described as 'natural'. It should be made by nature and not be man-made. If any chemicals are deployed to change its make-up, including additives and flavourings, then the product cannot be described as 'natural'. • Procedures which do come under the remit of 'natural' are smoking (no chemicals), baking, roasting, blanching, sieving, washing using water and classical dehydration methods. • Procedures which cannot be described as natural are freezing, concentration, pasteurization and sterilization. • Compound products, which have been made from at least two ingredients, cannot be described as 'natural'. • Uncertain terms like 'natural goodness', 'nature's way' are assertions which are best not used.
Pure	• This is to be used in products with only a single ingredient, of which no additions have been made and where there is no possibility of it being mixed with similar foods. • This term is also used to reinforce the optimum quality of the products ingredients. • Compound foods should not be described as pure but they can be 'made from pure ingredients'. • The description should encompass being plain or unflavored and should only be used if the above criteria is met.
Traditional	• This is a popular description of a product or procedure where other, more recent products are also on the market. • It can only be used where a method or main formula of a product has been in existence for a lengthy period. • 'Traditional' should not be used just to differentiate an original recipe from later versions of it. • Care should be taken when using and consideration should be given as to whether the term 'original' or alternative word is better suited as a description.
Home-made	• These products should be just that – food made at home, by an individual, using traditional methods. • This term is clearly defined in dictionaries. • Factory made products should never be described as home-made as this will be a clear misrepresentation of the facts.
Hand-made	• A product described as this should be mostly hand-made, as opposed to just one stage of the production process. Alternative descriptions include 'hand assembled', 'hand carved', or 'hand decorated/finished'. • It is acceptable though, for a hand-made product to be made within a commercial setting.
Farmhouse	• Will be perceived as misleading if the products being described as farmhouse are not actually produced on a farm. • If this term is used on foods other than bread and pate, then they must have been produced on a farm. • Just describing a food as 'farmhouse' (e.g. farmhouse vegetables) holds no weight and companies should refrain from using it. • Foods or other ingredients should not be stated as being 'country style'

Healthy marketing terminology

For the past 20 years, the media has taken positive steps to increase public awareness of the hazards and disadvantages of leading an unhealthy life. So many food products are aimed at an ever-growing number of consumers who are interested in being healthy.

Companies strive to ensure that supposed healthy foods are noticed by the consumer. Phrases are used to grab the attention of health-savvy people. For example, 'low in salt', 'sugar free' and 'low fat' are terms commonly seen on supermarket shelves, as they have been peddled as being the healthier choice.

Nutrition Facts

Serving Size 1 cup (200g)
Servings per Container 4

Amount Per Serving	
Calories 300	Calories from Fat 110
	% Daily Value
Total Fat 12g	20%
Saturated Fat 4g	22%
Cholesterol 0mg	0%
Sodium 70mg	6%
Total Carbohydrate 30g	10%
Dietary Fiber 0g	0%
Sugars 20g	
Protein 5g	
Vitamin A 5%	Vitamin C 0%
Calcium 10%	Iron 0%

* Percent Daily Values are based on a 2,000 calorie diet.

Refined sugars and sweeteners

People often add refined sugar to their foods. For many, this type of sugar can become addictive. It consists of calories that don't benefit the individual nutritionally. Foods aimed at people seeking to lose weight often contain sweeteners. Although the reduced calories aid weight loss, it is important that the dangers/risks associated with such compounds are known. Adding sweeteners to a product benefits the food companies financially as it also contains a slightly addictive compound which encourages repeat purchase of the product.

Examples of common added sugars and sweeteners:

- Dextrose
- Glucose syrup
- High fructose corn starch
- Inverted sugar syrup
- Mannitol
- Maltodextrin
- Sorbitol
- Xylitol

Organic food

Organic means:

- Working alongside nature as opposed to working against it
- High standards for animals
- Less pesticides
- No artificial herbicides or fertilizers
- No artificial colors & preservatives
- No regular use of antibiotics
- GM Free

Source: Soil association - https://www.soilassociation.org/

Greater continuous environmental development of the land and natural habitat encourages wildlife to increase.

All organic products purchased, whether its food or toiletries, drink or textiles, help to develop an improved world.

Organic food comes from reliable sources. All such food products must follow a set criterion before being allowed to have organic status. The criteria specify what farmers can do in the formation of organic food. Organic farms and organic food companies come under inspection a minimum of once every year. The standards that it needs to meet is set by EU law.

Food preparation

Even though USA protocols promote us eating fresh, whole foods, even these types of foods can vary in quality. Food is separated as being refined and unrefined (for example white pasta has less nutrients than wholewheat pasta), and beyond this, there is not much information available as to what makes good quality food. This is a valuable area because it decides the overall nutritional benefit of the food that we regularly eat.

There are multiple phases to food preparation in which food is handled, farmed, and manufactured from the time of its inception as a seed (or the moment its born if an animal), to when it is presented at the dining table. Every phase can influence the result, which is food eaten by us and the nutrients that are contained in them. We can choose good nutritious food for ourselves during our regular supermarket shop, but then go home and cook the food in an 'unhealthy' way, forcing it to lose all the nutritional benefits it has to offer. For example, chopping vegetables many hours before cooking it encourages important micronutrients to disappear; frying and roasting raises the fat within cooking whereas grilling or baking does not; slow cooking meat at a lower temperature reduces damage to proteins and allows more nutrients to be absorbed from the food. This process of food quality highlights some of the matters surrounding our food production process.

End of Chapter activities

Activity 2.2: Draw the Eatwell plate, listing food types in each category.

Activity 2.3: List the eight healthy eating tips given by FSA.

Activity 2.4: Prepare a two minute talk on the importance of healthy eating and the problems associated with a poor diet.

Activity 2.5: Review this food label and answer the following questions.

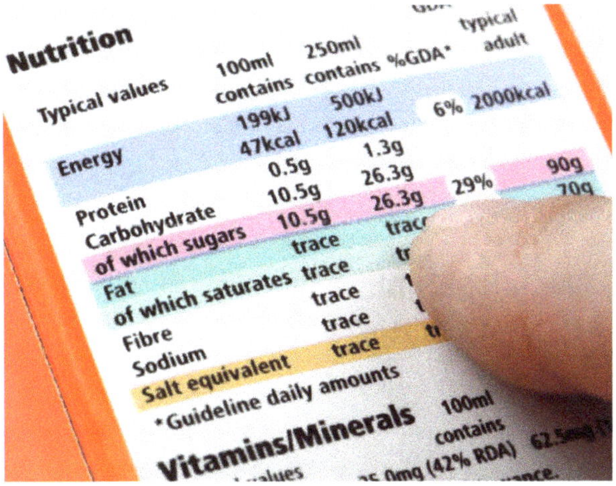

1. How many calories in every 100ml?

2. How much fat in every 100ml?

3. How much carbohydrate (non-sugar) in 100ml?

Activity 2.6: **Match the food sources to vitamins.**

Vitamin A

Vitamin B

Vitamin C

Vitamin D

Vitamin E

Vitamin K

Activity 2.7: **Separate these vitamins into fat soluble or water soluble.**

Vitamin A Vitamin B Vitamin C

Vitamin D Vitamin E Vitamin K

Fat Soluble	Water Soluble

End of Chapter checklist

1. What is protein made up of?
2. What is protein broken down to by the digestive system?
3. What are the functions of protein?
4. What are the three categories that protein can be split into?
5. What do you understand by the metabolic process – anabolism and catabolism?
6. What is the role of carbohydrate?
7. What is the difference between simple carbohydrate and complex carbohydrate?
8. What food contains insoluble starch?
9. What is refined carbohydrate and how does it differ from unrefined carbohydrate?
10. What are the three main types of fat?
11. What are the functions of fat in the human body?
12. Which type of fat is considered better for the human body?
13. What are the differences between the two types of unsaturated fat?
14. What are some of the sources of omega 3 and omega 6?
15. What minerals are needed by the body and why?
16. What are anti-oxidants and list some sources of antioxidants?
17. What is the definition of a balanced diet?
18. What health conditions can result from unbalanced diets?
19. How many calories does an average man need per day and how many does a woman need per day?
20. What are 'reference intakes' and 'dietary reference values'?
21. What is the main source of vitamin D?
22. What are refined sugars and sweeteners?
23. What does 'fresh' mean on a food label?
24. What does 'home made' mean on a food label?
25. Which method of food preparation increases the fat in the food?

Chapter 2B: Using the principles of nutrition with training programs

Chapter summary

This Chapter will demonstrate how to apply the principles of nutrition to exercise and fitness to develop suitable training programs specific to the needs of a client and their body.

Aim

The aim of this Chapter is to allow personal trainers to identify important elements of nutrition and use the knowledge on the function of nutrients to apply them practically when working with clients.

Learning objectives

After completing this Chapter, personal trainers will be able to:

1. Summarize how the body uses nutrients from food to convert them to energy for activity.
2. Match exercise intensity to energy systems used and main fuel type contributing to the energy systems.
3. Recommend food for exercise – before during and after.
4. Summarize the importance of hydration during exercise.
5. Provide guidelines on the amount of food to consume whilst participating in physical activities.
6. Guide clients on the different types of dietary methods they can adopt for weight loss or weight management and even weight gain.
7. Identify reasons that would imply the need to refer a client to a dietitian or nutritionist.
8. List the symptoms and signs of eating disorders.

Energy for activity

Adequate nourishment and sufficient physical activity play a valuable part in our lives. How much exercise one takes part in has an influence over their nutrition and health in general. A healthy level of fitness decreases the chances of getting life-long diseases like heart disease and obesity. Whether a person wants to preserve their health or take part in an athletic competition, sound nutrition is a good base from which to enhance physical fitness. The correct combination of the energy-rich nutrients carbohydrates, protein and fat (alongside water and micronutrients) improves the body's performance.

Fats, protein and carbohydrates are broken down by the body to produce adenosine triphosphate (ATP) when oxygen is available. All biological processes in the body such as food digestion, hormone production, cell and tissue repairs require energy in the form of ATP. Likewise, when we exercise ATP is required and so the body breaks down one of the phosphate bonds within ATP which then causes the muscles to contract and the body to generate heat. This is why we feel warmer during exercise sessions.

How the body uses the different energy systems to supply energy to the body during exercise was covered in *Chapter 1B: Impact of exercise on the body*. This section will focus on how the body uses up the nutrients (fat, protein and carbohydrate) to produce energy during physical activities.

All the body's faculties receive an instant supply of energy from the ATP. Where a muscle is dormant, it has sufficient ATP to maintain activity for several seconds. As the ATP muscle is utilized, enzymes break up another high energy compound called creatine phosphate (CP). This is so it can replace the source of ATP. Just like ATP, the amount of CP in the muscle is minimal. In the first 10-15 seconds of exercise, the ATP and CP source the muscles with energy. However, activity of longer time periods need the body to replace ATP from the metabolism of energy-rich nutrients.

Carbohydrates, protein and fats all help to make ATP where oxygen is in supply. Where no oxygen is present, just carbohydrates can be used. Even though carbohydrates make ATP quickly, they are not utilized effectively. The supply of oxygen in muscle cells relates directly to how fast the heart is able to pump oxygen through the blood to the working muscles.

Energy from carbohydrate

Carbohydrate (glucose) is stored in the body (muscles and liver) for release as and when required. The muscles store glucose as glycogen and glycogen is converted back to glucose for use during exercise. This cycle is referred to as glycolysis.

Glucose is converted to energy in two ways:

1. Aerobically (in the presence of oxygen)
2. Anaerobically (without oxygen)

Aerobic processes can only occur if oxygen is present. If the body is getting enough oxygen during a workout to keep up with the body's demands of the physical activity, the cells break pyruvate down aerobically. The process of releasing glucose via the aerobic system occurs within a specialized structure in the muscle cell called mitochondria. This glucose is then carried through the blood and stored in the body as a fast source of energy. If the intensity of the exercise intensity prevents the aerobic system from supplying the needed levels of oxygen the cells access a different pathway an anaerobic (no or low oxygen) pathway to release energy and produce pyruvate during glycolysis.

Both processes release waste products. The breakdown of glucose into ATP aerobically releases carbon dioxide, that needs to be removed from the body through respiration (why we breath harder and faster). As the aerobic process fails to keep up with energy demands and the body switches to anaerobic process, lactic acid is produced. The build-up of lactic acid reduces a cell's capacity to further process waste and this leads to fatigue and muscle soreness, forcing us to slow down or stop exercising. Cells then recover by breathing in more oxygen and the circulation of blood help carry away lactic acid.

Producing energy from fat

Like carbohydrate fat can only be used as energy by converting to ATP in the presence of oxygen, but without oxygen fat cannot be burnt. Whether the body is resting or participating in physical activities, to produce ATP, a mixture of both glucose and fatty acid is actually required, but in different proportions. At rest, approximately 70% of ATP is derived from fats and 30% from carbohydrate, but when physical activity commences there is a shift to derive more ATP from carbohydrate, with the shift increasing as the exercise intensity increases.

Lipolysis is the procedure that processes the utilization of fat for energy. In the course of exercise, the triglycerides in adipose tissue and in muscle fibers are broken up into fatty acids and glycerol. Fatty acids are dispersed into the bloodstream and then appropriated by the muscle cells. Within the muscle cells, fatty acids are taken to the mitochondria to make ATP.

Producing energy from protein

Proteins are broken up into amino acids and these can be used to make ATP when oxygen is present. For most exercises, protein represents a small amount of the energy which is used. It only becomes a main supplier of energy when exercise is maintained for several hours.

Exercises which challenge endurance boost amino acid usage as an energy supplier and help preserve blood glucose levels. If amino acids exceed the body's biological need, they are transformed into glycogen or fat in order to be used for energy metabolism. Using proteins for fuel makes carbon dioxide, water, ATP, urea and ammonia.

Exercise intensity and energy systems used

As intensity rises, the ATP is needed more rapidly. This is where carbohydrates start to give more to this process. Even though protein has the same number of calories as glucose, it will not produce sufficient energy, because carbohydrates are accessible. Regular aerobic training makes the body more efficient at transporting and oxidizing fatty acids because the body develops a greater number of mitochondria and fat-burning enzymes as it adapts to exercise. As a result, the body becomes increasingly efficient at burning fat and weight loss occurs.

The table below provide guidelines on what energy system and fuel is used during exercise based on intensity:

Intensity	**Primary energy systems**	**Main fuel used**
Very intense	Phosphocreatine	Carbohydrate
Intense	Phosphocreatine and lactic	Carbohydrate and fat
Heavy	Lactic	Fat
Moderate	Lactic and aerobic	Fat and carbohydrate
Light	Aerobic	Fat

Adapted from Earle and Baechle, 2004

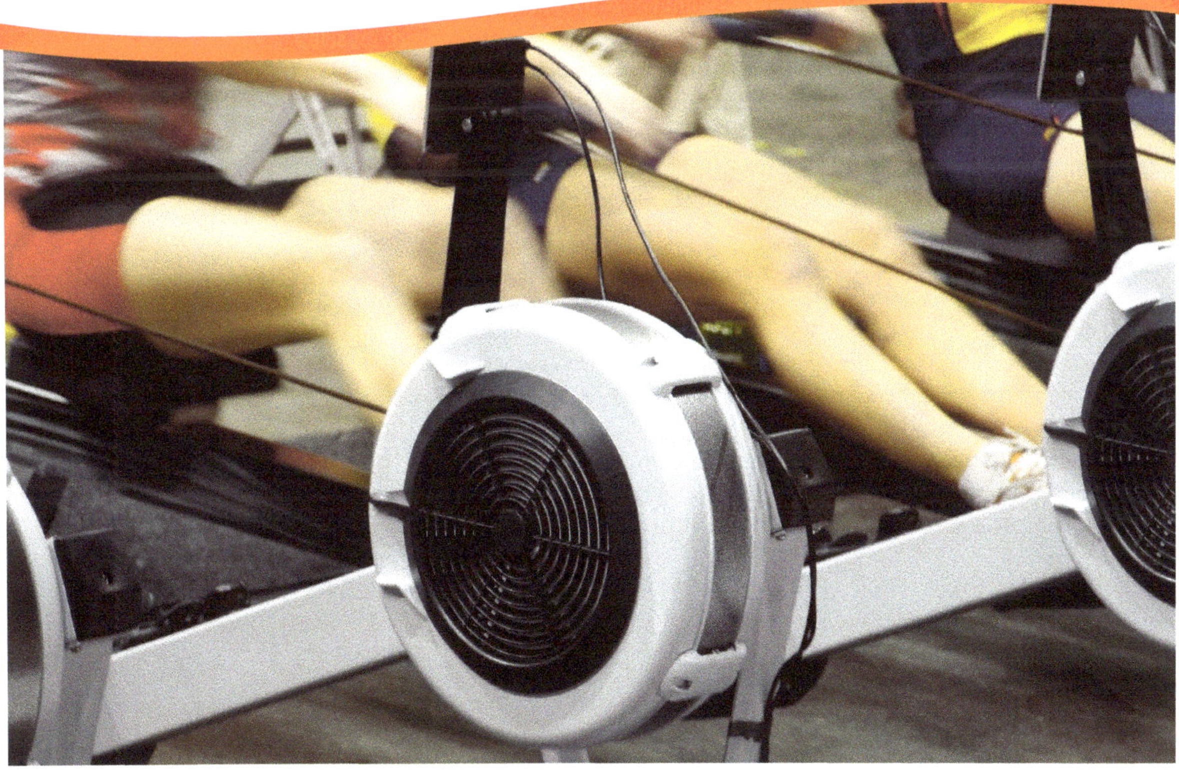

Nutritional recommendations for exercise

All people should try to eat a healthy diet, with ethos from the Eatwell Guide. This advice should also apply when participating in regular exercise, for example physical activity like visiting the gym, swimming, running, cycling or team sports.

A person can live an active life by leading a healthy life. However, it should be noted that exercising will use up more energy. Therefore, unless the intention is to lose weight, the person would need to eat more food to fuel the body with the extra energy that it needs.

Eating healthily to assist in exercise and sport can have many advantages including being able to achieve more, decreasing the likelihood of being injured or sick and to make sure you recover well after exercise or training.

A good diet to aid sport and exercise should include lots of foods which are rich in starch, a good supply of fruit and vegetables, protein and dairy products. Water is also very important to keep hydrated.

Food recommended for exercise

Carbohydrate – food for energy

Carbohydrate is the primary source of energy for the human body. Consumption of the right amount of carbohydrate is vital for exercise and sports activities.

The general rule is that carbohydrate consumption should increase the more exercise you do.

The body is able to keep carbohydrates within the muscles and liver in the form of glycogen. It can use these stores as fuel to supply the brain and muscles during exercise. These glycogen stores are restricted so the individual should have a sufficient store at the beginning of any exercise session.

Carbohydrates, during digestion are broken up into glucose in order to supply ins energy for the body so that it can use it efficiently. A challenging exercise progr utilize the reserved energy from carbohydrates rapidly it is important to inclu carbohydrates in most meals.

Insufficient portions of carbohydrates for people taking part in challenging exercise may result in them feeling tired and unable to perform their best. It can also mean a decline in concentration and longer periods spent in recovery.

Foods containing plenty of starch are a great source of carbohydrates. Types of wholegrain carbohydrates also supply us with fiber, (useful for digestion), many vitamins and minerals (including B vitamins), iron, calcium and folate.

A person wishing to go against the above advice and partake in a low carbohydrate meal program must seek advice from a specialist before doing so.

Carbohydrate loading

Anyone thinking of participating in heavy training, for example for a marathon, is advised to adopt a 'carbohydrate-loading' program.

This entails to firstly train to a limit where all energy in muscles are used up. This training should match (or very closely match) the forthcoming event to ensure the right energy stores are used from the correct muscles. After this, training should be reduced. At the same time, the amount of carbohydrates eaten in the last three days before the main event, should be increased. 8-10g of carbohydrates per kg of body weight should also be eaten.

Fat

Fat is an important nutrient and also provides the body with energy. Eating too much of it can lead to too much energy and may eventually lead to weight gain over a period. It is essential for health guidelines to be followed, so that the amount our body receives from fat is less than 35% and no more. Saturated fats should not go over 11% of all energy received from food. Generally, fats in food consist of both saturated and unsaturated fatty acids. However, opting for food which contain more amounts of unsaturated fat and less saturated fat, is better. More of us eat excessive amounts of saturated fat so it is advisable to reduce intakes of this. The following foods should therefore be eaten sparsely:

- Pastries
- Chocolate
- Certain savory snacks
- Hard cheeses like cheddar
- Oils such as palm oil and coconut oil
- Processed meats, for example sausages, ham, burgers and fatty cuts of meat
- Cakes, puddings
- Biscuits
- Cream, coconut cream and ice-cream
- Butter, lard, ghee, suet
- Fried foods including fried chips

Protein

Protein is essential for good health and for exercise. Its main job is to aid growth and to preserve and repair body cells and tissues, for example, muscle.

Various foods contain differing amounts and combinations of amino acids (the 'building blocks' of proteins). Important amino acids are ones that the body is unable to produce by itself and so these are required from the diet.

Consuming protein-heavy foods on their own will not produce big muscles!

A diet with energy from carbohydrates and fats, protein and muscle-strengthening exercise helps to build muscle.

Not all the protein we consume builds muscle. Excess protein is mostly used for energy once the body has used its protein store for muscle repair.

Most people who like exercising can source their daily protein supply from a healthy and varied diet. Protein should be included in every meal to encourage the building of muscle.

There is evidence to suggest that eating protein before and after an exercise session helps to reignite the muscle repair system.

Nutritionally beneficial sources of protein include:

- Beans, peas and lentils
- Dairy products, cheese, yoghurt and milk
- Fish, including oily fish salmon or mackerel
- Plant-based meat-alternatives for example tofu, tempeh
- Lean cuts of meat
- Poultry, chicken, turkey
- Eggs

Examples of training protein snacks:

- Milk of all types – but lower-fat types contain less energy
- Natural dairy yoghurt of all types – including Greek yoghurt and kefir
- Soy yoghurt and other plant-based alternatives
- Mixed nuts and seeds, unsalted
- Dried fruit, unsweetened
- Boiled eggs

Water

Water although not quite a nutrient is a necessity. The body becomes warmer as it exercises, and it tries to cool itself down by sweating. This leads to water and salt loss via the skin. The exercising person should drink adequate liquid for recovery.

How much a person sweats is dependent on many factors. The first is how intense it is and how long it lasts. The more intense and the longer the duration, the more sweat will be lost by the body. Another factor is the temperature of the surrounding environment. In hot surroundings, sweat loss may rise. What a person is wearing will also affect sweat levels. The more clothing they wear, the faster they will heat up, resulting in more sweat loss. Finally, sweat levels could purely be down to genetics.

The general rule is the more you sweat, the more you should drink.

Food for exercise

The time of day for eating and exercising can affect how the exercising person is feeling and have an impact on their overall performance. The body has to have the right energy within it to carry out its aim. However, a person should not be too full or feel too empty while they exercise.

People vary in what time and amount they decide to eat before exercise. For some, two hours is sufficient time to digest their meal, but others may feel discomfort after exercising two hours after eating and may prefer to leave a bigger gap. It is best to use a trial and error method to see how much and when to eat, to help decide what is best suited to them.

Food before exercise

Preferably, a pre-exercise meal needs to be low fat and include some food which is rich in starch – for example, porridge, pasta or potatoes. It should be eaten two to three hours prior to exercising. If a longer gap is left or if nothing is eaten at all, a person may suffer from low energy or feel light headed whilst exercising.

Some examples of meals that can be eaten before exercise:

- Tomato-based pasta and vegetables
- Porridge including skimmed or semi-skimmed milk
- Sandwich with a chicken filling
- Beans on toast

A small portioned snack between the pre-exercise meal and actual exercise can be eaten about 30-60 minutes before exercise. An easily digested snack should be chosen. Some examples of such snacks are listed below:

- Crackers with cottage cheese
- Fruit – banana is a popular choice
- Milk, or a non-dairy option
- A slice of wholegrain toast thinly spread with peanut butter
- Yoghurt or non-dairy alternatives
- Fruit or plain scone with cheese which is low-fat

There are some foods that should not be eaten before exercise. This is because often they may cause stomach upset. Most of these foods are either fatty foods or foods with high fiber content. Some examples of fatty foods include chips/french fries, crisps, olives, full fat cheese, big portions of nuts. High fiber foods include raw vegetables, cereals rich in fiber and raw nuts and seeds.

Keeping hydrated throughout the day is a must as well as drinking water with the pre-exercise meal.

Food during exercise

Eating a portion of carbohydrates whilst exercising can improve performance for those individuals taking part in challenging or extreme intensity sports lasting over an hour. This is because carbohydrate stocks may noticeably decline (for example, marathon training, football or swimming competitions).

It is critical that water is consumed during exercise, especially if sweating is profuse and if it is exceptionally hot. Water is also needed to replenish electrolytes which have been lost through sweating.

The most sensible thing to do to stay hydrated would be to take regular sips of water during exercise. Thirst is a sign of partial dehydration so it is important that you don't wait until you feel thirsty before drinking water.

Those taking part in exercise sessions lasting less than an hour only need water. If exercising for over an hour, it is best to have a fast digesting carbohydrate and some salts and minerals (electrolytes). A banana, isotonic sports drink, dried fruit, cereal bar or carbohydrate gel are all examples of such snacks.

Food after exercise

Food and fluids play a significant role when it comes to recovery after exercise.

Carbohydrate supplies will be lower after a long run or long workout so it is vital that these are replaced, especially if the person plans to exercise more later in the day.

Suitable foods to have straight after exercise should include protein like salt-free nuts or some milk. Wholegrain carbohydrates and good quality protein snacks should be selected.

As for the post-exercise meal, this should consist of preferably wholegrain starchy food with some good quality lean protein. The sooner this is eaten after exercise, the better for recovery as it will replenish levels of glycogen and muscle protein.

If a meal after exercise is not possible, then a little snack consisting of carbohydrates and protein should be eaten. For example, a banana and some low-fat milk can be consumed within 30 minutes to an hour after exercise so that the recovery process can be started. This is even more relevant when the next exercise session is planned within the next eight hours.

Fruit and vegetables should also be incorporated into meals to achieve balance.

It is crucial to replenish fluid and hydrogen levels lost through sweating so lots of water should be drunk after taking part in exercise.

Amount of food to consume when exercising

General guidelines suggest our daily energy consumption should be 2500 calories for men and 2000 for woman.

Formulas exist to help work out exactly how many calories you as an individual need to keep your energy levels sustained. One method is to work out your basal metabolic rate (BMR). This is the number of calories your body needs to be in a resting state. Listed below is the formula of how to calculate your BMR in kcal per 24 hours:

BMR calculation for men:
66.47 + (13.7 x your weight in kg) + (5 x your height in cm) – (6.8 x your age in years)

BMR calculation for women:
655.1 + (9.6 x your weight in kg) – (1.8 x your height in cm) – (4.7 x your age in years)

The number of calories you need based on your BMR is shown in the table below.

Primary energy systems	Calories required
Hardly any, or no exercise	BMR x 1.2
Mild exercise	BMR x 1.4
Some exercise (three to five days a week)	BMR x 1.5
Above average amount (six to seven days a week)	BMR x 1.7
Extremely active (to be very active and in a physically demanding job)	BMR x 1.9

Supporting clients with diet and nutrition

The support a client will require for dieting and improving their nutritional intake is similar to the support they would require whilst exercising. This includes supporting them in the following areas:

Weight loss

The objective of any plan managing weight is to stop an increase in gaining body fat. For people who already weigh more than they should, the aim is to lose body fat until a healthy level is reached. This would deter health implications linked to obesity.

A number of methods are used in order to obtain the ideal weight and size. Clients must have a good understanding of the background to their method of weight loss. They must also be aware of any side effects linked with their chosen weight loss method. The client and personal trainer should both have enough knowledge of the nutritional stages that the client can expect to encounter whilst on their chosen dietary program.

State	Possible health implications	Impact on performance
Losing weight	If one is overweight, then this could significantly reduce blood pressure and cholesterol.	May boost the power-to-weight ratio. It may also impair recovery because of the catabolic state.
Gaining weight	The most probable effect is a rise in blood pressure and increased bad cholesterol amounts if weight gain is long-term. Joints may also be increasingly strained.	This may help in recovery, in forming muscle and in developing strength. If the power-to-weight ratio is not preserved, then it may adversely affect performance.
Extreme energy limitation	This could lead to a low blood sugar level, being dizzy and fainting.	This could result in being lethargic and being low in energy.

WARNING

Showing empathy and understanding towards the client and communicating with them effectively will assist them in making the right decisions about their diet. It will also help prevent the client from forming 'yoyo' dieting habits and damaging their health.

Dietary Approach	Features	Potential issues
Eating low calorie meals	• These eating plans normally are limited to 1200-1500 calories per day • Sometimes consist of drinking calorie controlled shakes • No need for complicated calorie counting	• Meals may be repetitive and boring • Followers of this plan may lack energy • High rate of followers leaving this eating plan
Counting calories	• Usually requires food consumption of less than 800 calories a day • Sometimes includes bars or milkshakes to replace meals	• Tiredness, feeling nauseous, constipated or diarrhea • Gallstones may appear • Short-term results
Paleolithic eating plan	• Approximately 1/3 of all intake should be protein (depending on season) • Ration of omega 6 to omega 3 fatty acids should be 1:1 and up to a potential 1:4 • There should be a higher amount of monounsaturated fat and less intake of saturated fat • Carbohydrate should be restricted to seasonal fruit, wild vegetables, roots, legumes and nuts • Exercise is recommended as a key part of this plan	• The restriction in dairy and subsequent low calcium intake means it may not be suitable for all
Fasting approach	• Detoxifies many processes within the body • Allows the digestive system to rest • Enables energy levels to be balanced – resulting in weight loss	• Chance of becoming dehydrated • May result in low energy levels and more instances of headaches, general pains, allergies and smelly breath
Ketogenic approach	• Involves eating foods high in fat, an average amount of protein, and low carbohydrates • The lack of carbohydrate lowers blood glucose which results in changing metabolism • Increases fatty acids from stores in adipose tissue • The fatty acids travel to the liver. Here they are broken down into smaller constituents (known as keto acids/ketone bodies) and returned back into circulation • Many bodily tissues utilize ketones as a source of energy and so being in a 'ketogenic state' is the term used to describe being under such influences	• Higher intake of fat increases chance of CHD • Higher protein levels mean acidity in the kidneys and bloods • Reduced calcium in bones • May be unsuitable for people with a history of kidney dysfunction

Ethnic and cultural differences add another dimension to the task of sharing dietary advice. It is imperative that the personal trainer is aware of dietary lifestyles and any cultural traditions of the client. These could be affected by the clients or client's family heritage. It may include foods and ways of cooking from across the globe. Religious adherence can also influence what a client can or can't eat. Such customs must be honored when giving nutritional guidance and any choices made by the client with respect to their lives need to be supported.

Supplements

Fat burning supplements

These are taken by some clients in order to burn fat, boost metabolism and energy, and suppress appetite.

Fat burning supplements have the effect of increasing the number of calories burned off. Ultimately, this can lead to the client losing weight. Some of the constituents that make up these supplements can trigger some hormones such as epinephrine to break up fats and prepare them for the body to utilize as energy.

They can however, have an adverse effect, and may result in illness, heart attack, stroke or seizures. Other possible symptoms include arrhythmia, depression, insomnia and being overly nervous.

Clients who choose to take such supplements should take extra care when using them, analyzing any effects they may have to maximize safety.

Vitamin supplements

These are taken to enhance one's diet. Some supplements however do not possess many 'natural' nutrients. It must be stressed that vitamin supplements have a supportive function only. They are not meant to be a replacement for a poor-quality diet. Typically, a daily dose of multivitamin or mineral will not have a negative effect and it has the ability to help someone who lacks certain levels of nutrients. There is an opinion that a one-day supplement falls short of remedying any heavy deficiency and that the absorption process can be interfered with by the quality of the product. Taking individual vitamins or minerals can be hazardous if the dosage is high so they should only be given via prescription or on the advice of a registered dietitian. Under the guidance of a nutritionist or dietitian, a good quality supplement can provide adequate nutritional support when the dosage is at the correct level.

Protein supplements

Supplements such as protein shakes have become increasingly common over the last 20 years, partly because of the rise in bodybuilding and heavy advertising promoting its use. Protein shakes are popular also because they are user friendly and help to boost muscle mass quickly and easily.

A lot of protein shakes are marketed as including whey protein. Milk contains whey protein. In its bare state, it adds the most beneficial value to the body compared to other proteins. This is advantageous to the body in several ways. One advantage is that it fixes and grows muscle tissues. However, these types of supplements may also present themselves with some issues. Part of the manufacturing process of whey protein involves it being dried at temperatures exceeding 60 degrees Celsius. This level of processing strips its capacity to function. Manufacturers are also guilty of using sugars, sweeteners colors and flavourings to make proteins taste better for the consumer. Such products usually lack fat, despite fat being needed by proteins for effective metabolism. The general consensus is that even though protein supplements do no harm, they are still not a necessity. The body can easily access protein from different foods.

WARNING

If the following applies to a client, they need to be extra careful whilst using such supplements or be directed to a registered dietitian. This would be the safest thing to do:

- **Medical condition**
- **Takes regular, prescribed or over-the-counter medication**
- **Sees a dietitian/nutritionist**
- **Family history of kidney disease**

Energy intake versus energy expenditure

Simply put, energy balance assesses the number of calories ingested and the number of calories used.

The energy balance equation says that if the calories eaten are more than those used, then the extra calories will be saved most probably as extra body fat which results in the gaining of weight. Subsequently, a typical way to lose body fat is to create a 'negative energy balance' by eating fewer calories than what will be used.

The main focus of any functional weight plan is to reduce body fat without decreasing metabolic rate. An effective weight loss plan loses body fat whilst at the same time keeping as much fat free tissue (or FFM – fat free mass) as is possible. This would keep to a minimum any potential loss in metabolic rate. Research has shown that this is done best by slow, consistent weight loss. Drastic cuts in weight loss cannot be maintained.

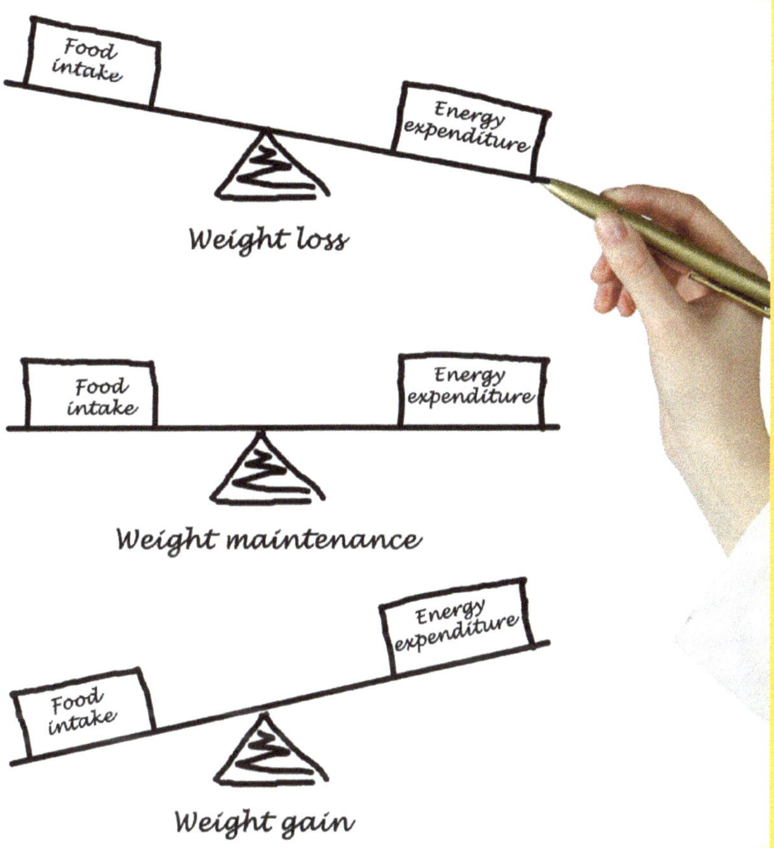

There are many ways to create an energy deficiency. One way is to limit food intake, and another way is to introduce exercise into your lifestyle (or by combining them). The most productive way is to moderately limit diet whilst taking part in exercise, rather than solely exercising or only limiting food.

The total calorific 'spending' is the result of many interacting variables:

- **Basal metabolic rate:** The overall total of the responses that happen within the body when it is in complete rest and whilst nothing is being digested. This is normally communicated as the amount of calories necessary to maintain core activity.
- **Thermal impact of food:** The level of energy consumed by the human body via the processes of
  - Ingestion
  - Digestion
  - Absorption
  - Usage and
  - Saving of food
- **Thermal impact of activity:** The level of energy needed for prepared and unprepared amounts of exercise. As evidence shows that poor amounts of activity are linked to the development of obesity, it means that rising levels of exercise should contribute towards turning around this process.

Referring clients to a dietitian

A personal trainer qualification will allow you to provide healthy eating advice to clients based on UK recognized guidelines. This may require you to communicate with professionals in the field of diet and nutrition as well as refer your clients to these professionals.

Professionals in the field of diet and nutrition

Dietitian

Only registered dietitians (RDs) can review, give a diagnosis of, and seek to treat diet related and nutritional issues on an individual and larger public health level. Their role involves:

- Working with people in good health and those that are ill.
- Using the latest public health and science based research on foods, health and disease. Dietitians can turn this information into practical and usable advice to help patients, clients, carers and colleagues to make good healthy choices.
- Working in the NHS, private sector, in industry, education, research sport, media, PR, publishing and government and NGOs.
- Having an impact on governmental and local policy in the areas of food and health.
- Advising and assisting people to preserve their nutritional position when people want to try different diets, for example exclusion diets, health supplements or intervening in areas where evidence is still being discovered, for example, autism.

Dietitians have the unique status of being the only skilled professional in the area of nutrition to be governed by law. Dietitians follow an ethical code to make sure their standards remain at a high level. All dietitians must register with the statutory regulator in their country, such as the Health & Care Professions Council (HCPC) to be able to be called a dietitian/registered dietitian (RD) (The British Dietic Association).

Some reasons to see a dietitian

The following are a list of possible reasons for referral to a dietitian:

- Digestion issues
- After diagnosis of a condition like diabetes, high blood pressure or heart disease
- Where a child has specific nutritional needs
- Where there is a need to lose weight safely
- Where there is a need to gain weight after being diagnosed with a medical condition or after a bout of illness
- Where surgery is an option for weight reduction
- Advice regarding breastfeeding and weaning
- To confirm the existence of an allergy or food intolerance
- Advice surrounding eating disorders
- To improve chances of conceiving a child
- Practical advice to carers on suitable nutrition for the people they are caring for
- Advice on how to enhance fitness levels and athletic achievement

How to find a registered dietitian

Deciding on whether to refer to a registered dietitian or a registered nutritionist is dependent on the type of advice that is required.

Details of registered dietitians can be found by contacting the local hospital or doctor, or referring to an online dietitian directory.

Nutritionist

Nutritionists are trained to give information about food and healthy eating. They work in many different sectors, in the fields of public health, improvement of health, health policy, animal nutrition, local and nationwide government, private sector, NGOs and education and research. Some nutritionists work together with dietitians. They commonly work on a self-employed basis. Nutritionists work with people who are in general good health, so that they can prevent disease. They cannot work with severely ill patients in hospital or those living in society requiring therapeutic interventions, without being supervised by a dietitian.

It is important to make a distinction between a nutritionist, a Registered Nutritionist, personal trainer, and qualified dietitian. Anyone can call themselves a nutritionist and personal trainer, but only dietitians are legally allowed to describe themselves as dietitians.

Nutritional therapists and diet experts

Nutritional therapists try to relieve and prevent illnesses, often using complementary 'medicine' that isn't recognized in the mainstream medical world. They may offer guidance on:

- Detoxing
- Colonic irrigation
- Prevention of ingestion/inhalation of toxins or allergens
- Using supplementary nutrients

Anyone can call themselves a nutritionist, nutritional therapist, clinical nutritionist or a diet expert, but they are not legally allowed to say they are a dietitian.

It is best to ask any potential health professional offering advice about their training and qualifications and be satisfied that they are suitably qualified to give the required advice. Alternatively, a doctor, consultant or health visitor can be approached for advice.

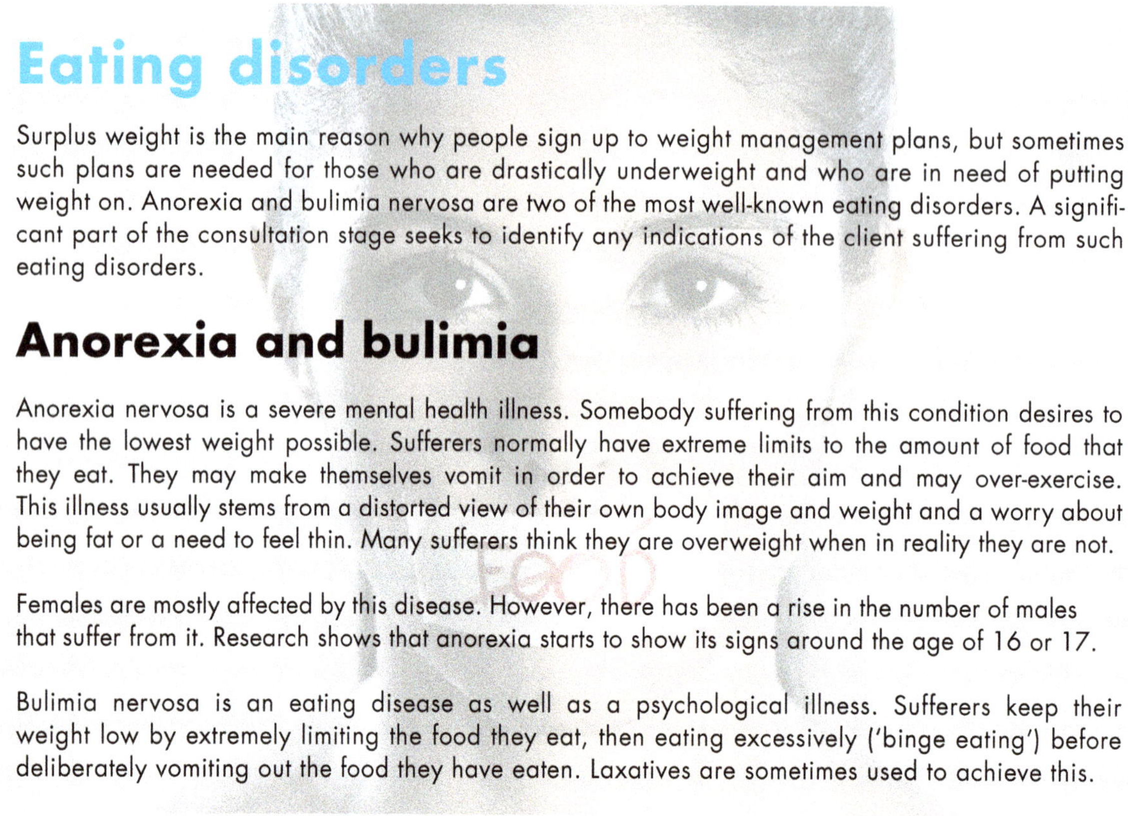

Eating disorders

Surplus weight is the main reason why people sign up to weight management plans, but sometimes such plans are needed for those who are drastically underweight and who are in need of putting weight on. Anorexia and bulimia nervosa are two of the most well-known eating disorders. A significant part of the consultation stage seeks to identify any indications of the client suffering from such eating disorders.

Anorexia and bulimia

Anorexia nervosa is a severe mental health illness. Somebody suffering from this condition desires to have the lowest weight possible. Sufferers normally have extreme limits to the amount of food that they eat. They may make themselves vomit in order to achieve their aim and may over-exercise. This illness usually stems from a distorted view of their own body image and weight and a worry about being fat or a need to feel thin. Many sufferers think they are overweight when in reality they are not.

Females are mostly affected by this disease. However, there has been a rise in the number of males that suffer from it. Research shows that anorexia starts to show its signs around the age of 16 or 17.

Bulimia nervosa is an eating disease as well as a psychological illness. Sufferers keep their weight low by extremely limiting the food they eat, then eating excessively ('binge eating') before deliberately vomiting out the food they have eaten. Laxatives are sometimes used to achieve this.

Signs and symptoms of anorexia

Physical signs

- Loss of hair
- Feeling dizzy
- Lack of energy
- A drastic loss of weight
- Dry skin
- Skin coloring distorted
- Constipation
- Stomach pains
- Painful menstruation in female sufferers
- Clothes hanging of them due to being too loose

Psychological signs

- Being moody
- Extreme anxiety about putting weight on
- Impaired view of their body
- Obsessively counting calories
- Feeling down and in discomfort
- Mood swings

Behavior of concern

- Skipping meals
- Restricting types of food to few low-calorie foods like lettuce or celery
- Excessively weighing themselves
- Excessively checking appearance
- Showing discontent about weight
- Being anxious and overactive
- Wearing overly loose clothes to hide their 'fat'
- Making excuses about why they aren't eating
- Cooking lavish meals for others but not eating any or a tiny portion
- Visiting websites which encourage anorexia
- Over-exercising

Associated health problems

- May suffer from osteoporosis
- Could damage the body internally and make it harder for females to conceive
- If the disease takes hold and is not treated, it could ultimately result in death

Signs and symptoms of bulimia

Physical signs

- Painful menstruation in female sufferers
- Swelling of the face and salivary glands
- Decaying teeth and sore throat
- Feeling lethargic and extremely tired
- Fluctuation in body weight
- Dehydration

Psychological signs

- Feelings of:
  - Guilt and shame
  - Low self-confidence
  - Anxiousness
- Depression
- High and low mood swings
- Impaired view of their own body
- Extreme desire to eat

Behavior of concern

- Skipping meals and fasting
- Binge eating and vomiting
- Use laxatives obsessively
- Excessively weighing themselves
- Excessively checking appearance
- Showing discontent about weight
- Being uneasy in public dining areas
- Declining to eat in public places
- Visiting the toilet after eating a meal
- Eating secretly
- Exercising too much
- Wearing overly loose clothes to hide their 'fat'

Associated health problems

- Risk of choking, heart attack, teeth corrosion and rupture of the stomach

TIP

Because sufferers of these disorders are often in denial, speaking to the client directly about it is not recommended. It is best to slowly build a relationship with the client and show concern for their well-being. Once a rapport has been established, the client can be directed to a doctor where the client can go on to be referred to a dietitian, counselor or psychologist. The personal trainer can then evaluate their training program.

Treating eating disorders

Personal trainers must know the procedure of referring clients with eating conditions. They should know how to direct them to the right person who can help. Although eating disorders present themselves with physical symptoms, the cause is usually psychological. Many people hide their condition for years and some deny they even have a problem, so bare nutritional guidance will not have much of an effect. Suitable professional guidance should be obtained for people gripped by these disorders.

Guidance for practitioners dealing with eating disorders is available in the National Institute for Health and Care Excellence (or NICE) website. Advice can also be sought from eating disorder support groups.

End of Chapter activities

Activity 2.8: Complete the table below to show the energy systems and fuels used, depending on the intensity of the exercise.

Intensity	Primary energy systems	Main fuel used
Very intense		Carbohydrate
Intense	Phosphocreatine and Lactic	Carbohydrate and fat
Heavy	Lactic	
Moderate	Lactic and aerobic	Fat and carbohydrate
Light		Fat

Activity 2.9: List three side-effects of insufficient portions of carbohydrate whilst exercising.

Activity 2.10: Prepare a two minute speech on how weight loss can occur when you exercise.

Activity 2.11: As part of a healthy diet, we should keep saturated fat to approximately what percentage of total energy received?

100% ☐ 50% ☐ 25% ☐ 10% ☐

Activity 2.12: The following food will be high in which nutrients?

Food	Nutrients (protein, carbohydrate, fat)
Grilled chicken	
Fried potato	
Butter	
Chocolate pudding	
Banana	
Bread	

Activity 2.13: Write benefits and problems associated with the following dietary methods.

Dietary method	Benefit	Problems
Fasting		
Ketogenic diet		
Low calorie meals		

Activity 2.14: Which plate of food would you recommend for after exercise and why?

2.15: List the symptoms of the eating disorders below.

Anorexia	Bulimia Nervosa

End of Chapter checklist

1. What is lipolysis?
2. How does the body store carbohydrate in the body?
3. What is carbohydrate broken down into during digestion?
4. What is meant by a 'carbohydrate loading' program?
5. What are some of the side-effects of insufficient portions of carbohydrate whilst exercising?
6. What supplements may clients choose to take as part of a diet and why?
7. What is the difference between a nutritionist and dietitian?
8. What is Bulimia Nervosa?
9. A client with digestion issues / symptoms should be referred to a dietitian or nutritionist?
10. How should a personal trainer deal with a client with an eating disorder?
11. What is basal metabolic rate?
12. How is glucose converted to energy aerobically?
13. How is glucose converted to energy anaerobically?
14. Which gas is required to produce ATP?
15. Why do we feel warmer during exercise?
16. How much water a person requires whilst exercising is dependent on what factors?
17. What are the risks associated with not drinking enough water whilst exercising?
18. The building of muscle requires which nutrient in addition to carbohydrate?
19. What is a Palaeolithic diet?
20. How can an energy deficit be created?

THE KINETIC PULSE COLLECTIVE KPC

Chapter 3
INTRODUCTION TO PERSONAL TRAINING

Chapter 3A: Personal training overview

Chapter 3B: Knowing your client

Chapter 3A: Personal training overview

Chapter summary

This Chapter will cover the role of a personal trainer and what is expected of them when working with clients.

Aim

The aim of this Chapter is to allow personal trainers to gain a broad understanding of what personal training will involve and identify the skills required to become a good personal trainer.

Learning objectives

After completing this Chapter, personal trainers will be able to:

1. Summarize what personal training is and the qualifications required to become a personal trainer.
2. Explain what a personal trainer does on a day-to-day basis.
3. List some of the benefits of personal training.
4. List what clients expect of a good personal trainer.
5. Summarize the difference between a personal trainer and a gym instructor.

What is personal training?

Personal training is a form of direct guidance which involves exercise screening, setting goals and educating a person about health in general. After an initial consultation, the trainer formulates an exercise plan which tests the body, tailored to a client's specific needs. The trainer can give advice on correct ways to lift, and can show exercises that help the client to reach their aims and objectives. The personal trainer also helps to motivate, helping to fulfill the client's potential.

Personal trainer job and skills

Personal trainer skills include:

1. A good understanding of the human body, the notion of functional exercise, the fundamentals of nutrition and the science of exercise.
2. Formulating exercise plans for both individual clients and for groups. These exercises are adapted to the needs of the specific client or group, and the goals which they would like to achieve.
3. Having a real understanding of the need to screen and assess a client, undertaking this task at the earliest stage and regularly during any program.
4. Delivering an exercise program safely and effectively.
5. Having a passion to assist clients in reaching their goals by undertaking relevant cardiovascular, flexibility and resistance exercises.
6. Encouraging people to develop their health and fitness levels overall.
7. Maintaining their own health and fitness levels and having a commitment to uphold personal training principles.

The National Federation of Personal Trainers state that personal trainers deliver key exercise science 'rules' to plan and formulate exercise programs. These programs help clients to achieve their goals both in the public and private environment. These personal trainers must practice safe exercise methods. Personal trainers need to ensure they are aware of the latest standards that regulate the industry in which they are in. They achieve this by regularly fulfilling educational obligations.

Required qualifications

To be a personal trainer you need (In general, as different countries may differ):

- Level 2 fitness instructor qualification
- Level 3 personal trainer qualification
- First aid certification
- Personal training insurance

Where do personal trainers work?

The fitness industry is continuing to grow. Business minded personal trainers are creating jobs for themselves in many ways. Here are some of the options:

- Gym / fitness center
- Private training studio
- Sports arena
- Office building
- Client's home
- Park
- Online support

Job summary

Screening and gathering information

Every potential client must be screened by the personal trainer to decide whether the client is capable of being trained. Health conditions such as obesity and diabetes need to be identified. Information including previous medical history is also collated by the personal trainer, as well as any chronic sicknesses, biomechanical issues and any medication currently being taken. Consent must be sought from the client's doctor where the client is on blood pressure, heart or blood glucose medicine.

General information like the client's age, gender, height and weight should also be gathered. Knowledge of the client's job would also help the personal trainer to assess their daily activity rate. Information like sleeping habits, dietary routines, water consumption and information on any recent exercise program should also be collated.

Fitness assessments

Another requirement for a personal trainer is to carry out an appraisal of the client's fitness level. The results of this help the trainer to formulate a training plan for the client. In this assessment, a body composition test is performed, to check the client's body fat percentage. Also included in the assessment are muscle strength and muscular endurance tests. This helps the trainer to decide on the level of intensity to factor into their training plan.

Program design and training

Programs should be designed and training should be planned around the client's fitness level and their precise objectives or reason for their intention to exercise (for example, to lose weight). Personal trainers give guidance on set resistance movements and how many sets and repetitions a client should undertake within a typical workout, followed by the required rest period.

Dietary advice

Personal trainers also need to provide general nutritional advice to clients. This can be in the form of literature or they may recommend food that will help most with post-exercise body recovery. A trainer should demonstrate the link between daily activity and consumption of calories. Tables and charts should be shown to the client for them to make an educated decision when choosing the content and timing of their meals.

Benefits of personal training

Flexible locations

Unlike gym instructors, personal trainers can hold sessions with their clients in their own homes, offices, or wherever it suits the client within reason. Gym Instructors can only conduct their role from the gym.

Achievement of goals

A personal trainer can help a client ascertain their fitness aims and objectives. Even though a client may be sure of what these are, the trainer can break them down into more manageable and achievable goals. The trainer can then regularly monitor progress towards achieving them. The trainer also identifies the client's current fitness level and considers with the client what the desired result of the sessions should be.

Tailored exercise session

An exercise plan which is tailored to a client's specific needs will be more effective than a general workout plan. As the trainer is aware of the client's medical and physical background, they are better equipped to design a program that suits them and a program that is likely to achieve the results desired by the client.

Motivation

Another reason clients hire a personal trainer is to keep motivated. Exercise can often become burdensome and harder to perform regularly when doing it alone. The client will be more motivated to perform well at the gym even if they do not meet the trainer at every session, as they know they may see their trainer soon. The client would feel a sense of achievement when meeting the trainer next.

Keeping track of progress

Working with a trainer keeps the client on top of their achievements and helps them to keep track of their progress. Knowing they are accountable to someone else will increase the likelihood of the client keeping to their exercise plan.

Choice and variety of exercises

A personal trainer with experience can share what they know about the many methods of exercise. This would reduce boredom and keep the client interested in their exercise program. Where the client is dissatisfied with an exercise, the trainer can replace it with another type, and one that brings the same physical advantage. As the client's fitness progressively gets better, the trainer can tweak their plan to accommodate this development.

Mistakes correction

A personal trainer will often correct any mistakes a client has been making with exercise. They will demonstrate the right way of performing each exercise and will watch the client practice, correcting any issues relating to posture or method. Knowing how to conduct an exercise is vital and helps to lower the possibility of injury. Exercises demonstrated by the trainer can also be performed at home or whilst at the gym.

Maximized efficiency

A good personal trainer can get the most out of exercise time. This maximizes the efficiency of the session. This is particularly advantageous when the client has a short amount of time compared to their regular session. The trainer will instantly know how to adjust the session, burning the same amount of energy in the reduced time, as well as achieving the same physical benefits.

What makes a good personal trainer?

So, what makes a good personal trainer? The following are some key attributes which a good personal trainer will have. Mastering these qualities will ensure happier clients leading to greater success for both the client and the trainer:

Patience

Some clients may want instant results and they may become anxious if they don't notice bodily changes soon after starting a program. It is here that the personal trainer should explain to the client that patience is the best way forward, advising that a gradual build-up of fitness levels is the most effective way of improving fitness levels in the long-term.

Empathy and compassion

A personal trainer should be a 'people's person', someone the client can connect with. It is essential that a personal trainer has a good understanding of the client's fitness aims and objectives. The trainer should have empathy for the struggles that a client may be going through. It is not necessary for the trainer to have been unfit in the past for them to relate to the client, but demonstrating empathy and compassion will lead to a successful relationship. This would have an impact on how the client is trained and how motivated they remain throughout the course of the program. Lack of empathy and compassion could result in a client feeling isolated with adverse effects on their training.

Technical knowledge

Personal trainers should have sound knowledge and an understanding of the core areas of fitness. These include study of basic movement patterns, body toning methods, how to improve cardio training and conditioning, how to bulk up and lean out as well as other aspirations the client may have. They should also have knowledge of teaching points related to different movement types, any precautions that should be taken and the impact of the movement type on the body.

Accommodating and adaptable

Personal trainers must be able to accommodate the client by being flexible. For example, amending an exercise plan that isn't quite compatible or being able to change an appointment with a client at the last minute should never be a problem for a personal trainer.

Personal trainers should also be careful not to categorize themselves or the types of training they do. Limiting the equipment or methods used hinders professional success. Trainers should be open to using a variety of teaching methods, as some methods may suit some clients more than others. For example, a smartphone app which helps to monitor activity may suit some clients but not others. The key is to know what the desired result is, and to expend methods which will achieve this. Training and the methods used should be formulated and changed around the needs of the client, not around the trainer themselves.

A final example of why being adaptable is important is the fact that in modern times, there is a new, two-fold phenomenon of a drastic increase in overweight and obese people. At the same time, people are living a lot longer, meaning there is an increase in the older population. In the past, these two markets have been misunderstood, resulting in a poor approach to improving their fitness. Trainers need to adapt their approaches to cater for these two markets to ensure greater success through recommendations.

Motivation and drive

Often, personal trainers find they are the main driving force behind the client. People nowadays are busier than ever and may be tired and feel deflated. During these times, the personal trainer's drive and motivation is key in helping the client to achieve their fitness goals. The trainer themselves should be open to learning new techniques and evolving their methods to stay driven.

Judge intensity levels wisely

Many members of the public have a perception of personal trainers working their clients too hard, to the extent of a typical client being extremely sore or even vomiting after an excessively intense workout. Some trainers may do this to justify their fees. A trainer guilty of encouraging such unsuitably intense sessions will have a short-lived career in the fitness industry!

The decision to go for a low, medium or high intensity should be made according to each individual client's ability. A good trainer will gradually increase intensity and match it to the client's need and ability.

Make sessions fun

Having fun should always be promoted by taking a professional and light-hearted attitude. Personal training should not be stressful or unenjoyable and therefore it is the trainer's role to select activities that the client is likely to enjoy. For example, if a client has specified a dislike for jogging then it is better to find other cardiovascular exercise for them such as step machines or cycling.

Good communication

The key to formation and maintenance of a relationship in any context is good communication. Communication is only successful if the receiver understands what the sender is trying to convey.

Effective communication entails active listening between both parties, appropriate verbal language, tone and body language and making clear observations of the other person's behavior, attitude and body language. Different clients may also have different needs when it comes to communication and therefore as a personal trainer you need to be adjustable, tweaking your communication skills to ensure your clients understand exactly what you are saying.

Active listening is key to good communication. It involves not just listening to the spoken word but also looking for the meaning behind those words. This means clarifying any information that you are uncertain about rather than making assumptions and demonstrating empathy to let the other person know that you have understood.

When talking, it is important to use good grammar and pronounce words correctly as well as using an appropriate tone. It is also important to speak at a volume that clients can hear you and to speak at a pace suitable for clients. Avoid using slang such as "yep", "um", "yeah", "you know what I mean". Also, avoid using too much technical jargon and explain using simple terminologies. If technical terminologies are used, ensure clients understand the meaning. If abbreviations and acronyms are used, also ensure clients have understood what they stand for.

Punctual	Being punctual is a mark of professionalism. Being late suggests a not caring attitude to clients and in an exercise environment, not only does it demotivate a client but they may start losing confidence in the personal trainer.
Organized	Being organized is also a mark of professionalism and gives clients confidence that they have invested well. When clients are paying for a service, they expect the supplier to be organized even if they themselves lack these skills. A client turning up late doesn't do much damage but the trainer being late and unprepared can irreversibly damage their reputation as well as the reputation of the organization they are working for. Another sign of demonstrating you are organized is to have a contingency plan should a specific activity on the program not be possible due to faulty equipment or any other reason.
Reliable and trustworthy	Closely linked to professionalism is being reliable and trustworthy. Ensure all commitments are met and never discuss information about clients with a third party without their consent.
Confident	If the personal trainer appears confident then in return the client will feel confident about their decision to participate in physical activities under the trainer's directions. The personal trainer should communicate confidently and avoid using passive language like "maybe this exercise will be good, but I am not entirely sure". Clients expect you to know, however, bear in mind that appearing over confident can turn people off. It's simply case of finding the right balance.
Knowledgeable	Clients will expect their personal trainer to have in depth knowledge and therefore it is a good idea to plan what you will say and do in a session. If the session will involve a lot of verbal communication, plan and even rehearse what you are going to say. If the client asks you a question that you do not know the answer to, find out!
Compassionate and sensitive	Different customers will have different, needs and weaknesses as well as knowledge level and therefore it is essential that personal trainers are understanding and supportive to a client's needs and expectations.
Enthusiastic and motivational	If the personal trainer is enthusiastic, so will be the client. Always provide positive feedback and plenty of encouragement. "We are almost there, just a few more sessions" is likely to encourage a client rather than a statement like "We still have a long way to go!".
Role model	It is essential that as a personal trainer you 'practice what you preach' to encourage a client and keep them motivated.

What NOT to do as a personal trainer

Personal trainers often assume multiple roles with their clients, which sometimes includes being a coach, cheerleader and even a friend. However, as a personal trainer:

1. **Do NOT** push your fitness goals and preferences onto your clients as they may not seek out those same goals.
2. **Do NOT** criticize clients. They have come to you for help and not criticisms.
3. **Do NOT** give medical advice or attempt to make a medical diagnosis.
4. **Do NOT** give physical therapy advice or massage any area that requires physiotherapy.
5. **Do NOT** try and work as a nutritionist or dietitian prescribing specific diets. Only general advice is acceptable.
6. **Do NOT** provide body massage or any similar service that can be interpreted as inappropriate touching.
7. **Do NOT** offer a counseling service.
8. **Do NOT** become romantically and intimately involved in personal client relationships.
9. **Do NOT** allow your credentials, liability insurance and any other certifications required to lapse.
10. **Do NOT** share client information with anyone unless the client has consented whilst seeking services from another professional.

The difference between a personal trainer and gym instructor

Whilst both roles are similar, they are at the same time significantly different. Gym instructors are normally employed with a fixed salary, whereas personal trainers are usually self-employed. The latter therefore has more earning potential. Gym instructors are responsible for gym inductions for people who are new to the gym. They show the new joiner how to use equipment. According to the gym facility, they may also conduct a routine fitness assessment and possibly draft a basic program based on the new member's fitness aims and objectives. Instructors also have the task of 'floating' around the gym area, offering advice and help to gym users. Gym instructors may also open and close the gym and undertake customer service duties. If they hold a qualification, they can to lead some group exercise sessions. Some instructors are able to offer a service to update a member's fitness program every few weeks and again conduct a fitness assessment to monitor progress. Gym members receive the service as part of their monthly membership. Gym instructors also have the task of cleaning and maintaining the fitness equipment. In most private fitness centres, there are few or no roles for gym instructors when a personal trainer is also working there. However, local authority gyms tend to employ many more gym instructors.

It is now commonly agreed that merely increasing activity levels will not answer all our fitness and health issues. It is arguable that people need more than just an exercise plan to follow if they want to see real results. This is where a personal trainer can help. Personal trainers act as a mentor to help clients successfully reach their fitness aims and objectives.

So how do personal trainers achieve this?

Thorough consultation and getting to know the client

In personal training a lot of preparation goes into training a client even before the physical exercise stage commences. This is all after the initial, thorough consultation. A personal trainer will need to spend time getting to know the client at a far deeper level than gym instructors (covered in *Chapter 3B*).

Diet and nutrition support

Food is attributed to success when trying to lose weight or simply get fit. Phrases like 'you are what you eat' and 'abs are made in the kitchen, not in the gym' hold some truth. Personal trainers would have a better knowledge base when it comes to nutrition in order to support their client in achieving their fitness goals.

Other lifestyle factors consideration

A personal trainer will also look at other influences that can have an effect on a client's health, such as sleep habits and stress levels. If these are not handled competently then they can have a harmful effect on the client's overall health whilst exercising. Overall, a client wants to feel better about themselves and a good personal trainer can help to achieve this even before the client steps into the gym!

Personalized training programs

Fitness instructors will often give clients a list of exercises to follow. However, a list of exercises may not always be effective. A person can follow a list regularly for a number of weeks and see results the first few times. However, after this, and in the absence of guidance on how to progress further, a person may struggle. A personal trainer's program which would have been more tailored will be more effective in producing consistent results.

Close monitoring

In contrast to the basic program drafted by the gym instructor, a personal trainer's program will have more in-depth and detailed monitoring of progression. There would be more precise monitoring of weights, intensities, durations, repetitions and complexity of exercise. This will make sure the body is changing and slowly improving.

Motivating clients

Being a personal trainer isn't just about attending training sessions. A personal trainer needs to keep their sessions interesting and varied. When a client hires a personal trainer, they are paying for a whole experience, the latest exercise knowledge and its application. They should leave each session feeling good about themselves. The personal trainer can achieve all this if they have a sound understanding of psychology and behavioral patterns. This knowledge will equip them with the ability to keep the client motivated and progress them towards their fitness aims and objectives. The ultimate personal trainer will keep the client focused throughout their journey – results are achieved over a period of time after all.

To summarize, the service provided by a personal trainer outweighs that of a gym instructor. It is far more flexible, varied and overall a far more personal service. The earning potential is also much more, as clients will pay depending on the level of service and experience that is offered.

End of Chapter activities

Activity 3.1: List 10 tasks a personal trainer will be involved in when working with clients on a day-to-day basis.

1.	6.
2.	7.
3.	8.
4.	9.
5.	10.

Activity 3.2: Prepare a one minute talk for a potential client on the benefits of personal training.

Activity 3.3: Write down six things clients expect from a personal trainer.

1.	4.
2.	5.
3.	6.

Activity 3.4: Create a table of dos and don'ts from a personal training perspective.

Do	Don't

End of Chapter checklist

1. What is personal training?
2. What skills are required to be a good personal trainer?
3. What qualifications are required to become a personal trainer?
4. Where do personal trainers work?
5. Why does a client need to be screened by a personal trainer?
6. Why should a personal trainer gather general information on a client?
7. Why do clients hire personal trainers?
8. What is the difference between the role of a personal trainer and a gym instructor?
9. What does good communication entail?
10. What advice must a personal trainer be able to give confidently?

Chapter 3B: Knowing your client

Chapter summary

This Chapter will build on the role of a personal trainer and demonstrate the importance of personal trainers getting to know their clients.

The Chapter covers various fitness tests and measurements that can be used to understand a client's fitness level.

Aim

The aim of this Chapter is to teach personal trainers how to collect information on a client and what tests and procedures they can follow to obtain the information required to develop personal training programs.

Learning objectives

After completing this Chapter, personal trainers will be able to:

1. Explain what a profile is and how it is used.
2. Collect information to build a client profile.
3. Summarize the different test types they can use to obtain information on a client's fitness level.
4. Carry out tests to measure body composition.
5. Carry out tests to assess cardiorespiratory fitness.
6. Perform muscular strength tests.
7. Perform flexibility tests.
8. Take a client's blood pressure.
9. Calculate a client's pulse rate.
10. Develop objectives for a personal training program.

A personal trainer must know each and every client at a far deeper level than gym instructors. This is so they can provide them with the best possible training program to meet their individual needs and fitness goals.

Creating a client profile

With a number of clients to support, a good personal trainer would consider building a client profile taking into consideration the following factors as well as anything else they feel is appropriate.

Physical profile

- Age and gender
- Height
- Medical conditions
- Any disabilities
- Post-surgery issues
- Birthing experience – vaginal delivery, c-section
- Medications client is taking

Reasons for seeking personal training

- Weight loss
- Strength building
- Medical conditions
- Post-surgery requirement
- Training for a competition
- Post pregnancy

Current fitness level

- Blood pressure
- Heart rate
- Body composition

Past experience

- Any exercises in the past
- Any anxieties they may have
- Barriers to exercises

Personal likes and dislikes

- Activities liked / disliked
- Hobbies
- Exercising time preferred

Eating habits and lifestyle choices

- Vegetarian / vegan
- Type of food consumed regularly
- Cooking method used
- Smoking and number smoked per day
- Alcohol consumption and amount

Family situation

- Marital status
- Number of children
- Family medical history – any known illnesses that runs in the family
- Support network available
- Access to equipment in the home

Financial circumstances

- Employed
- Unemployed
- Business owner
- Gym member

Time constraints

- Employed part time / full time
- Traveling required for work and business
- Family commitment
- Holiday plans

The above are just examples of information the personal trainer should obtain and there is not an exhaustive list.

How to gather information

Consultation

An important part of knowing the client is understanding their health, fitness level and suitability to exercises. This requires a thorough consultation and carrying out of a variety of tests. The consultation process can be divided into three stages:

- Screening the client
- Gathering information
- Physical measurements and tests

TIP

Carrying out tests is a useful way to motivate the client from the start. As it educates the client on their fitness level, it becomes easier to start formulating goals.

Screening

A thorough assessment of health-related fitness should begin with some form of medical screening. This helps to identify any person needing further medical assessment prior to starting an exercise program. Once such individuals are identified, appropriate steps can be taken. Completing a health check form is a good start to the screening process.

L2

A health check is a simple form given to the user. It asks the user whether they need to consult with their doctor before taking up a physical activity.

Personal trainers have a legal duty to minimize risk and maximize the benefit of exercise participation. A thoroughly completed form should always be kept on file and can provide protection from any legal proceedings from clients against the personal trainer.

Some questions from a health check form

Health Check Form

This form is designed to help you help yourself. Many health benefits are associated with regular exercise, and the completion of the form is a sensible first step to take if you are planning to increase the amount of physical activity in your life.

For most people, physical activity should not pose any problems or hazard. This form has been designed to identify the small number of adults for whom physical activity might be inappropriate or those who should have medical advise concerning the type of activity most suitable for them.

Common sense is your best guide in answering these few questions. Please read the carefully and check YES or NO opposite the question if it applies to you. If yes, please explain.

QUESTION	YES	NO
1. **Has your doctor ever said you have heart trouble?** If yes, please state:	☐	☐
2. **Do you frequently have pains in your heart and chest?** If yes, please state:	☐	☐
3. **Do you often feel fain or have spells of severe dizziness?** If yes, please state:	☐	☐
4. **Has a doctor ever said your blood pressure was too high?** If yes, please state:	☐	☐
5. **Has your doctor ever told you that you have a bone or joint problem(s), such as arthritis that has been aggravated by exercise, or might be made worse with exercise?** If yes, please state:	☐	☐
6. **Is there a good physical reason, not mentioned here, why you should not follow an activity program even if you wanted to?**	☐	☐

If a client answers 'yes' to any medical conditions in the form, the personal trainer should have evidence of medical approval before training the client. A medical clearance form completed by the client's doctor should be requested and kept on file.

If the form reveals intervention from another specialist such as a physiotherapist or nutritionist, this should also be acted upon and the personal trainer should refer the client to seek specialist advice.

As part of health screening it is a legal requirement to obtain client consent prior to fitness testing and exercising. However, it should only be obtained by the personal trainer after they have made the client aware of facts, implications, and future consequences of participating in an exercise program. Informed consent should be given verbally by the client after the personal trainer has explained the procedures and risks. The consent form should also be filled in and kept on file with other health screening documents.

Initial screening should then be followed by a series of assessments in the following areas:

- Body composition
- Cardiorespiratory fitness
- Blood pressure
- Flexibility
- Muscular strength
- Core stability

Making conversations

A good way to obtain information is to make the client comfortable and calm, then have a conversation with them in a relaxed manner. Interviews and questionnaires are helpful, but a relaxed client is more likely to open up to the personal trainer and discuss any anxieties they may have and barriers to exercising they are trying to overcome.

The gathering information process is continuous. As stated above a client profile should be developed and the profile should be updated as further information is obtained, for example upon completion of screening.

Activity

Activity 3.5: Create your own client profile.

Physical tests and measurements

An element of 'knowing the client' requires taking physical measurements and carrying out suitable fitness tests. This gives the personal trainer a greater understanding of a client's fitness level and helps them formulate a personal training program.

Any tests involving the measurement of girth and body composition should be carried out in a suitable environment. A client may feel embarrassed by certain tests and personal trainers should show sensitivity and respect with regards to this. Sometimes it may be more appropriate to only take the most necessary measurements around the girth if the client is notably obese. Calculating BMI by weighing them may also be more appropriate. Any process should be explained to the client, after which they should give informed consent.

When choosing which tests to conduct, the client's needs, goals and capability must be considered. Not all tests are appropriate for all clients. For example, a person who has typically led a sedentary lifestyle will not be suited to a muscular power test which requires them to do a vertical jump. This would become too high risk. A test which involves a cardiorespiratory test would be better suited to such a person.

Pre-test procedures

Clients should be advised to follow a set of pre-test procedures. They must be explained the importance of following these tests, and that failure to do so will invalidate the test. The personal trainer must make sure that the client arrives in a 'neutral state' – i.e. variables to be at a minimum. Good practice is to have at the back of an appointment card a list of the pre-test procedures. This can be handed to the client during booking.

Pre-testing procedures differ according to the type of tests being conducted. The following table details the typical advice given to clients:

Procedure relating to	Advice
Consumption	Avoid: • Heavy meals less than three hours before any test. • Drinking excessive amounts of alcohol a day before test and NONE at all on day of test. • Drinking caffeinated drinks (e.g. tea, coffee) and any fizzy drinks two hours before the test. • Smoking at least a few hours before the test.
Action	• Do have a good night's sleep the night before. • Try not to exercise or do any form of trying physical activity on the day of the test. • Avoid using a jacuzzi, sauna or sunbed less than two hours before the test.
Clothing and other items	• Wear appropriate clothes. • Wear clothes that allow easy access to the arms e.g. loose sleeves will make it easier to take blood pressure. • Do not wear any form of jewelry.
Timing	Something that seems insignificant as the time of the day can affect test results. A female client's menstrual cycle can influence a test due to the fluctuation in fluid levels and body temperature. Try and keep the time of day constant. If this is not possible, the personal trainer must record this so it can be taken into account when assessing results.
Environment	The heart rates response is affected by temperature and humidity. Environmental factors should be kept the same from test to test. If this is not practically possible, the personal trainer should record the temperature and take this into account.
Equipment	All equipment should be of good quality, well maintained and inspected regularly. If an equipment is suspected to be faulty, it should not be used and reported to the person in charge of equipment within the facility.
Medical conditions	Any test should be canceled if the client is feeling unwell or has a temperature. Any current medication should be brought to the test.
State of mind	Clients can appear nervous and stressed which can affect the test results. The personal trainer should make the client feel at ease and reassure them of any concerns.
Situation on the day	A person's personal circumstances on the day can affect test results. If the client reports any issues at the beginning of the test or during the test, it should be carefully taken into consideration.

Tests should be stopped immediately if the client presents themselves with any of the following circumstances:

- Onset of symptoms indicating angina
- Sizeable drop (20mmhg) in systolic blood pressure
- BP fails to rise, despite increased activity
- Excessive increase in BP systolic pressure >260 mHg or diastolic pressure >115mmHg
- Light-headedness
- Ataxia
- Pallor
- Cyanosis
- Nausea
- Cold, clammy skin
- Heart rate fails to increase with greater exercise intensity
- Significant changes in heart rhythm
- Client expressly states they want to stop, or says they are very tired/fatigued
- Physical signs of severe fatigue
- If testing equipment stops working

TIP

Personal trainers should maintain the highest of professional standards at every stage of the appraisal procedure. A sign of good customer care involves continuously informing the client of any sensations they should be experiencing during each test. A good personal trainer would make sure the client is comfortable at all times.

The importance of safety

SAFETY FIRST

Clients with no history of exercise should not be tested to the point of exhaustion. The reasons for this include:

- An intense test is strenuous, painful and can put the client off from future resistance training.
- An all-out test may result in Delayed Onset Muscle Soreness (DOMS) which again may deter clients from further training.
- If the client is solely focused on going to the absolute peak, they will lose their form. At this early stage of resistance training, good technique is more valuable than maximum exertion.
- Absolute beginners expose themselves to more risk if exercising too intensely. Ligaments and tendons are at particular risk, as these sites take longer to gain strength than muscles. Using heavy free weights before this muscle strength is developed, is potentially dangerous.

Body composition tests

A person's body weight can be divided into two categories:

1. **Fat Mass (FM):** Includes internal and external fat (adipose tissue)
2. **Fat Free Mass (FFM), or lean mass:** Includes muscle, bone, and internal organs

Fat Mass + Fat Free Mass = Total body weight

Historically, height and weight tables have been calculated to provide clients with advice on how to achieve a healthy weight. However, these tables do not measure the proportion of total weight that is made up of fat.

Indications of total weight are a good starting point in evaluating health status. However, the composition of a client's body should also be assessed. Personal trainers must understand the difference between weight loss and fat loss – they must also know the optimum level clients should be seeking to achieve.

Body Mass Index (BMI)

In order to define overweight or obesity, a measurement is required that allows for differences in weight due to height. Body Mass Index (BMI) is a widely accepted measure of weight for height.

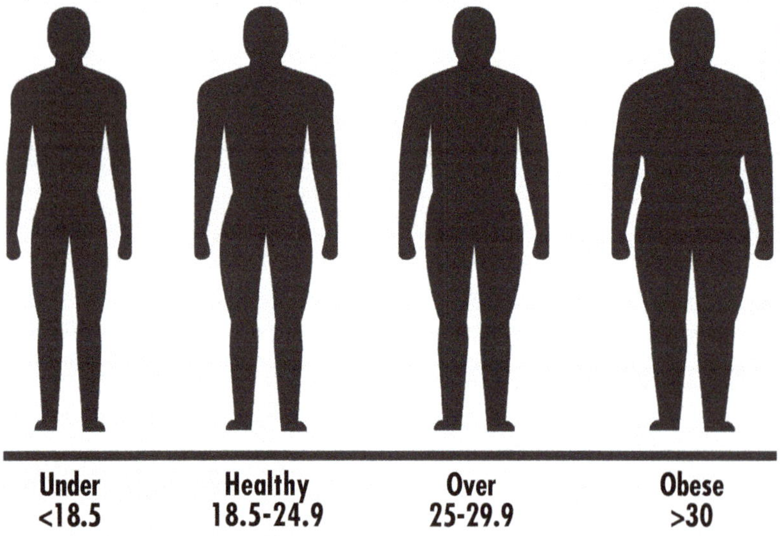

The equation to calculate BMI is:

$$\text{BMI} = \frac{\text{weight in kg}}{(\text{height in m})^2}$$

Source: HSE 2013, Vol1

Assessment method

Method of assessment: weight	Method of assessment: height
• Calibrated scales • Client to remove shoes and heavy clothing • Any re-tests should be conducted on the same day	• Check calibration of equipment • Be aware that height decreases as the day progresses, measure to highest part of head and record this as the height • Client to remove shoes and stand tall

Circumferential measurements

Circumferential measurements can also be used to assess the status of one's weight by converting them to body compositions using the relevant formula. However, these readings are often not accurate but quick and convenient to give some indications.

The way body fat is distributed around the body gives some indication on a person's health and fitness status. More fat around the abdomen is an indication of higher risk of chronic diseases and premature death compared to people with the same level of fat distributed around the limbs.

Circumferential measurement procedures:

- Take measurements under clothing if possible. If not, note details of clothing
- Take average of three readings

Circumferential areas and how to measure

Area of body	How to measure
Arm 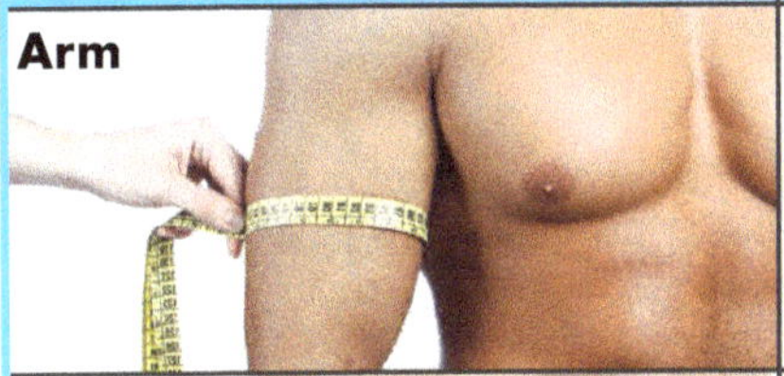	Client arm to be relaxed. Take horizontal measurement at the midpoint between the acromion process and the olecranon process.
Chest 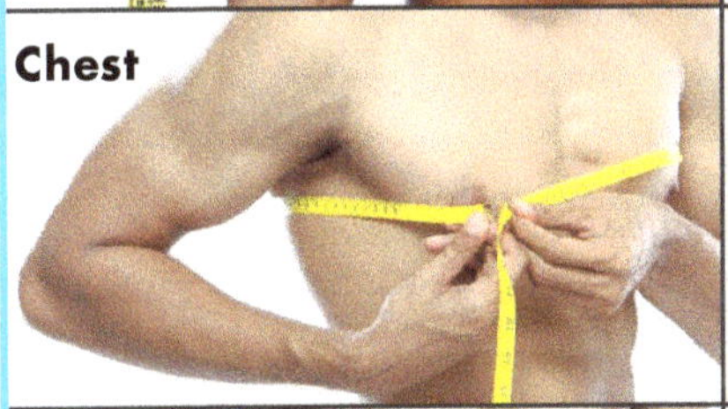	Client to stand straight – measurement taken at the maximum circumference. Note: Female subjects may wish to measure themselves from the front whilst the personal trainer takes measurement from the side of the client.
Waist 	Client to relax abdomen muscles. Take horizontal measurement at the umbilicus level, or the navel. This measure is taken after a normal breath. Note: Fat stored in the abdominal area is particularly seen as a risk factor for CHD (as opposed to being on the legs, hips and arms). This is because abdominal fat is carried directly by the body to the coronary arteries.
Hips 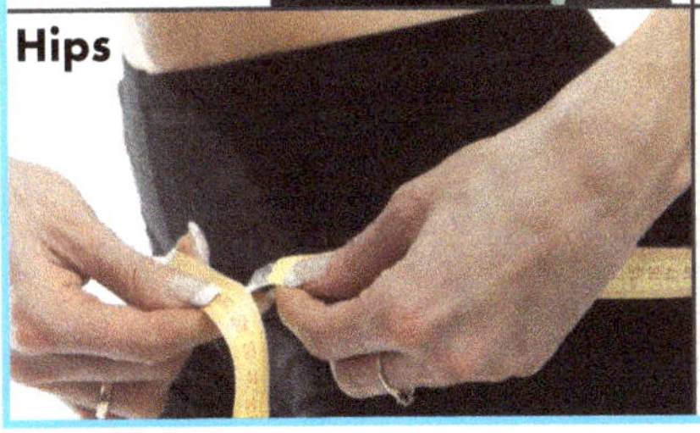	Client stands straight. Horizontal measurement taken at maximum circumference.

Waist to hip ratio

The size of the waist in comparison to the hip is known as the waist-to-hip measurement and is an indication of the fat distribution around the body. Studies suggest that health risk increases with higher waist to hip ratios.

Measurement procedures

- Take at least three measurements moving the tape measure up and down slightly to find the largest measurement of the waist.
- Repeat the above for the hip.
- Divide the waist measurement with the hip measurement to calculate the ratio.

Waist circumference and health status

Nowadays, many seem to prefer the simpler method of waist circumference measurement which is independent of height, instead of waist/hip ratio.

Formula: Waist (cm) / Hips (cm) = Ratio   e.g: 95cm / 75cm = 1.26

The 2006 NICE guidance infers that waist circumference is a valid measure of abdominal fat mass and disease risk in individuals with a BMI less than 35. If BMI is greater than or equal to 35, waist circumference adds little to the absolute measure of risk provided by BMI. The NICE categories are defined as follows:

Risk category	Waist circumference male	Waist circumference female
Low	Less than 94cm	Less than 80cm
High	94-102cm	80-88cm
Very high	Greater than 102cm	Greater than 88cm

Source: Nice Guidelines, cited in HSE Vol 1, Chapter 10.

Further reading: HSE 2013: vol 1 | chapter 10: Adult anthropometric measures, overweight and obesity.

Activity

Activity 3.6: Use a friend or family member to take circumferential measurements and write down your findings.

Arm:	Waist:
Chest:	Hip:

Skinfold measurement

Skinfold testing, also known as caliper testing is a commonly used method to estimate a client's body fat percentage by using a skinfold caliper to measure the thickness of fat tissue to get the best and most consistent measurements. Skinfold measurements correlate strongly with a person's body density measurements from underwater weighing and although the values are estimates, if taken properly by trained personal trainers, the values are a good estimation of body fat. (Earle and Baechle, 2004). However, proficiency in taking measurements is required and the personal trainer should practice this procedure to become proficient.

Measurement procedures

Skinfold measurements should be taken on the same side (usually the right side). Also, a minimum of two measurements should be taken at each location. If the two measurements differ by more than 2 millimeters or 10%, a third measurement is recommended for a more accurate estimation. The four site method is commonly used by personal trainers, although it is possible to use less or more sites.

Measurements should be taken when the client's body is dry and free of lotion. Measurements should always be taken before exercise as exercise can induce changes in the client's hydration status which can affect the thickness of the fold.

Procedures for the four site test are provided below:

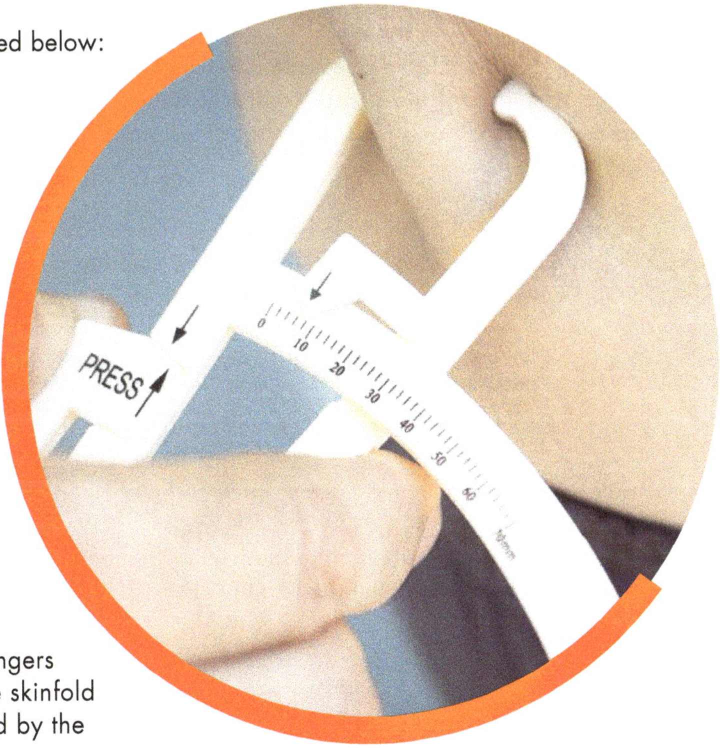

To take the measurements:

1. Identify, measure and mark the four skinfold sites (biceps, triceps, subscapular and suprailiac) with a pen.
2. Firmly grasp the skinfold firmly between the thumb and fingers and lift up the skin.
3. Keep the fold elevated and place the contact surface of the calipers at a 90-degree angle to the skinfold, approximately 1cm below the fingers, so that the skin fold is between the two contact surfaces.
4. Release the pressure between the fingers slightly whilst continuing to hold the skinfold so that a greater pressure is applied by the calipers.
5. Release the handle of the calipers and take the readings to the nearest 0.1mm. Readings should be taken within four seconds of releasing pressure.
6. Repeat the above for the other sites.

Notes on taking skinfold measurements

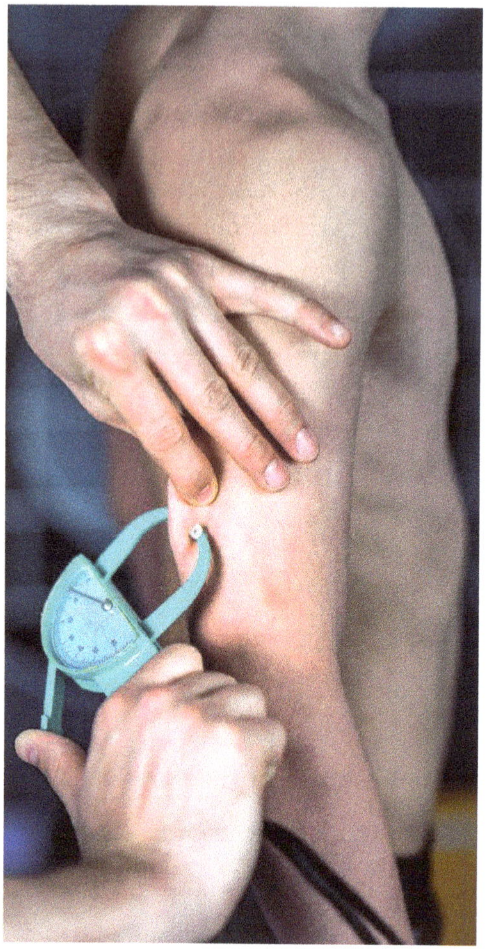

Always ensure that you mark the relevant skinfold areas first and then take the following into consideration:

Chest: For men, a diagonal fold should be created, one which is half the length between the anterior axillary line (this is the theoretical line which stretches from the forward-facing part of the armpit, downward) and the nipple. For women, follow the same procedure for men, but the fold should be made one third of the length from the anterior axillary line (theoretical line) to the nipple.

Midaxilla: Take an upward fold on the midaxillary line (theoretical line stretching from the center of the armpit, downwards; it splits the body into halves, front and back) at the base of sternum.

Subscapula: A diagonally lined fold should be made from the margin of the vertebrae (central) to 1-2cm or 0.8 inches from the lesser angle (lowest point) of the scapula.

Triceps: Take an upward fold behind the mid-line of the top area of the arm (above the triceps) midway between the upper shoulder and elbow. The elbow should be protracted and composed.

Suprailium: Make a diagonal fold over the highest point of the ilium (top end of the pelvis), at the site where a theoretical line would descend from the anterior axillary line.

Abdomen: Make an upwards fold, sideways, which is around 2cm (one inch) from the umbilicus.

Thigh: On the anterior view of the thigh, take an upwards fold half way between hip and knee junctures.

Medial calf: The client should position their right leg on a chair or bench with knee bent at 90 degrees.

On the medial margin, the level of the highest girth measurement should be marked. Move up an upright skinfold on the middle side of the right calf by 1cm (0.4 inches) over the mark. Measure the fold where the girth level is at its greatest.

Interpreting skinfold test results

Several methods can be used to interpret skin test results. One approach is using the measurements to calculate body density using an equation and then using a second equation based on the body density to calculate the body fat. However, a more common and simplified approach is to take measurements at four sites and then dividing the total from the four sites by four:

Skinfold (four sites) ÷ 4

The value can then be used to assess % of body fat using the table below.

Rating	Males % body fat (16-40 years)	Females % body fat(16-40 years)
Very low fat	<7	<13
Slim	7-12	13-20
Acceptable	13-17	21-25
Overweight	18-28	26-32
Obese	28+	32+

Bioelectrical impedance analysis (BIA)

Bioelectrical impedance analysis is another method for measuring body composition. It works by measuring the way the body conducts electricity using a specialized machine called bioelectric impedance analyzer (BIA). During the test, a current is generated by the BIA machine and passed through the body by placing electrodes on the hands and feet.

The test measures the body's resistance to the current passing through it. It is possible to assess the body fat level in the body because the current will flow more easily through parts of the body composed of less fat and more water and muscle. Based on this information on current flow and by combining other factors such as height, weight, gender, age and fitness level, mathematical equations can be used to predict how much body fat a person has.

Advantages and disadvantages: This is a very simple and quick way to perform body composition and can be done at home if you have the equipment. However, the equipment tends to be relatively expensive and not all clients will have access to it.

Test procedures

Before test

For accurate results that can be replicated when retested, it is important to ensure that the client is hydrated closely to their normal level as possible. A clinical nurse may carry out assessments to ensure the right hydration level.

The client being tested should refrain from the following:

- Caffeinated drinks such as tea, coffee, cola and other energy drinks 24 hours before the test
- Alcohol consumption 24 hours before the test
- Exercise for 12 hours before the test
- Eating for 4-5 hours before the test

Source: NIHR Southampton Biomedical Research Centre in www.uhs.nhs.uk/

As the impedance measure is affected by body hydration status, body temperature, time of day and requires strictly well controlled conditions to get accurate and reliable measurements, some specialists have questioned the validity and sensitivity of this test type (Earle and Baecle, 2004). Nevertheless, it is an option that a personal trainer has to measure body composition of a client.

Testing

The test surface should be comfortable and free of other equipment. Make sure the machine's battery is relatively new and well charged. Regularly check the machine's calibration using instructions and notes provided in the machine's user guide.

Testing can be performed in different ways. Some devices require a pair of electrodes to be placed on the hand and wrist, and another pair placed on the ankle and foot (usually opposite sides of the body), whilst other devices simply require you to stand on two foot plates. You should follow the instructions provided with the device.

If using machines with electrodes, place the electrodes on the client's right hand and right foot. Regularly check the client's cables using standard protocol. Ensure that the client lies quietly and without motion during the test.

The machine will give you two values. These values will be used in an equation to estimate the amount of fat and lean tissue on the body.

Body composition prediction equations

Known BIA equations:

$$TBW = 0.40 \frac{H^2}{R_{50}} + 0.148W + 3.32$$

Ramiz et al, 2012 cited in "https://bmcpediatr.biomedcentral.com

$$FFM = 0.661 \frac{H^2}{R_{50}} + 0.200W - 3.32$$

Bray et al, 2001 cited in https://bmcpediatr.biomedcentral.com

R50 = Resistance measured at 50 kHz (ohm)

H = Height (cm)

W = Weight (kg)

A hydration fraction 0.732 ml/g was used to convert total body water (TBW) to fat-free mass (FFM).

A well-known machine used for BIA is the Bodystat 1500.

Blood pressure assessment

During the cardiac cycle, pumping of the heart combined with the narrowness of the blood vessels produce considerable pressure on the arteries. Blood pressure can therefore be described as "a measure of the force that the blood applies to the walls of the arteries as it flows through them."

Blood pressure varies according to what you are doing. Anything which makes the heart beat faster or makes the arteries narrower can affect blood pressure. Short term increases in blood pressure can be due to various factors such as anger, fear, excitement and exercise. Long term increases or decreases in blood pressure can be due to health issues such as heart problems. The exact reasons for increases in blood pressure are hard to identify although sometimes lifestyle choices such as poor eating habits, smoking and excessive drinking can be connected.

Blood pressure is measured in millimeters of mercury (mmHg) and is expressed as a fraction using two numbers:

$$\frac{\text{Systolic blood pressure measurement}}{\text{Diastolic blood pressure measurement}}$$

The systolic blood pressure is generated at the peak of ventricles contraction, while the diastolic pressure isolates the lowest point at which the heart relaxes. The systolic measurement indicates the pressure exerted on the walls of the artery when the cardiac muscle is contracting and the diastolic pressure is the measurement of pressure exerted on the walls of the artery when the heart relaxes.

To take blood pressure manually, a device known as a sphygmomanometer will be used. This typically includes a stethoscope, an arm cuff, pump and dial, although nowadays some automatic devices use sensors as well as digital displays. Blood pressure can also be measured using a digital blood pressure monitor.

Manually taking blood pressure procedures

1. Remove excess clothing that might interfere with the blood pressure cuff or constrict blood flow in the arm. Make sure the client is relaxed by allowing five minutes to relax before proceeding.
2. The client should sit upright with their feet flat on the floor and the upper arm positioned so it is level with their heart. If wearing a long-sleeved top, the sleeves should be rolled up or remove the long-sleeved clothing.
3. Place the blood pressure cuff on the client's arm.

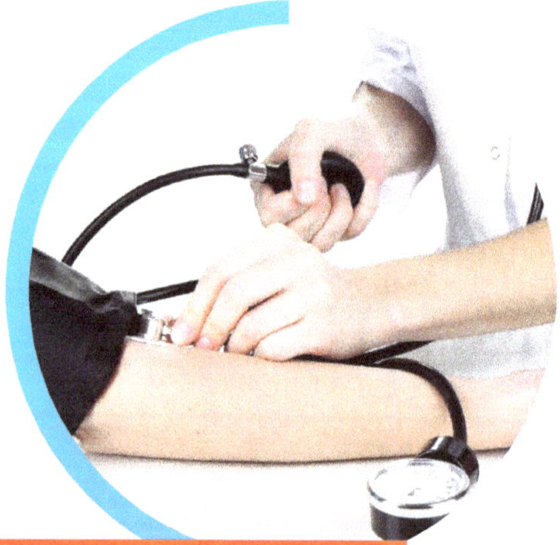

It is important to choose the proper blood pressure cuff size. Most measurement errors occur by not taking the time to choose the proper cuff size. Once the cuff is wrapped around the arm, use the index line to determine if the client's arm circumference falls within the range area marked on the cuff. Otherwise, choose the appropriate smaller or larger cuff. Both client and tester should refrain from talking during the reading.

4. Locate the brachial artery and position the cuff so that the artery marker points to the brachial artery and then wrap the cuff snugly around the arm.
5. With the cuff on, palpate the arm at the crease to locate the strongest pulse sounds and place the bell of the stethoscope over the brachial artery at this location.
6. Inflate the blood pressure cuff by pumping the cuff bulb as you listen to the pulse sounds. When the cuff has inflated enough to stop blood flow you should hear no sounds through the stethoscope. The gauge should read 30 to 40 mmHg above the client's normal blood pressure reading if it is known or if unknown, the cuff should be inflated to 160-180 mmHg. If pulse sounds are heard right away, continue inflating the cuff to the highest pressure until you don't hear a sound.
7. Slowly deflate the blood pressure cuff. It is recommended that the pressure should fall at 2-3 mmHg per second, anything faster may likely result in an inaccurate measurement.
8. Take note of the systolic reading by listening for a sound that may resemble a tapping noise at first. The first occurrence of rhythmic sounds heard as blood begins to flow through the artery is the client's systolic pressure.
9. Take note of the diastolic reading by continuing to listen as the cuff pressure drops and the sounds fade. The diastolic reading is when the rhythmic sounds stop.

Digital measurements

1. Remove excess clothing that might interfere with the blood pressure cuff. Make sure the client is relaxed by allowing five minutes to relax before proceeding.
2. The client should sit upright with their feet flat on the floor and the upper arm positioned so it is level with their heart. If wearing a long-sleeved top, the sleeves should be rolled up or remove the long sleeved clothing. Ensure the client is sitting still, as moving and talking can affect the reading.
3. Following the instructions that came with the monitor, position the cuff around the arm and press the start button. This will automatically start the monitor and inflate the cuff. The reading will be displayed on the monitor once it has completed the reading.

It might be worthwhile taking two or three readings, each about two minutes apart, and then working out the average. Sometimes the first reading can be higher due to anxiety. People find that their first reading is much higher than the next readings. If this is true for you, keep taking readings until they level out and stop falling, then use this as your reading.

Interpreting results

Blood pressure range guide

- Normal blood pressure is considered to be between 90/60mmHg and 120/80mmHg
- High blood pressure is considered to be 140/90mmHg or higher
- Low blood pressure is considered to be 90/60mmHg or lower

High blood pressure or unusually low blood pressure could be signs of clinical significance and should be investigated by a health professional.

Cardiorespiratory fitness

L2

Cardiorespiratory fitness is the ability to perform dynamic movements using large muscle groups for a prolonged period of time at moderate to high intensity. Our body's cardiorespiratory system ensures oxygen is breathed in and is sent to the muscles in our body, producing energy. Exercise makes our body work harder to produce more energy. This increases the demand for oxygen until the cardiorespiratory system is unable to supply enough oxygen to meet the increase in energy demands. This point of 'maximum oxygen uptake' is also known as VO_2 max (ml_kg-1_min-1).

VO_2 max indicates the ability of the lungs, heart, blood and vascular system to transport oxygen. It also shows how able the tissues are in extracting and using oxygen. VO_2 max is a good way of measuring how aerobically fit a person is. An aerobically fit person will be better at utilizing oxygen compared to someone who is unfit.

It is a fact that aerobically fit adults enjoy a better quality of life than those who are unfit. There is considerable evidence correlating obesity with numerous physiological health risks. Many studies have linked being overweight and obesity directly to middle-age mortality and a range of chronic diseases including diabetes, cardiovascular disease and some cancers. (HSE 2013, Vol1).

All fitness assessments should include tests to understand the client's cardiorespiratory fitness, as it can give indications of coronary heart disease risks.

There are several tests that can assess cardiorespiratory fitness, including:

- Rockport walking test
- 1.5 mile run test
- 12 minutes run/walk test
- Cycle ergometer test

Before we look at the actual tests, the components of the tests need to be understood. VO_2 max and heart rates are usually two measurements required for cardiorespiratory tests.

Calculating VO_2 max

There are several equations that can calculate VO_2 max depending on the measurements available. Some of the common ones are provided below:

Equation for rockport walking test

132.853 - (0.0769 x weight) - (0.3877 x age) + (6.315 x gender) - (3.2649 x time) - (0.1565 x heart rate)

Measurement units:

- Weight is in pounds (lbs)
- Gender: male = 1 and female = 0
- Time - expressed in minutes and 100ths of minutes
- Heart rate - beats/minute
- Age is in years

Equation for 12 minutes walk /run test

VO_2 max (ml.kg-1 . min-1) = (0.0268 x D) – 11.3

D = The distance in meters covered in 12 minutes or

VO_2 max ≈ (35.97 * $dmiles_{12}$) - 11.29

where $dmiles_{12}$ is distance (in miles) covered in 12 minutes

Equation for 1.5 mile run test

VO_2 max (ml.kg-1 . min-1) = 88.02 – (0.1656 x BW) – (2.76 x T) + (3.716 x G)

BW = Body weight in kilograms

T = Time – i.e. the time taken to run 1.5 miles in minutes

G = Gender – 0 for women and 1 for men

The VO_2 max score can then be compared to the normative rates agreed on by researchers shown in the table below:

Normative VO_2 max

	Age									
	20-29		30-39		40-49		50-59		60+	
Percentile	M	F	M	F	M	F	M	F	M	F
10	34.5	28.4	32.5	26.5	30.9	25.1	28.0	35.2	20.8	20.8
20	37.1	30.6	35.4	28.7	33.0	26.5	32.2	32.3	22.8	22.8
30	39.5	32.3	37.4	30.5	35.1	28.3	32.3	30.9	23.8	23.8
40	41.0	33.8	38.9	32.3	36.7	29.5	33.8	29.4	24.5	24.5
50	42.5	35.2	41.0	33.8	38.1	30.9	35.2	28.2	31.8	25.8
60	44.2	36.7	42.4	34.6	39.9	32.3	36.7	26.9	33.6	27.2
70	46.8	38.1	44.6	36.7	41.8	33.8	38.5	25.5	35.3	29.4
80	48.2	41.0	46.8	38.6	44.1	36.3	41.0	24.3	38.1	31.2
90	51.4	44.2	v50.4	41.0	48.2	39.5	45.3	22.3	42.5	35.2

Percentile values for VO_2 max. Adapted from Earle and Baechle, 2004. Interpretation of percentiles: 10 = well below average; 30 = below average; 50 = average, 70 = above average; 90 = well above average.

Measuring resting heart rate

Resting heart rate (RHR) is the amount of times the heart beats every minute while a person is resting. Lower readings generally mean a higher level of aerobic fitness. However, it should be noted that hereditary factors can influence results, so RHR cannot be solely relied upon as a measure of fitness.

The table below shows estimated target heart rates for different ages. Your maximum heart rate is about 220 minus your age. The figures are averages, so use them as general guidelines.

Age	Target HR Zone 50-85%	Average Maximum Heart Rate 100%
20 years	100-170 beats per minute	200 beats per minute
30 years	95-162 beats per minute	190 beats per minute
35 years	93-157 beats per minute	185 beats per minute
40 years	90-153 beats per minute	180 beats per minute
45 years	88-149 beats per minute	175 beats per minute
50 years	85-145 beats per minute	170 beats per minute
55 years	83-140 beats per minute	165 beats per minute
60 years	80-136 beats per minute	160 beats per minute
65 years	78-132 beats per minute	155 beats per minute
70 years	75-128 beats per minute	150 beats per minute

Source: American Heart Association

Measuring procedures

Pulse rates can be taken in several ways. The common way is to locate the most commonly used sites, which are the carotid or radial artery.

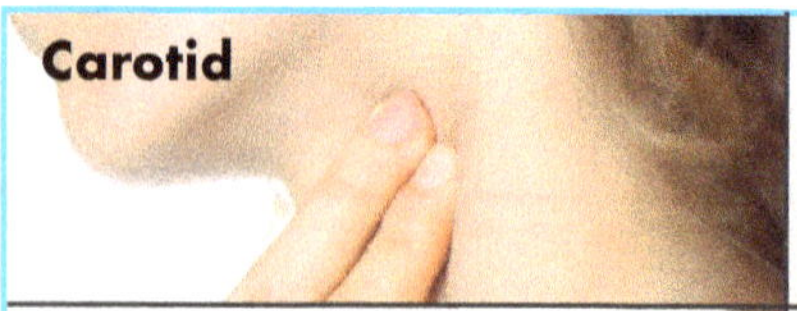 **Carotid**	The common carotid artery sites are on both sides of the front of the neck. Each are in the groove formed by the larynx (Adam's apple) and the sternocleidomastoid muscles (muscles on the side of the neck) just below the mandible (lower jawbone).
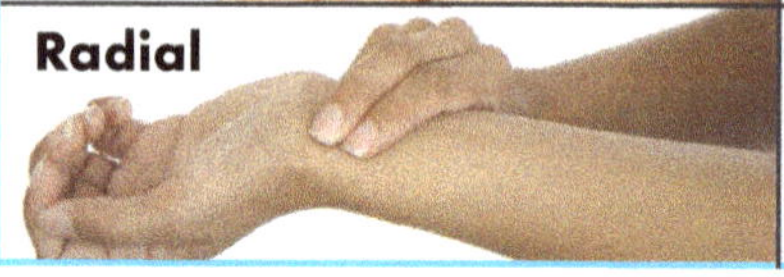 **Radial**	The radial artery courses deeply on the anterolateral (thumb side) aspect of the forearm and becomes superficial near the distal head of the radius (directly in line with the base of the thumb).

If the carotid or radial artery cannot be located, RHR can be taken at any arterial site, such as the temporal, femoral and brachial.

Measuring pulse rates procedures

- Ensure client has rested for five to ten minutes in a seated or horizontal position, before measuring heart rate.
- Only use the tips of the middle and index fingers. Do NOT use the thumb, as this has a pulse of its own and may affect the accuracy of the count.
- Do NOT apply heavy pressure when palpating the carotid site, as baroreceptors in the carotid arteries detect this pressure and cause a reflex slowing of the heart rate.
- Wait 30-60 seconds for the client to get used to the measurement. Many clients feel a little anxious at the beginning of this check, which may adversely affect results if taken immediately.
- If the stopwatch is started simultaneously with the pulse beat, count the first beat as a zero. Count the first beat as one if the stopwatch is already running.
- Count pulse for 60 seconds. Record the result and repeat.
- If the results are markedly different, repeat for a third reading.

Interpreting results

If the heart rate is too high this is an indication that a person is straining and therefore needs to slow down. If it's too low, and the intensity feels fairly 'light', they may want to push themselves to exercise a little harder.

In the first few weeks of commencing exercising, one should aim for the lower range of their target zone (50%) and gradually build up to the higher range (85%). After six months or more, they may be able to exercise comfortably at up to 85% of ones maximum heart rate.

Bradycardia

Sometimes a person's RHR can be less than 60 bpm. This is a condition known as Bradycardia. Causes of bradycardia include:

- Extremely fit athletes
- Hypothermia (very low body temperature)
- Hypothyroidism (low thyroid function)
- Hyperkalaemia (when the potassium level in the bloodstream is higher than what should be normal
- Myocardial infarction (damage to or death of heart tissue)
- Genetics
- Certain drugs (e.g. beta blockers)

Tachycardia

Opposite to Bradycardia is a condition called Tachycardia, which is when a RHR is over 100 bpm. Causes of Tachycardia include:

- Consumption of alcohol, caffeine, or nicotine
- Stress, anxiety or arousal
- Heart failure
- Pulmonary embolism
- Hypovolaemia (abnormal decrease in blood volume/blood plasma)
- Hypermetabolic states (e.g. fever or a raised body temperature)
- Certain drugs (e.g. adrenaline, ephedrine, atropine)
- Poor cardiovascular fitness levels

The figure below demonstrates the ECG traces of the different conditions against normal RHR.

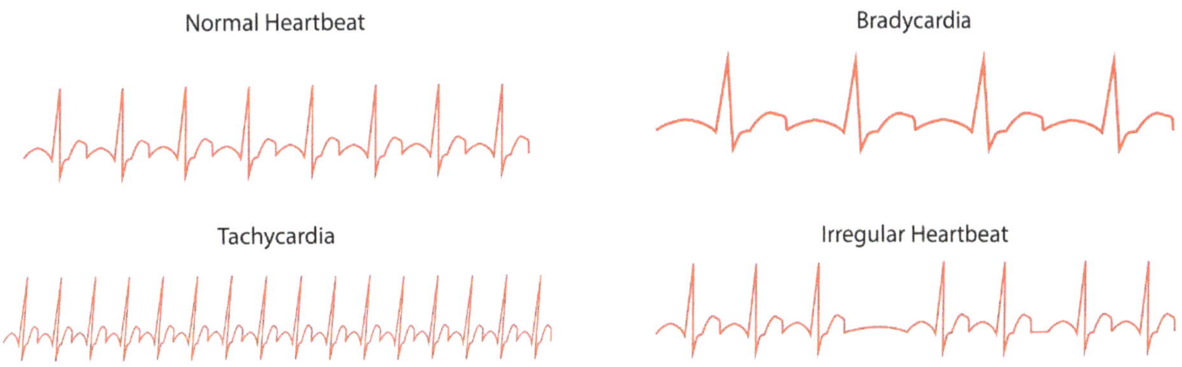

Rockport walking test

The Rockport walking test involves the client walking one mile before taking the pulse rate. Other variables of the test are: finish time, body mass, gender and age which are incorporated in a mathematical equation to predict aerobic fitness by calculating the VO_2 max.

Test procedure

1. Inform the client of the start and finish point on the race track and explain that the test must be completed as quickly as possible but not speed walking.
2. On your mark, get set go and start the stopwatch.
3. Record the elapsed time in minutes and seconds as the client crosses the finish line.
4. Convert the seconds to minutes by dividing the seconds by 60, for example, 30 seconds is 0.5 minutes (30÷60) and add this to the minutes to obtain the total time in minutes.
5. Record the client's heart rate immediately upon the completion of the mile. It is preferable to have the participant wearing a heart rate monitor for this measurement but the assessment of heart rate via palpation (using a 15 seconds' count from the carotid or radial artery) is a suitable alternative.
6. Estimate the client's VO_2 max using the following formula:

132.853 - (0.0769 x weight) - (0.3877 x age) + (6.315 x gender) - (3.2649 x time) - (0.1565 x heart rate)

Measurement units:

- Weight is in pounds (lbs)
- Gender: male = 1 and female = 0
- Time - expressed in minutes and 100ths of minutes
- Heart rate - beats/minute
- Age is in years

You can now compare the estimated results against the VO_2 max normative values shown on page 171. The table below can also be used to interpret results based on the time taken:

	Age 18-30 (min:sec)		Age 30-69 (min:sec)	
	Male	**Female**	**Male**	**Female**
Well above average	≤11:08	≤11:40	<10:12	<11:40
Above average	11:09-11.42	11:41-12:49	10:13-11.42	11.41-13:08
Average	11:43-12:37	12:50-14:11	11:43-14:44	13:08-16:04
Below average to poor	>13:38	>14:12	>14:45	>16:05

Normative values for Rockport test. Adapted from Earle and Baechle, 2004

1.5 mile run test

The 1.5 mile test is designed to measure how quickly a client can run 1.5 miles. The time taken in minutes is then used in an equation to calculate the VO_2 max.

The test should take place on a flat course running track (400 meter if possible) and the personal trainer should measure and mark the required area the client needs to run. A stopwatch should be used to note down the time it takes the client to complete the run.

Test procedures

Inform the client of the start and finishing points and explain that the test must be completed as quickly as possible but walking is permissible if required for a short time if they feel severe fatigue.

1. On your mark, get set go and start the stopwatch.
2. Record the elapsed time in minutes and seconds as the client crosses the finish line.
3. Convert the seconds to minutes by dividing the seconds by 60, for example, 30 seconds is 0.5 minutes (30÷60) and add this to the minutes to obtain the total time in minutes.

Use the following VO_2 max equation to estimate the client's VO_2 max.

VO_2 max (ml.kg-1 . min-1) = 88.02 – (0.1656 x BW) – (2.76 x T) + (3.716 x G).

BW = Body weight in kilograms.

T = Time – i.e the time taken to run 1.5 miles in minutes.

G = Gender – 0 for women and 1 for men.

You can now compare the estimated results against the VO_2 max normative values on page 171.

Example

30-year-old male client who weighs 80 kilograms has completed the 1.5 mile test in 10 minutes and 15 seconds (10:15) = 10.25 minutes.

VO_2 calculation:
VO_2 max (ml.kg-1 . min-1) = 88.02 – (0.1656 x BW) – (2.76 x T) + (3.716 x G)
= 88.02 – (0.1656 x 80) – (2.76 x 10.25) + (3.716 x 1)
= 88.02 – (13.248) – (28.29) + (3.716)
= 50.198

Comparing the value with VO_2 max normative values shown on page 171, the percentile rank for 50.198 is just below the 90th percentile (well above average).

12 minutes run/ walk test

The 12 minutes walk / run test also known as the Cooper 12 minute test, is a popular maximal running test of cardiovascular fitness. It requires clients to try and cover as much distance as they can in 12 minutes and then the measurement is used in a regression equation to calculate VO_2 max.

The test should take place on a flat course running track (400 meter if possible) and the personal trainer should measure and mark the required area the client needs to run. A stopwatch should be used to note down the time it takes the client to complete the run.

Test procedures:

TIP

The personal trainer may find it useful to place visible markers dividing the track by distance on so that they can measure the distance covered easily.

1. Inform the client of the starting position and explain that they must run as quickly as possible but walking is permissible if required for a short time if they feel severe fatigue.
2. Set the stopwatch to 12 minutes counting down or 0 counting up.
3. On your mark, get set go and start the stopwatch.
4. Mark the area in the track when on exactly 12 minutes and record the distance covered.
5. Convert the seconds to minutes by dividing the seconds by 60, for example, 30 seconds is 0.5 minutes (30÷60) and add this to the minutes to obtain the total time in minutes.

Use the following VO_2 max equation to estimate the client's VO_2 max.

VO_2 max (ml.kg-1 . min-1) = (0.0268 x D) – 11.3

D = The distance in meters covered in 12 minutes

You can now compare the estimated results against the VO_2 max normative values shown on page 171.

Advantages and disadvantages: The running tests are cheap and easy to perform. You can also test multiple clients at the same time if required. However, performance on this test can be affected greatly by motivation.

Example

A 25 year old female client weighs 55 kilograms and was able to run 1,500 meters.

VO_2 calculation:

$$VO_2 \text{ Max (ml.kg-1 . min-1)} = (0.0268 \times D) - 11.3$$
$$= (0.0268 \times 1{,}500) - 11.3$$
$$= 40.2 - 11.3$$
$$= 28.9$$

Comparing the value with normative VO_2 max values shown on page 171, the percentile rank for 28.9 is just over the 10th percentile (well below average).

Step tests

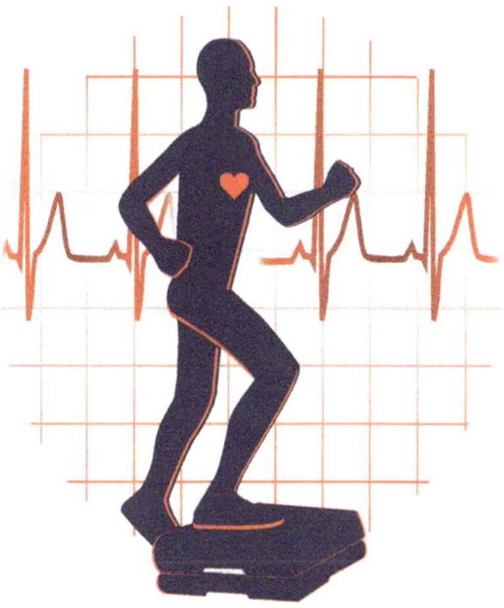

Step tests have been developed to measure aerobic fitness using a simple test requiring minimal equipment and space. Most of the tests would require a step or solid platform between 15-50cm. Depending on test type, the personal trainer may need a stopwatch, metronome or pre-recorded cadence tape depending on procedure selected.

Advantages and disadvantages: Step tests require minimal equipment and cheap to carry out. They can be self-administered if required. **However,** as the step is the same size for all people, biomechanical characteristics such as gender, height and length of lower limbs may give an advantage.

Step test

The step test is commonly used by personal trainers and described below.

1. Place the step on an even surface.
2. Step one foot up on the bench (1st beat), step up with the second foot (2nd beat), step down with one foot (3rd beat), and step down with the other foot (4th beat.) The client steps up and down on the platform at the given rate for a total of three minutes. The client immediately stops on completion of the test and sits down and remains still, whilst their pulse is taken by the trainer.
3. The client's pulse should be counted for a full minute and then recorded.

The client's fitness level can then be assessed by comparing the post exercise heart rate against the normative rate as shown in the table below.

MALE	18-25	26-35	36-45	46-55	56-65	66+
Percentile						
Excellent	70-78	73-79	72-81	78-84	72-82	72-86
Good	82-88	83-88	86-94	89-96	89-97	89-95
Above average	91-97	91-97	98-102	99-103	98-101	97-102
Average	101-104	101-106	105-111	109-115	105-111	104-113
Below average	107-114	109-116	113-118	118-121	113-118	114-119
Poor	118-126	119-126	120-128	124-130	122-128	122-128
Very poor	131-164	130-164	132-168	135-158	131-150	133-152

FEMALE	18-25	26-35	36-45	46-55	56-65	66+
Percentile						
Excellent	72-83	72-86	74-87	76-93	74-92	73-86
Good	88-97	91-97	93-101	96-102	97-103	93-100
Above average	100-106	103-110	104-109	106-113	106-111	104-114
Average	110-116	112-118	111-117	117-120	113-117	117-121
Below average	118-124	121-127	120-127	121-126	119-127	123-127
Poor	128-137	129-135	130-138	127-133	129-136	129-134
Very poor	142-155	141-154	143-152	138-152	142-151	135-151

Adapted from Earle and Baechle, 2004

Examples of other step tests:
(http://www.topendsports.com/testing/tests/step.htm)

- **Harvard Step Test**
- **Chester Step Test**
- **Canadian Home Fitness Test**
- **Balke Step Test**
- **Sharkey (Forestry) Step Test**
- **Queens College Step Test**
- **Home Step Test**

Cycle ergometer tests

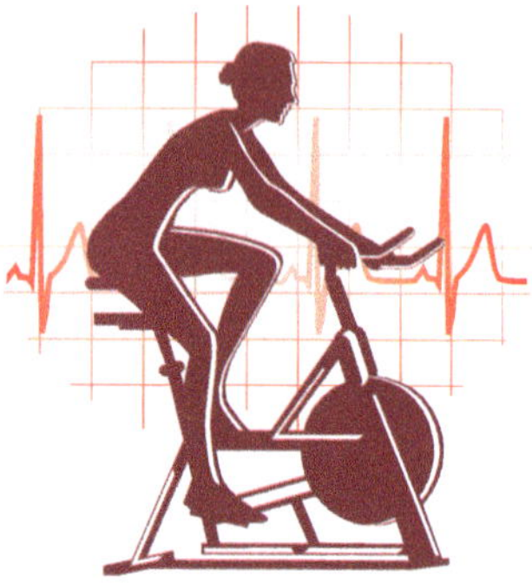

Cycle ergometer tests are another way to test a client's fitness level. There are various types of cycle ergometer tests and a common one is the Astrand-Rhyming cycle ergometer test. It is a single stage test that lasts for six minutes using a mechanically or electrically braked cycle ergometer.

Test procedures

1. Set the cycle's pedaling cadence at 50 rpm
2. Set the work rate based on gender and fitness level as specified

	Males	Females
Conditioned	600 or 900 kg.m.min^{-1}	450 or 600 kg.m.min^{-1}
Unconditioned	300 or 600 kg.m.min^{-1}	300 or 450 kg.m.min^{-1}

Adapted from Earle and Baechle, 2004

The work rates to set for this test type are based on gender and a client's fitness level (condition or unconditioned). If there is uncertainty about the fitness level, the recommendation is to choose the unconditioned rates specified (Earle and Baechle, 2004).

3. Client should sit on the cycle and start pedaling when the stopwatch is started.
4. After two minutes take the first heart rate measurement.
   - If the heart rate is ≥ 120, request the client to continue at the chosen work rate throughout the test.
   - If the heart rate is ≤ 120, increase the resistance to the next increment or until the heart rate is ≥120 after two minutes.
5. At the end of the 5th minute take the 2nd heart rate measurement.
6. At the end of the 6th minute (test end) take the 3rd heart rate measurement.
7. Calculate the average of heart rates and use this average value to estimate the VO_2 max in liters. per minute (L . min^{-1}) using the maximal oxygen consumption from heart rate prediction table below on page 179.
8. Age correct the VO_2 max calculated above by multiplying the value with the appropriate age correction factor as shown in the age correction factor table below on page 180.

After age correction you can convert the value to ml . kg^{-1} . min^{-1} by using the following equation:
VO_2 max (ml . kg^{-1} . min^{-1}) = VO_2 max in L .kg^{-1} . min^{-1} x 1000 ÷ BW
BW = Body weight in kilograms

You can now compare this value with the cycle test performance normative rates specified on page 171.

Maximal oxygen consumption from heart rate prediction

Heart rate (HR) beats/min	Work rate (kg.m.min^{-1}; Watts)									
	300; 50	300; 50	600; 100	450; 75	900; 150	600; 100	1200; 200	750; 125	1500; 250	900; 150
	Maximal oxygen consumption (L . min^{-1})									
	M	F	M	F	M	F	M	F	M	F
120	2.2	2.6	3.5	3.4	4.8	4.1		4.8		
121	2.2	2.5	3.4	3.3	4.7	4.0		4.8		
122	2.2	2.5	3.4	3.2	4.6	3.9		4.7		
123	2.1	2.4	3.4	3.1	4.6	3.9		4.6		
124	2.1	2.4	3.3	3.1	4.5	3.8	6.0	4.5		
125	2.0	2.3	3.2	3.0	4.4	3.7	5.9	4.4		
126	2.0	2.3	3.2	3.0	4.4	3.7	5.8	4.4		
127	2.0	2.2	3.1	2.9	4.3	3.5	5.7	4.2		
128	2.0	2.2	3.1	2.8	4.2	3.5	5.6	4.2		
129	1.9	2.2	3.0	2.8	4.2	3.4	5.6	4.1		
130	1.9	2.1	3.0	2.7	4.1	3.4	5.5	4.0		4.7
131	1.9	2.1	2.9	2.7	4.0	3.4	5.4	4.0		4.6
132	1.9	2.0	2.9	2.7	4.0	3.3	5.3	4.0		4.5
133	1.8	2.0	2.8	2.6	3.9	3.2	5.3	3.8		4.4
134	1.8	2.0	2.8	2.6	3.9	3.2	5.2	3.8		4.4
135	1.7	2.0	2.8	2.6	3.8	3.1	5.1	3.7		4.3
136	1.7	1.9	2.7	2.5	3.8	3.1	5.0	3.6		4.2
137	1.7	1.9	2.7	2.5	3.7	3.0	5.0	3.6		4.2
138	1.6	1.8	2.7	2.4	3.7	2.9	4.9	3.5		4.1
139	1.6	1.8	2.6	2.4	3.6	2.8	4.8	3.5		4.0
140	1.6	1.8	2.6	2.4	3.6	2.8	4.8	3.4	6.0	4.0
141		1.8	2.6	2.3	3.5	2.8	4.7	3.4	5.9	3.9
142		1.7	2.5	2.3	3.5	2.8	4.6	3.3	5.8	3.9
143		1.7	2.5	2.2	3.4	2.7	4.6	3.3	5.7	3.8
144		1.7	2.5	2.2	3.4	2.7	4.5	3.2	5.7	3.8
145		1.7	2.4	2.2	3.4	2.7	4.5	3.2	5.6	3.7
146		1.6	2.4	2.2	3.3	2.6	4.4	3.2	5.5	3.7
147		1.6	2.4	2.1	3.3	2.6	4.4	3.1	5.5	3.6
148		1.6	2.4	2.1	3.2	2.6	4.3	3.1	5.4	3.6
149			2.4	2.1	3.2	2.6	4.3	3.0	5.4	3.5
150			2.3	2.0	3.2	2.5	4.2	3.0	5.3	3.5
151			2.3	2.0	3.1	2.5	4.2	3.0	5.2	3.4
152			2.2	2.0	3.1	2.5	4.1	2.9	5.2	3.4
153			2.2	2.0	3.0	2.4	4.1	2.9	5.1	3.3
154			2.2	2.0	3.0	2.4	4.0	2.8	5.1	3.3
155			2.2	1.9	3.0	2.4	4.0	2.8	5.0	3.2
156			2.2	1.9	2.9	2.3	4.0	2.8	5.0	3.2
157			2.1	1.9	2.9	2.3	3.9	2.7	4.9	3.2
158			2.1	1.8	2.9	2.3	3.9	2.7	4.9	3.1
159			2.1	1.8	2.8	2.2	3.8	2.7	4.8	3.1
160			2.1	1.8	2.8	2.2	3.8	2.6	4.8	3.0
161			2.0	1.8	2.8	2.2	3.7	2.6	4.7	3.0
162			2.0	1.8	2.8	2.2	3.7	2.6	4.6	3.0
163			2.0	1.7	2.8	2.2	3.7	2.6	4.6	2.9
164			2.0	1.7	2.7	2.1	3.6	2.5	4.5	2.9
165			2.0	1.7	2.7	2.1	3.6	2.5	4.5	2.9
166			1.9	1.7	2.7	2.1	3.6	2.5	4.4	2.8
167			1.9	1.6	2.6	2.1	3.5	2.4	4.4	2.8
168			1.9	1.6	2.6	2.0	3.5	2.4	4.3	2.8
169			1.9	1.6	2.6	2.0	3.5	2.4	4.3	2.8
170			1.8	1.6	2.6	2.0	3.4	2.4	4.3	2.7

Adapted from Earle and Baechle, 2004

Age correction factor

Age	CF	Age	CF	Age	CF	Age	CF	Age	CF
15	1.10	25	1.00	35	0.87	45	0.78	55	0.71
16	1.10	26	0.99	36	0.86	46	0.77	56	0.70
17	1.09	27	0.98	37	0.85	47	0.77	57	0.70
18	1.07	28	0.96	38	0.85	48	0.76	58	0.69
19	1.06	29	0.95	39	0.84	49	0.76	59	0.69
20	1.05	30	0.93	40	0.83	50	0.75	60	0.68
21	1.05	31	0.93	41	0.82	51	0.74	61	0.67
22	1.03	32	0.91	42	0.81	52	0.73	62	0.67
23	1.02	33	0.90	43	0.80	53	0.73	63	0.66
24	1.01	34	0.98	44	0.79	54	0.72	64	0.66

Adapted from Earle and Baechle, 2004

Cycle test performance normative rates

Fitness levels	Low	Fair	Average	Good	High	Very high
Men – oxygen consumption (ml.kg^{-1}. min^{-1})						
20-29	<25	25-33	34-42	43-52	53-61	>61
30-39	<23	23-30	31-38	39-48	49-57	>57
40-49	<20	20-26	27-35	36-44	45-53	>53
50-59	<18	18-24	25-33	34-42	43-49	>49
60-69	<16	16-22	23-30	21-40	41-45	>45
Women – oxygen consumption (ml.kg^{-1}. min^{-1})						
20-29	<24	24-30	31-37	38-48	49-57	>57
30-39	<20	20-27	28-33	34-44	45-53	>53
40-49	<17	17-23	24-30	31-41	42-50	>50
50-59	<15	15-20	21-27	28-37	38-42	>42
60-69	<13	13-17	18-23	24-34	35-39	>39

Muscular strength tests

Muscular strength is an important aspect of one's fitness and a minimum level of muscular strength is required to function comfortably on a day to day basis. Muscular strength can be expressed either as 'absolute' strength or 'relative strength'. Absolute strength is the raw scored achieved whilst the relative strength is based on body weight. There are several muscular strength tests that a personal trainer can carry out to understand the client's strength level.

Two test types to measure upper body strength and lower body strength are described below.

1-repetition maximum bench press test

The 1-repetition maximum (1RM) bench press test using a barbell is a good way to measure a client's upper body strength. The barbell needs to be adjustable to allow low resistance increments (2.5-40kg) and a spotter will be required to assist with the test.

L2

Teaching points

- Lie on the bench, head up with upper body and head supported by the bench. The natural spinal curve should be evident whilst lying on the bench.
- If using a bench with weight support, grip the bar firmly with hands outside shoulder width and keep the wrists straight. Otherwise the bar should be given by a spotter.
- Barbell should be level with the chest.
- Extend the arms and return the bar to mid-chest level without resting on the chest. The arms should be kept vertical as the bar is lowered.

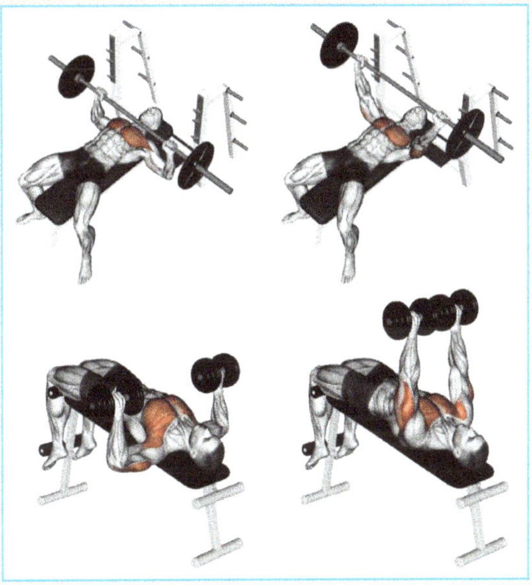

Bench presses can also be done using dumbbells following the same techniques.

Muscles worked: Pectoralis major, anterior deltoids and triceps.

Precautions: Avoid twisting the back during this exercise and ensure the head is not hanging off the bench.

Test procedures

- Client should warm up adequately, for example do 5-10 reps of light-to-moderate free weight exercises, then after a minute rest perform two heavier warm up sets of 2-5 reps, with a two-minute rest between the sets.
- After warm up, the client should rest for two to four minutes and then perform the one-rep-max attempt with proper bench press technique, where the weight load is estimated to one near the maximum load. If the lift is successful, rest for another two to four minutes and increase the load 5-10%, and attempt another lift. If the subject fails to perform the lift with correct technique, rest two to four minutes and attempt a weight 2.5-5% lower.

- Keep increasing and decreasing the weight until a maximum lift is performed. This is the 1RM score.

TIP

Selection of the starting weight by estimating sensibly is important so that the maximum press is completed within approximately five attempts after the warm up sets.

- Divide the 1RM value by the client's body weight to calculate the relative strength. You can now compare the relative strength values to normative values shown in the table below.

	Age									
	20-29		30-39		40-49		50-59		60+	
Percentile	**M**	**F**	**M**	**F**	**M**	**F**	**M**	**F**	**M**	**F**
10	0.80	0.30	0.71	0.27	0.65	0.23	0.57	0.19	0.53	0.25
20	0.88	0.33	0.78	0.32	0.72	0.20	0.63	0.23	0.57	0.26
30	0.93	0.35	0.83	0.34	0.76	0.30	0.68	0.26	0.63	0.28
40	0.99	0.37	0.88	0.37	0.80	0.32	0.71	0.28	0.66	0.29
50	1.06	0.40	0.93	0.38	0.84	0.34	0.75	0.31	0.68	0.30
60	1.14	0.41	0.98	0.41	0.88	0.37	0.79	0.33	0.72	0.32
70	1.22	0.42	1.04	0.42	0.93	0.38	0.84	0.35	0.77	0.36
80	1.32	0.49	1.12	0.45	1.00	0.40	0.90	0.37	0.82	0.38
90	1.48	0.54	1.24	0.49	1.1	0.46	0.97	0.40	0.89	0.41

Strength norms for 1rm bench press. Adapted from Earle and Baechle, 2004. Interpretation of percentiles: 10 = well below average; 30 = below average; 50 = average, 70 = above average; 90 = well above average.

1-repetition maximum leg press test

The 1RM leg press test is a good way to test a client's lower body strength.

L2

Teaching points:

- Choose a suitable weight for your training and then place your feet a little more than hip width on the foot plate. Ensure a 90 degree bend at the knees and ankles. Grip the handles, keeping a neutral spine. Chest should be up and looking forward. This will form your starting position.
- Using force through the heels of your feet, push through hips and knees extending the legs. Be careful not to lock out the knees.
- Hold this position for a moment, then go back to the starting position but without letting the weights touch each other.

Main muscles worked: Quadriceps, gluteals, hamstrings, gastrocnemius and soleus.

Test procedures

- Client should sit in the leg press machine and place legs on the footplates. Seat should be adjusted so that the knee angle is approximately 120 degrees.
- Client should warm up adequately, for example do 5-10 reps of a light-to-moderate free leg presses.
- After warm up, the client should rest for two to four minutes and then perform the one-rep-max attempt with proper leg press technique, where the weight load is estimated to one near the maximum load. If the press is successful, rest for another two to four minutes and increase the load 5-10%, and attempt another press. If the subject fails to perform the lift with correct technique, rest two to four minutes and attempt a weight 2.5-5% lower.
- Keep increasing and decreasing the weight until a maximum press is performed. This is the 1RM score.

TIP

Selection of the starting weight by estimating sensibly is important so that the maximum press is completed within approximately five attempts after the warm up sets.

- Divide the 1RM value by the client's body weight to calculate the relative strength.

You can now compare the relative strength values to normative values shown in the table below.

	Age									
	20-29		30-39		40-49		50-59		60+	
Percentile	**M**	**F**	**M**	**F**	**M**	**F**	**M**	**F**	**M**	**F**
10	1.51	1.02	1.43	0.94	1.35	0.76	1.22	0.75	1.16	0.84
20	1.63	1.13	1.52	1.09	1.44	0.94	1.32	0.86	1.25	0.94
30	1.74	1.23	1.59	1.16	1.51	1.06	1.39	0.95	1.30	0.98
40	1.83	1.25	1.65	1.21	1.57	1.12	1.46	1.03	1.38	1.04
50	1.91	1.32	1.71	1.26	1.62	1.19	1.52	1.09	1.43	1.08
60	1.97	1.36	1.77	1.32	1.68	1.26	1.58	1.18	1.49	1.15
70	2.05	1.42	1.85	1.47	1.74	1.35	1.64	1.24	1.56	1.18
80	2.13	1.66	1.93	1.50	1.82	1.46	1.71	1.30	1.62	1.25
90	2.27	2.05	2.07	1.73	1.92	1.63	1.80	1.51	1.73	1.40

Strength norms for 1rm leg press. Adapted from Earle and Baechle, 2004. Interpretation of percentiles: 10 = well below average; 30 = below average; 50 = average, 70 = above average; 90 = well above average

Muscular endurance tests.

Press up test

The press up test is a good way to measure muscle endurance and the chart below can be used to identify their fitness level. The required measurement is the total number of completed press ups to the point of exhaustion.

Age	17-19		20-29		30-39		40-49		50-59		60-69	
	M	F	M	F	M	F	M	F	M	F	M	F
Excellent	>56	>35	>47	>36	>41	>37	>34	>31	>31	>25	>30	>23
Good	47-56	27-35	39-47	30-36	34-41	30-37	28-34	25-31	25-31	21-25	24-30	19-23
Above average	35-46	21-27	30-39	23-29	25-33	22-30	21-28	18-24	18-24	15-20	17-23	13-18
Average	19-34	11-20	17-29	12-22	13-24	10-21	11-20	8-17	9-17	7-14	6-16	5-12
Below average	11-18	6-10	10-16	7-11	8-12	5-9	6-10	4-7	5-8	3-6	3-5	2-4
Poor	4-10	2-5	4-9	2-6	2-7	1-4	1-5	1-3	1-4	1-2	1-2	1
Very poor	<4	0-1	<4	0-1	<2	0	0	0	0		0	

Source: Adapted from Golding, et al. (1989). The Y's way to physical fitness (3rd ed.)

Test procedures

- Client should be in normal press up position – body straight and arms shoulder width apart.
- The client should lower him/herself to 90 degrees of elbow flexion.

For those that are unable to complete the left version, the client may instead be raised from a position where the knees are in contact with the ground.

Abdominal curl test

The abdominal curl test is also a good way to measure muscle endurance and the chart below can be used to identify their fitness level. The test involves counting the number of times the client can raise the shoulder blades off the mat (trunk at 30° of spinal flexion), in order for the fingers to touch a line which is equal to three inches away from the resting position.

The table below shows what would be considered, average poor or good.

Age	18-25		26-35		36-45		46-55		56-65		65+	
	M	F	M	F	M	F	M	F	M	F	M	F
Excellent	>49	>43	>45	>39	>41	>33	>35	>27	>31	>24	>28	>23
Good	44-49	37-43	40-45	33-39	35-41	27-33	29-35	22-27	25-31	18-24	22-28	17-23
Above Average	39-43	33-36	40-45	29-32	30-34	23-26	25-28	18-21	21-24	13-17	19-21	14-16
Average	35-38	29-32	35-39	25-28	27-29	19-22	22-24	14-17	17-20	10-12	15-18	11-13
Below Average	31-34	25-28	31-34	21-24	23-26	15-18	18-21	10-13	13-16	7-9	11-14	5-10
Poor	25-30	18-24	22-28	13-20	17-22	7-14	13-17	5-9	9-12	3-6	7-10	2-4
Very Poor	<25	<18	<22	<13	<17	<7	<12	<5	<9	<3	<7	<2

Source: Adapted from Golding, et al. (1986). The Y's way to physical fitness (3rd ed.)

Test procedures

- Area should be matted in order to cushion the lumbar spine.
- Client should lie on their back, knees bent to 90 degrees, palms down and arms straight.

One minute sit up test

The one minute sit up test can be used to measure abdominal and hip flexor muscles strength. A mat and stopwatch will be required for this test.

Test procedures

- Client should be in supine position on a mat with arms crossed touching the shoulders. The hips and knees should be flexed with the angle at the knee being approximately 90 degrees (feet are about 30-45cm away from the buttocks).
- On start of stopwatch, the torso should be raised until it is perpendicular to the floor with chin tucked into the chest and hands remaining in contact with the shoulders.
- Lower the torso until the shoulders are once again in contact with the floor and repeat until the minute is over. Rest period is acceptable if required. The score is the number of sit-ups performed in the one minute.

The score can then be compared against normative values as shown below:

	Age											
	18-25		26-35		36-45		46-55		56-65		>65	
Percentile	M	F	M	F	M	F	M	F	M	F	M	F
10	27	25	21	20	21	16	16	13	20	8	12	9
20	33	32	30	24	25	20	24	21	24	12	19	11
30	37	34	33	28	29	23	29	25	28	18	22	16
40	41	38	36	32	32	28	33	28	32	22	24	20
50	46	44	38	34	36	31	39	31	36	24	27	22
60	52	51	51	37	43	35	44	33	41	27	31	26
70	57	57	57	41	45	38	51	36	46	32	35	29
80	66	61	61	46	52	44	53	40	49	38	40	32
90	77	68	62	54	60	54	61	48	56	44	50	34

Norms for sit up tests. Adapted from Earle and Baechle, 2004. Interpretation of percentiles: 10 = well below average; 30 = below average; 50 = average, 70 = above average; 90 = well above average.

Flexibility testing

This involves the movement available at a joint. It is the ability to extend a muscle without it resulting in structural damage. A number of factors influence this, namely the individual's muscle mass, bone structure, adipose tissue and skin.

Several tests measure flexibility. The personal trainer should use their own observational skills to evaluate flexibility issues when possible. However, this may be difficult to diagnose through just observation.

Sit and reach test

This is generally a fair test to perform unless the client has previously had low back injury, in particular a prolapsed disc. If the client does have a prolapsed disc, they should be referred to their doctor for further assessment. This test measures the flexibility of the hamstrings and lower back. It measures how flexible the hamstrings and lower back are.

Testing procedures

1. Client to warm up prior to this test, or to perform it after an aerobic test.
2. Client to remove shoes and any items of clothing that will restrict movement.
3. Position client with his/her feet flat against the board. His/her legs and back to be straight.
4. Client to reach forward gradually, keeping his/her back straight for as long as possible.
5. Measure hamstring flexibility by noting down the point that the client starts to bend his/her back.
6. Measure the hamstring and lower back flexibility by instructing the client to continue to reach forward as far as possible bending his/her back. Record the furthest point.

Goal setting

Once a personal trainer has gathered information and feels they know enough about the client to proceed with training, the first thing to do is to work with the client to set goals.

A goal can be defined as 'the object of a person's ambition or effort; an aim or desired result.' Setting goals is one way of increasing motivation and commitment to any set task.

Goal types and categories

Goals are not only used in the health and fitness industry, but also to motivate ourselves in everyday life. There are many types of goals and some of the common ones are:

1. Personal goals: These may be in family and social life, sporting and fitness objectives, and things that generally make us happy. They may also include self-improvement goals relating to personal growth and development.

2. Career: These may be about one's career, business and the financial rewards that they bring.

3. Performance related goals: These types of goals centre on the result of an action or process, like winning a contest or beating a challenger. Being successful in this is dependent on the client's own effort as well as the ability of the challenger.

Goals can be short-term, medium-term or long-term. With regards to exercising, short-term goals are usually set over a period of one day, one month or up to six months. These goals are related to what the personal trainer wants to accomplish in a single session or set of sessions. Long-term goals are associated with periods of six months to more than several years and sometimes even set as 'lifetime goals'.

Setting goals helps an individual to persist with a task over a period of time, and helps them focus their attention on its important aspects. It promotes the client's creative mind, encouraging them to think of new ways in which to achieve the required outcome. It is important that the personal trainer works with the client to set both long-term and short-term goals as the fulfilment of short-term goals will contribute to the achievement of long-term goals.

Components of effective goal setting

Formulating goals and objectives on their own is not likely to increase motivation and performance. The most effective way to increase motivation is to incorporate the following six methods:

1. Goals and objectives should be precise and not too broad.
2. Recognize and help foster the commitment shown by the client in achieving their goal.
3. Give a constructive evaluation to the client of their short-term and final goals.
4. Give rewards for the completion of short-term goals and for the achievement of the final desired goal.
5. There should be a good supply of resources and support made available to the client.
6. Clients should be given the required knowledge, skills and competence to achieve the desired goal.

SMART goals

When setting goals, it is useful to use the acronym **SMART**.

Specific - This means that goals must relate to specific aspects of fitness, such as body area, aerobic fitness or muscle endurance.

Measurable - The goal must be quantifiable and as such stated in figures. For example, I want to lose five kilograms, rather than I want to lose weight.

Achievable - Goals must be within the realms of possibility depending on client's immediate capability. Never set someone a goal if they cannot achieve it.

Realistic - The trainer and client must be realistic in setting goals, taking into account any external factors that may hinder progress.

Time constrained – Goals should be set with a time limit to achieve them, for example end of the year.

A good set of goals will follow all the above criteria. An example of a SMART goal is to reduce waist size by 5cm in three months' time. This goal is specific to one aspect of fitness; it is measurable, time constrained and achievable.

Goals should be challenging but achievable. Carelessly set goals could result in demotivating the individual. For example, if unrealistic goals are set that are very difficult to accomplish, or if the timescale is too long, the client may lose motivation and be put off exercising altogether. The client may become stressed if goals are set too high. This type of stress on top of the pressures of regular life may overwhelm them – they do not need additional things to be worrying about. Conversely, if the goals set are too easy, the client will quickly complete them and may then be in danger of resuming previous bad habits.

TIP

It is good practice to let the individual contribute to the formation of the goals. Psychological evidence suggests that people do not react well to restrictions being placed on them. They are more likely to resist if they are constantly harassed with instructions and orders. By helping to develop the goals, the client is much more likely to be committed to completing each one. This will also assist in promoting their own strategy for motivation and compliance.

Achieving set goals

Tools used to help with achieving set goals

1. A written record: Goals are written on paper. The client holds this record as well as the personal trainer. The client is encouraged to place a copy of these targets in a place where they and their support network (family, friends) can see it easily.

2. Use of images: Using pictures of where the client wants to be once the goal has been reached is a good way of creating an emotional and psychological link. This use of visual aids can make the goal seem more real and in turn help the client to succeed.

3. Compliments and reminders of their progression: It is not just children who perform better with praise. Adults react well to praise too. Personal trainers should regularly give credit to worthy performances and maintain a positive feedback system.

4. Follow up an achievement with a reward: Often, rewarding the client after they have reached a goal can encourage them to improve further. It is good practice to discuss with the client which rewards they would like to link with their achievement. There is no need for the reward itself to be significant or grand – just reaching the goal should give the client the motivation and incentive to continue with the plan. An example of a reward could be a T-shirt or a small item inscribed with an inspirational message. Acknowledgement by the personal trainer of the client's efforts is sometimes a reward in itself.

5. Support network: At times, a client can find it hard to stick to a plan and keep themselves motivated. Having a support network can help the client keep on track. The personal trainer could assist with forming a support network.

6. Diary: It is good practice to advise clients to write a diary. This is an excellent way of measuring how far the client has progressed. It can also have the effect of encouraging the client to reach their goal.

7. Using reminders: This can be any reminder which will help the client to complete their goal and motivate them to continue.

Reviewing and revision of goals

There is little point in setting goals if there is no follow up system or evaluation of progress. Reviewing progress is usually followed up by the setting up of further goals.

Regular sessions should be pre-arranged with clients in order to keep a check on the client's progress in meeting short and long-term goals. Setting up these sessions in advance is important in ensuring the client is adhering to the plan.

The difficulty level and complexity of the goal should be reviewed also. Taking away a reward for a goal that was too difficult in the first place may only frustrate and upset the client.

Instead, reward should be given every time the client completes short-term objectives within a final goal. This method is very effective when dealing with complicated goals. It helps to combat any feelings of disappointment and failure.

These guidelines are not considered to be an exhaustive list but rather a framework or reference point to assist professionals developing a goal-setting program.

Incorporating goals into a training program

Once goals have been set, the personal trainer should formulate training programs around these goals. Exercises should be selected that will help the client to achieve these goals. For example, if one of the goals is to lose weight, then aerobic exercises good for fat burning will need to be included in the training program.

Designing training programs is covered in *Chapter 4.*

End of Chapter activities

Activity 3.7: Calculate your own BMI and write down what category you fall under (under, healthy, over or obese).

BMI:

Category:

Activity 3.8: Put these steps of taking blood pressure in the correct order by writing a number 1-7 next to the steps.

	With the cuff on, palpate the arm at the crease to locate the strongest pulse sounds and place the bell of the stethoscope over the brachial artery at this location.
	Locate the brachial artery and position the cuff so that the artery marker points to the brachial artery and then wrap the cuff snugly around the arm.
	Slowly deflate the blood pressure cuff.
	Inflate the blood pressure cuff by pumping the cuff bulb as you listen to the pulse sounds. When the cuff has inflated enough to stop blood flow you should hear no sounds through the stethoscope.
	Take note of the systolic reading by listening for a sound that may resemble a tapping noise at first. The first occurrence of rhythmic sounds heard as blood begins to flow through the artery is the client's systolic pressure.
	Place the blood pressure cuff on the client's arm.
	Take note of the diastolic reading by continuing to listen as the cuff pressure drops and the sounds fade. The diastolic reading is when the rhythmic sounds stop.

Activity 3.9: Which of these tests can be used to assess a client's muscular endurance?

- [ ] 1.5 mile run test
- [ ] 1-repetition maximum leg press test
- [ ] One-minute sit-up test
- [ ] Press up test

Activity 3.10: Which of these tests can be used to assess a client's cardiovascular fitness?

- [ ] Rockport walking test
- [ ] Cycle ergometer test
- [ ] 1-repetition maximum bench press test
- [ ] Skinfold test
- [ ] 3-minute step test

Activity 3.11: Take a friend or family member's pulse rate and assess whether they have a normal heart rate or any conditions.

Activity 3.12: Carry out consultation on a family member or friend and do the following:

- **Gather information on their lifestyle**
- **Assess cardiovascular fitness**
- **Carry out one body composition test**
- **Measure blood pressure (optional)**
- **Create a set of smart objectives**

Test findings:

Objectives:

End of Chapter checklist

1. Why is client screening important?
2. What kind of information on a client should a personal trainer gather?
3. What is BMI?
4. What is a Health Check Form and why is it used?
5. What factors can affect fitness tests?
6. In what circumstances should tests be stopped immediately?
7. What is the meaning of 'waist to hip ratio'?
8. What is a caliper used for?
9. What is bioelectrical impedance analysis?
10. What methods can be used to take a client's blood pressure?
11. What is the formula for calculating BMI?
12. What is a cycle ergometer test used for?
13. What is VO_2 max and how is it calculated?
14. What is bradycardia?
15. What are the variables of Rockport walking test?
16. What tests can be used to assess a client's muscular strength?
17. What is a goal?
18. What are smart goals?
19. What are the main components of effective goal setting?
20. What tools can a personal trainer use to help a client achieve their goals?

Chapter 4
PROGRAMMING AND DELIVERING PERSONAL TRAINING SESSIONS

Chapter 4A: Programming personal training with clients

Chapter 4B: Delivering personal training sessions

Chapter 4C: Training special populations

Programming personal training with clients

Chapter summary

This Chapter will cover the components that need to be taken into consideration to develop personal training programs.

Aim

The aim of this Chapter is to teach personal trainers how to develop training programs by selecting exercise types depending on the objectives of the client.

Learning objectives

After completing this Chapter, personal trainers will be able to:

1. Summarize the different training approaches – aerobic, resistance and flexibility.
2. Summarize the specificity and components of aerobic training and then design an aerobic training program.
3. Summarize the specificity and components of resistance training and then design a resistance training program.
4. Summarize periodization and apply the principles to training programs.
5. Apply flexibility exercises to training programs, including partner stretching exercises.
6. Discuss what can impact core stability and adapt core balance exercises to a program.
7. Discuss the different resistance training methods and select them for training programs.
8. Select a variety of exercises for aerobic training and incorporate them within training programs.

Designing principles

Once the consultation process has been completed (*Chapter 3B - Knowing a client*) the personal trainer needs to plan a safe and effective training program combining information they gathered with the available approaches to training. Training program design is an area of controversy and no doubt, different personal trainers will have varying ideas about what is right and wrong and what a session should include.

It is important for a personal trainer to personalize the training! This means taking into consideration client specifics throughout the program. At all times, the client's desired goals should be kept in mind along with the client's competence and other information gathered during the consultation process. A typical training program will usually last for about an hour, although the duration will vary between clients depending on their objectives and competence and thus it is up to the personal trainer to recommend length of each component in line with their client's ability and goals.

When designing the training program, consideration should be given to the following:

- Variables of sets
- Number of repetitions
- Rest
- Level of intensity
- Frequencies
- Client's likes and dislikes
- Results from the tests
- Injuries and medical conditions
- Client's personal circumstances
- Client's financial circumstances
- Different training approaches
  - Cardiovascular training
  - Resistance training
  - Flexibility training
  - Core stability approaches

Key to a successful training program is the establishment of objectives specific to the desired outcome. Therefore, it is vital that the personal trainer determines exactly what the client wants. Often clients will have broad objectives, such as "I want to get fit" and the personal trainer should ask questions to understand what being fit means to the client and then to develop more specific smart and measurable objectives.

The fundamental principles of designing programs are the same. The principles of training are:

- **FITT:** This acronym stands for Frequency, Intensity, Type and Time. The FITT approach can be applied to both aerobic and anaerobic exercise.
- **Specificity:** This relates to the particular ways in which the body adapts to particular types of exercise. The idea is that if only a particular set of muscles are worked, then the body will make adaptions that maximally support that activity, but less so to other activities.
- **Reversibility:** This is the principle that relates to a particular activity that has evoked physiological adaptions, then to cease the activity will cause the adaptions to diminish. It is therefore necessary to maintain training activity to retain the benefits
- **Progressive overload:** This describes the gradual increase of stress placed upon the body during training required for body adaptions to take place.
- **Adaptability:** This principle describes how the body reacts differently to variations in activity. For example, whilst long distance running will provide benefits of bone density and aerobic development, including a sprint element will increase anaerobic development.
- **Recovery:** Many of the adaptions the body makes in response to training do not occur during the activity itself. Instead it is during the period after exertion ceases that the changes take place. Therefore, recovery is of vital importance when designing training programs.
- **Individuality:** This principle ensures that each client is considered distinctly and as a whole. A 'one-size-fits-all' approach to meeting common goals such as weight loss or a sporting achievement is not at all appropriate in providing a training program. Instead, a comprehensive range of factors need to be considered to ensure safe and efficient development.
- **Progression:** The rate of improvement will not be a linear process. Beginners will almost always benefit more rapidly over the initial weeks of a program than when further into a program. Fortunately, once the benefits begin to show, motivation is generally already increased and so the slowing of tangible progress is less of a concern in maintaining a training application. However, as the rate is not constant and will also be affected by other factors, the trainer needs to recognize this and take it into account.

Training session composition

Training sessions should follow a consistent pattern to optimize efficiency, safety and enjoyment. Each session should begin with a warm up, followed by the main part of the workout which is then wrapped up with a cool down as per the instructions in the warm up and cool down section.

A warm up can be said to have three main objectives:

- To increase the body temperature
- To raise the heart rate
- To make the joints more mobile in preparation for the session

The need to raise the body temperature slowly by moving the major muscles is to increase the blood flow to the muscles, bringing with it oxygen to produce energy.

The aim of cool down is simply the opposite to the aim of warm up and therefore the three objectives of cool down are:

- To return the heart rate to normal
- To return the muscle to their original pre-exercise length
- To remove waste products built up during the exercise session

The different training approaches

In level 2, the various training types and associated equipment were covered along with the movement types possible with the equipment. The same movements and equipment would be used for personal training but the sessions should be customized based on the client's objectives and fitness goals.

A summary of each training type and the associated equipment and movement types are provided below.

Aerobic training

Cardio exercises also commonly known as aerobic exercise refers in general to light-to-moderate exertion that can be carried out for extended periods of time. Swimming, jogging, dancing, kickboxing and cycling are good examples of aerobic activities. 'Aerobic' refers to the activity requiring energy at a rate that the normal, if heightened, operation of the cardiorespiratory system can support i.e. the oxygen that can be made available to the muscles is sufficient to carry out the activity.

Cardiovascular training equipment include: Treadmills, step machines, rowing machines, cross trainers and exercise bikes.

Anaerobic training

Anaerobic exercise is a form of exercise that consists of short exertion, high intensity movements, intense enough to cause lactic acid to form. When performing at elevated intensity levels, the cardiovascular system is challenged to deliver the required oxygen fast enough to the muscles. Anaerobic exercises can only continue for short periods of time because muscles require oxygen to maintain prolonged exertion. Examples of anaerobic exercise include heavy weight training, sprinting and most athletic sports. This type of exercise tends to be used by body builders to increase muscle mass and athletes to promote strength, speed and power.

Resistance training

There are many types of resistance machines and they tend to vary from manufacturer to manufacturer. Personal trainers should therefore ensure they have familiarized themselves on how to use the machines before teaching clients. With all resistance machines, it is important to highlight the full range of movements that can be achieved and their benefits. Examples of resistance training equipment are machines for shoulder press, peck deck, lateral pull down, assisted pull up machines, lower back machines, ab machines, leg extension machines, leg press machines, abduction and adductor machines.

Flexibility training

In general terms, flexibility can be defined as the range of motion about a joint and its surrounding muscles during movement. By increasing the range of motion at this joint, performance may be enhanced and the risk of injury reduced. The rationale for this is that a limb can move further before an injury occurs. However, flexibility training carries with it an increased risk of injury and so should be considered carefully before being incorporated into a program. A flexibility training program can be made up of different types of stretching, including:

- Dynamic stretching
- Static stretching
- Ballistic stretching
- Isometric stretching

Using free weights

Free weight exercises allow a greater range of movements and more accurately reflect the movements we participate in everyday, thus working and strengthening the muscles we use on a day to day basis. There are two main types of equipment for free weight movements:

- Dumbbells come in a pair, each with equal weight and can be of many different weights and sizes, although most are about 15-38cm long. The weight of dumbbells can be fixed or adjusted by adding or removing weight plates.

- Barbells are long, straight metal bars with sleeves on the ends to hold weight plates. The weight of the barbell can be adjusted by adding and removing plates.

Movements using dumbbells:

- Bench press
- Shoulder press
- Bent arm pull over
- Bicep curls
- Lateral rise
- Front rise
- Single arm row
- Standing triceps press
- Lunges
- Chest flyes
- Prone flyes

Movements using barbells:

- Deadlift
- The clean
- Upright row
- Back squat
- Bench press
- Bicep curls
- Shoulder press
- Lying triceps press

Exercises using body weight

There are a number of exercises that can be performed unassisted using one's own body weight that a personal trainer can incorporate in a training program. Examples of these exercises are:

Lunges

Squats

Wall sit

Sit ups

Leg lifts

Hip bridge

Donkey kicks

Planks

Push ups

Many body weight exercises like press ups, sit ups and planks are not suitable for pregnant women. The personal trainer should incorporate suitable exercises depending on the stages of pregnancy.

Aerobic training overview

Aerobic fitness also known as cardiovascular fitness can be defined as the ability to take in, circulate and use oxygen. Key to any physical adaptation are the training principles known as 'overload' and 'specificity'. These principles say that a person's fitness can only be improved if they train more than usual. The oxygen system in our body needs to be exerted in a way that increases breathing and heart rate.

Designing aerobic training programs is dependent on the short-term and long-term manipulation of program variables including intensity, frequency and duration to stress the aerobic energy systems. Designing aerobic training programs require an examination of the client's current fitness level, exercise history and overall fitness goals. A common fitness goal for clients taking up exercise is fat loss and aerobic training programs, if well designed are excellent for fat loss and generally to improve and maintain an efficient cardiorespiratory system.

L2

Aerobic exercise benefits

Cardiovascular fitness:

- Strengthens the heart and entire cardiovascular system
- Increases cardiac output and decreases resting heart rate
- Increases the oxygen levels in the blood and the volume of blood per stroke from the heart
- Improves circulation by removing cholesterol and plaque build-up from the arteries
- Increases blood vessel capacity and volume of blood
- Increases cardiovascular endurance
- Increases haemoglobin (gas transport molecules)
- Increases good cholesterol levels (HDL) while reducing bad cholesterol levels (LDL)
- Lowers blood pressure
- Decreases the probability of contracting diseases such as heart attacks, strokes and type 2 diabetes

Cardiorespiratory fitness:

- Increases lung capacity and tidal volume
- Gas exchange efficiency improvements
- Increases the efficiency in which oxygen is utilized
- Improves muscle tone
- Improves blood vessel supply to muscles
- Increases in mitochondria for better oxygen transfer in to muscles

L2

Weight loss

- Body adapts to burn fat as its primary fuel source which increases the basal metabolic rate, resulting in a greater number of calories being burned per day
- Improves muscular tone while reducing body fat

Mental well being

- Reduces stress levels, calms and centres the mind
- Improves co-ordination, balance and posture

Activity

Activity 4.1: Design your own aerobic training program for a client, whose main objective is to reduce their body mass index (BMI) and tone their abdominal muscles. You can use the sample template below:

program card				
Day	**Exercise**	**Sets X reps**	**Recovery**	**Special instructions**
Monday				
Tuesday				
Wednesday				
Thursday				
Friday				
Saturday				
Sunday				
Monday				
Tuesday				
Wednesday				
Thursday				
Friday				
Saturday				
Sunday				

Specificity and components

Specificity

According to the principle of specificity, the results of a training program will be directly related to the type of training performed. This means that the training that involves one type of aerobic exercise will not mean equal improvements in another type. In other words, a training program that is focused on cycling and where a client can exercise at high intensity, will not mean the client can also do another aerobic exercise like jogging at the same intensity. This is because the muscle activation and the oxygen intake and transportation varies between exercise modes and so the body's responses and adaptations are not equal. However, improvements in VO_2 and as a result from one aerobic exercise mode will no doubt help in other exercise modes to an extent (Earle & Baechle, 2004).

Components

An aerobic training program consists of several components that can be manipulated in different ways to achieve variable outcomes.

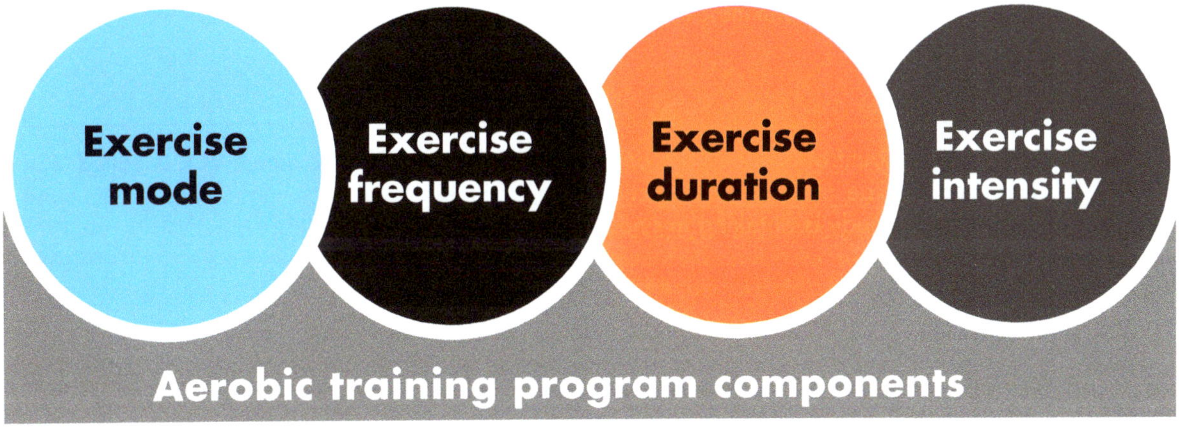

Exercise mode

One of the first steps in designing an aerobic training program is to decide on the mode of exercise. Aerobic exercises can be machine or non-machine based as shown in the table below:

Gym based exercise	Studio-based group exercise	Body weight exercise	Other modes
• Treadmills	• Choreograophed aerobics	• Walking	• Cycling
• Step machines	• Step aerobics classes	• Jogging	• Skipping
• Exercise bike	• Boxercise classes	• Marching	• Swimming
• Rowing machine	• Circuit training classes	• Running	• Dancing
• Elliptical trainers	• Spin classes	• Jump jacks	• Cross country
		• Squat jumps	• Hill walking
		• Jumping lunges	• Trekking
		• Leg curls	• Sports
		• Knee raises	
		• Donkey kicks	

If designing a program for athletes, the exercise modes selected by the personal trainer should reflect the specific sport or movement that the athlete performs during competitions. For non-athletes, exercise modes chosen should be related the client's overall fitness goals. For example, if the client's goal is to complete a 5km race, then a large part of the program will involve running outdoors or on a treadmill.
On the other hand, a program for an overweight client wishing to lose body fat can include a wide variety of exercises, if the exercises burn calories.

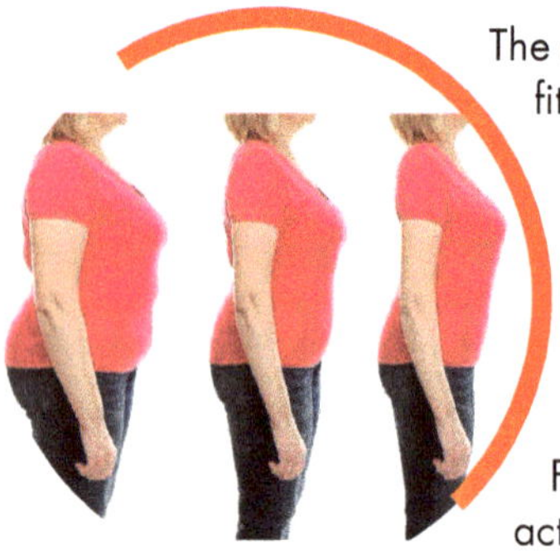

The exercise modes incorporated within a program must also be within the client's fitness capacity if known. For example, if theprogram includes running in the park when the client is incapable of even walking briskly, it would be highly unlikely that they will adhere to the program. If the fitness capacity is unknown then it is a good idea to choose activities that the client is known to enjoy or likely to enjoy.

The mode of exercise must also be matched to a client's physical abilities. For example, a client with diagnosed shoulder strain, is unlikely to be suited to activities like swimming that involves arm rotation, whilst a client with knee injuries but strong-arm muscles may thrive from swimming.

Intensity

L2

VO_2 is the amount of oxygen your body uses in a minute. The maximum VO_2 is called VO_2 max and can be used as a prediction of your fitness level - the higher this is the more effective your body is at taking in and using oxygen.

The intensity level chosen for the client is dependent on what would be required to reach the client's goals. Therefore, if the goal is to run 5km at a speed of 10km per hour, then the program would have to include intense running sessions but a gradual build up may be necessary, depending on the client's current fitness level.

Regulating and monitoring the intensity of exercise is vital to prescribe the correct aerobic endurance training program that will reach the client's fitness goals. Over training can be just as much a hindrance as under training and therefore as a personal trainer it is essential that the correct intensity is prescribed and that the intensity is increased / decreased depending on progression.

During a session, it is important to attain the Heart Rate Reserve (HRR) which is the difference between the client's maximal heart rate (MHR) and their resting heart rate. The client's oxygen uptake reserve (VO_2R) which is the difference between the VO_2 max and resting VO_2 has been shown to be fairly equal to the HRR. (Earle and Baechle, 2004) and this measurement is acceptable for monitoring purpose in personal training as the use of laboratory assessed HRR is uncommon.

For healthy adults, the intensity threshold is generally considered to be approximately 50% to 85% of HRR depending on fitness levels (Earle and Baechle, 2004). The key to beginning at an intensity that is right for the client is to examine the client's exercise and medical history and any test results available.

TIP

It is better to begin at a slightly lower intensity and building up, rather than commencing too high and risking overtraining or injury resulting in poor adherence.

Target heart rate

There is a correlation between heart rate and VO_2. As the heart rate increases in response to exercise and increases in workload, this necessitates an increase in oxygen consumption. This means that as the heart rate increases to the client's maximal heart rate (MHR), a large percentage of the VO_2 max is being used.

The table below shows a range of age predicted maximal heart rate (APMHR) and their related percentages of VO_2 max.

Age predicted maximal heart rate (APMHR)	Percentages of VO_2 Max
66	50
70	55
74	60
77	65
81	70
85	75
88	80
92	85
96	90
100	95

Source: Adapted from Earle and Baecle, 2004

This relationship has been found to be consistent regardless of gender, heart diseases, fitness levels, testing mode and muscle groups exercises and therefore heart rate is often regarded as a quick and easy method to determine the intensity of exercise (Earle and Baechle, 2004).

The APMHR is a predicted value because the only way to really determine a person's maximal heart rate is to perform a graded test that takes the client's heart rate to a point where it no longer increases. This can have medical concerns and is recommended to be done in the presence of a physician. Thus, a personal trainer can use the APMHR equation (Earle and Baechle, 2004):

APMHR = 220 – age

This equation gives an estimate with an error of 1+/- 10-15 breaths, but as it is rare that during aerobic exercise training a client will reach MHR, the age predicted estimate is seen to provide a close approximation that is acceptable for a personal trainer to use when designing aerobic training programs.

Aerobic training is proven to be advantageous when performed at an intensity of 60-90% of the maximum heart rate (MHR). Moderate intensity causes a person to be slightly out of breath without much fatigue. A brisk walk or cycling gently would equate to this for most unfit people. This is related to the lower end 60-90% MHR, though it does depend on the individual fitness level. Vigorous exercise results in a person becoming sweaty and out of breath. This means such exercise would come nearer to the higher end 60-90% MHR. Again, this is reliant on individual fitness levels.

RPE

Another recognized way of measuring intensity during aerobic activity is to use the Borg Rating of Perceived Exertion (RPE) Scale. This approach requires the client to rate their level of exertion using a number from 6 to 20 based on the physical sensations they experience whilst exercising, including increased heart and breathing rate, increased sweating and muscle fatigue. The numbers 6 to 20 in the RPE scale relate to phrases used to rate how easy or difficult an activity is perceived to be. This scale sees moderate intensity as being 'light', measured at number 11 and exercise of vigorous intensity is defined as 'somewhat hard' to 'hard', with a number of 13-14.

The original Borg RPE scale is provided below.

RPE Scale	Level of Exertion
6	No exertion at all
7	
7.5	Extremely light
8	
9	Very light
10	
11	light
12	
13	Somewhat hard
14	
15	Hard (heavy)
16	
17	Very hard
18	
19	Extremely hard
20	Maximal exertion

Source: Adapted from Earle and Baecle, 2004

Although the RPE number given by the client is a somewhat subjective measure, it can provide a good estimate of the actual heart rate during physical activity. Each number on the scale 6-20 corresponds to an approximate heart rate calculated, simply by multiplying the RPE number by 10. An RPE of 9 therefore would indicate a heart rate of 9x10=90 beats per minute. It should however be noted that this formula is an estimate and can be influenced by various factors such as client's age and fitness level as well as health conditions. By using the RPE method, it is possible to define a training program on numerical goals. Thus, if a new or unfit client states they are finding an activity 'hard' it would be possible to tell them to slow down or ease off so that they do not incur problems associated with overtraining. If the intensity of the exercise remains constant (i.e. 50% of a person's maximum heart rate, or an RPE of 13 throughout) then the heart rate will rise until it reaches what is known as 'steady state' where it stays relatively constant as the cardiovascular system meets the demands placed on it by the exercise. Achieving 'steady state' to train at a set intensity for a prolonged period is the goal of many aerobic fitness training programs.

Determining lactate threshold

Being able to determine when the anaerobic or 'lactate' threshold occurs in clients is a very useful measure during aerobic training as it enables intensities to be set for maximum effect and prevent intensities from becoming excessive. Of course, this is not easy to determine directly but in labs the lactate threshold has been consistently shown to occur between 13 and 15 on the Borg RPE scale where clients would describe exercise to be between 'somewhat hard' or 'hard'.

Talk test

The talk test is an alternative method used to monitor exercise intensity. Put simply, if the client can talk and exercise at the same time the oxygen needs of the exercise are still being met. If the client is out of breath, it is likely that they are working too hard (especially if they have to stop and catch their breath). If the client can talk and maintain the training intensity, they have more than enough oxygen and are not working hard enough to illicit the challenge required for adaptations to occur.

Frequency and duration

The frequency of exercise must be balanced with duration, intensity and training experience of clients. Exercise sessions of longer duration and intensity would need a longer rest period than shorter low intensity sessions. Exercise duration (measure of how long an exercise lasts) is directly related to the intensity of the exercise. Vigorously intense exercise realistically will be of shorter duration than sessions of moderate intensity.

Sample exercise frequency options are provided below for aerobic exercise.

	Frequency	Rest
Beginner	3 days per week	2 days after each session
Intermediate	4 days per week	1 day after 2 sessions
Advanced	6 days per week	1 day after 2-3 sessions
Duration	> 30 minutes to promote health and > 20 minutes to improve health or 10 minutes if intensity is moderate to high	

Source: Adapted from Earle and Baechle (2004) and American College of Sports Medicine (1998)

A personal trainer should set the duration of exercise based on the client's fitness level, exercise mode and the client's fitness goals. High intensity exercise should in general be of shorter duration than low to moderate intensity exercise.

Aerobic exercise types and considerations

LSD training is traditionally known as aerobic training and usually performed over a longer time (over 10 minutes) and low intensities of 50-70 and MHR. This type of training is suitable for those new to exercise programs. For intermediate and advanced exercisers, LSD is incorporated into training for endurance based sports or marathons. LSD is beneficial to gain fitness, however if it is the only type of exercise done, the improvement shown will eventually stagnate. One limitation of LSD is that it lacks specificity in relation to many sporting activities e.g. football players move in many different directions at different intensities, whereas LSD training is more or less in a straight line, thus it doesn't make sense for a footballer to continuously take part in LSD training as adaptations are specific to the type of stimulus applied.

Interval training are structured higher intensity workouts with some recovery periods in between. The time of work varies from a few seconds to several minutes. The higher intensity workouts can usually be kept up for two minutes. This is because the oxygen demand is greater than its supply. To keep the intensity high, the body's lactic acid energy system 'kicks in' to supply the remaining energy needed. Many athletes and sports participants benefit from the interval training because it promotes a person's ability to tolerate a high amount of lactic acid and the speed at which it is disposed of from the muscles. When a personal trainer formulates an interval program, they should consider its intensity, duration and the number of intervals including recovery periods. For example, an intermediate exerciser can be advised to carry out three minutes work followed by the same number of minutes in recovery, repeated two to five times. In contrast, an advanced exerciser may be advised to do three minutes activity followed by 90 second rest period, repeated four to six times. These scenarios clearly demonstrate the differences in fitness levels needed to perform, more so the ability to recover after each period of activity.

Fartlek (Swedish term that means speed play) training involves periods of fast activity mixed with periods of slower activity. This type of training is unstructured and the total work performed is approximately 30-40 minutes, working at different intensities. An example of an outdoor fartlek run would be to sprint from one pole to another, jog to the corner, giving a slower intensity for a few meters, then sprinting to a stop sign. This can be calculated for a set total time or distance.

Circuit training

A great way to promote mobility, endurance and strength is through circuit training. This type of training is made up of 6 to 10 exercises testing strength. These are conducted consecutively. Every exercise is undertaken a certain number of times for a limited period before the next exercise is started. There is a stage of rest in between each circuit. Each rest period increases after every stage. The entire number of circuits undertaken within a training session varies from two to six, dependent on:

- The training level of the participant (for example beginner, intermediate, advanced)
- Duration of the training
- The training goals

The length of the session can be dependent on time (e.g. 60 seconds) or can be measured by half the amount of repetitions of the exercise the participant can finish in 60 seconds of 100% effort. The circuit should be set up in such a way so as to exercise all the body parts, namely:

- Total body
- Upper body
- Lower body
- Core and trunk

Cross training
Cross training is where different exercises are mixed together in order to train the participant up in their usual exercise. For example, a runner who cross-trains may take part in other types of workouts including cycling, swimming, aerobic exercise or strength training to complement their running. This would help to promote strength and make muscles flexible in a way that running alone could not do. Cross training helps stop risk of injury by adjusting muscular irregularities. The varied number of exercises also helps stop the participant from getting bored with their usual routine.

Training clients at different levels

As a personal trainer, it is vital to personalize training taking into consideration the client's training experience and fitness level.

Beginners stage

Beginners should only take part in moderate intensity activities that do not result in fatigue, discomfort or soreness in the muscles. Training should initially be three to four times a week gradually building towards the recommended guidelines of five times a week. The length of the exercise session should aim to eventually reach 30 minutes of continuous exercise. Clients who are exceptionally unfit may not be able to reach 30 minutes of exercise and so should be advised to do as much as possible using an interval style approach. It should be noted that beginners may show vast improvements quite soon into the process but this may plateau in as little as three weeks. The personal trainer should therefore increase the exercise stimulus accordingly until the intermediate stage is reached.

Intermediate stage

This intermediate stage is reached once the client can carry out 30 minutes of moderate intensity activity, five times a week. This is achieved by amending the training guidelines. The first change would be to increase the intensity of the activity within each session. For example, increasing the intensity from 60% MHR to 70% MHR after 30 minutes of exercise. Alternatively, the personal trainer could gradually build the duration of exercise to one hour. The personal trainer must take care not to move the client forward too fast, as this has the potential to put off the client and could even result in an injury linked to overuse (due to the increased duration of exercise). Remember, it is best to only change one variable at a time.

Advanced stage

As fitness levels improve, the personal trainer should continue to increase intensity up to 'vigorous', alongside the changes in exercise duration. A good way of gently entering the waters of vigorous intensity, is to take part in interval training. This can perhaps be a 'stepping stone' to vigorous activity, with the client working with a mixture of moderate and high intensity exercises. The long-term goal to be working towards would be to complete a whole session at a high intensity vigorous level.

Periodization and aerobic training

An exercise program should include a variation of activities. Lasting success can be achieved by changing training patterns over the course of time.

A term 'periodization' is the process where training methods are changed over the course of time. The process is normally split into stages (Hawley and Burke, 1998). Grouping training into stages has several advantages:

- Helps to stop the client from burning out
- Provides a better experience for the client
- Makes training goal orientated
- Goals are completed in less time

An example of the stages involved are:

- Base training stage
- Transitory stage
- Power stage

1. Base training stage

At this stage, an 'aerobic base' is set up. This stage is also used to boost those changes linked with promoting VO_2 max. This stage usually features LSD (Long Slow Distance) training. It is measured by engaging in activity at AeT (zone 2) and AnT (zone 3) or RPE 11-15 for a minimum of 30 minutes. Other exercises which can be undertaken parallel to this may include postural correction and conditioning and muscular endurance resistance training.

2. Transitory stage training

This second stage of training is at times called the threshold stage (Hawley and Burke, 1998) or 'early quality work' (Daniels, 2001). The reason this is conducted is to boost the client's capacity to withstand the blood chemistry changes linked with work conducted at a higher pace. This can result in extreme tiredness.

This stage is usually made up of interval training work (zone three and four). Here, the client undertakes repetitions made up of five to ten minutes duration. Intensity should be equal to 85% to 95% VO_2 max or 85%-95% HR max (RPE 16-17).

3. Power stage training

Rapidity and power training allow the client to experience what it feels like to push oneself harder than usual. It should have a biochemical and neuromuscular effect with regards to 'teaching' the appropriate muscles to accommodate quicker rapidity. Intervals are normally followed in this stage where the client takes part in activity at a strength equal to 95 to 100% MHR RPE 19.

As well as this, clients will complete an extra stage which can be called the 'taper' or final quality stage of training. This is related to exercise that is of optimum standard, but which results in the client feeling more rejuvenated so that they can maximize their performance. Athletic training is a highly-disputed area, associated with a variety of theories. It should be noted that most clients are not professional athletes and are time constrained. As a result, the simplest guidance would be to keep the quality of the work optimal, and to minimize the length and how often it is conducted. It is often wise to ensure the client rests well and eats adequately.

Finally, training intensity MUST be increased steadily through the course of each stage. All stages are made up of multiple differing training techniques, which vary during the program. Personal trainers must also make sure that the client has enough rest and recovery in between exercise periods and stages.

Sample aerobic training program

Overall goal summary: Lose weight – 5kg. Increase cardiac fitness. Be able to run continuously for 40 minutes to run at least 5km in that time. **program duration:** 12 weeks

Week	Number of sessions per week	Duration of each session	Intensity	Exercise types, per session
1	3	30 minutes: 5 min warm up 20 min main session 5 min cool down	RPE 5-6	Session 1: Run 1 minute and walk 90 seconds on treadmill x 8 sets
				Session 2: Step machine (15 min) Rowing machine (5 min)
				Session 3: Run 1 minute and walk 90 seconds x 8 sets
2	3	30 minutes: 5 min warm up 20 min main session 5 min cool down	RPE 5-6	Session 1: Run 2 minutes and walk 1 minute on treadmill x 7 sets
				Session 2: Cross training machine (15 min) Rowing machine (5 min)
				Session 3: Run 2 minutes and walk 1 minute on treadmill x 7 sets
3	3	2 days 35 minutes and 1 day 35 minutes	RPE 5-7	Session 1: Jogging on treadmill 4 minutes at 8km per hour and building intensity and walking 1-minute x 6 sets
				Session 2: Step aerobics session / class
				Session 3: Jogging on treadmill 4 minutes at 8km per hour and building intensity and walking 1-minute x 6 sets
4	3	2 days 35 minutes (increasing main session by 5 min) and 1 day 30 minutes.	RPE 5-7	Session 1: Run 6 minutes and walk 2 minutes x 5 sets
				Session 2: Step machine (20 min) Rowing machine (5 min)
				Session 3: Run 6 minutes and walk 2 minutes x 4 set
5	3	40 minutes	RPE 6-7	Session 1: Run 9 minutes on treadmill or in the park and walk 2 minutes x 3 sets
				Session 2: Step aerobics
				Session 3: Run 9 minutes on treadmill or in the park and walk 2 minutes x 3 sets
6	3	45 minutes	RPE 6-8	Session 1: Run 12 minutes, walk 1-minute x 3 sets
				Session 2: Step machine (25 min) Rowing machine (10 min)
				Session 3: Run 12 minutes, walk 1-minute x 3 sets

Mid program review: Personal trainer to discuss the last six weeks of training, give feedback, and create a new program for the next six weeks, adding some muscle strengthening exercises.

Resistance training overview

Resistance training is a form of exercise that improves muscular strength and endurance. During a resistance training workout, a person moves their limbs against resistance provided by their body weight, gravity, bands, weighted bars or dumbbells. There are also exercise machines that can be used for resistance training. Clients new to this type of training will need a methodical and easy to understand introduction. Understanding the basics will enable them to build on this as they progress to higher stages. A typical beginner with little or no previous experience of resistance training may present themselves with the following:

- Inadequate technique
- Poor proprioception
- No muscular strength and endurance
- Inadequate aerobic conditioning
- Poor tissue tolerance
- Connective tissue which is weak
- Improper posture
- Poor core strength

In resistance training, two factors will greatly impact the outcome of the training:

- The type of exercises selected
- The order in which these exercises are implemented

Choosing exercises

When choosing exercises, the personal trainer should make a conscious effort to provide exercises that enhance posture, co-ordination, proprioception and core strength. The focus should be on the development of muscular balance, to allow the body to develop as a complete Chapter rather than promoting individual muscles. The number of exercises should coordinate with the objective of the workout, client's training experience and the time available for the workout (this information was extracted in the consultation stage). Roughly speaking, the number of resistance exercises to be chosen for each workout ought to be between four and ten.

Order of exercises

1. Concentrate on large muscles first

If a workout is targeting several muscles, the largest muscle group must be trained first. The reason for this is that large muscle groups need the most energy so if these are trained earlier in the workout while the client's energy level is high, the greatest training effect will be achieved. Examples of the large muscle groups are those of the legs, back and chest. Working on these muscle groups will speed up the fat burning potential and improve the muscular fitness of the client.

2. Complex and highly skilled exercise to be performed at the early stages

Exercises that need more energy and a lot more neuromuscular (nervous system efficiently recruits muscle group to perform a task) co-ordination to be safe and effective should be performed early in the workout when the client is unlikely to be experiencing neural and metabolic fatigue. This in particular is applicable to beginners as they potentially are restricted in undertaking exercise prior to fatigue and may also lack techniques which restricts the level of workout.

3. Train synergists and fixators last

If synergists (a muscle that increases the action of another) are trained before the agonists (muscle whose contraction moves a part of the body directly), then the fatigue that ensues will invalidate its synergistic effect when it comes to training the agonist. Synergists and fixators should therefore be trained in the most effective order, which is last.

Frequency

When deciding on the frequency of a weekly workout, the training experience of the client should be considered. The table below shows how a personal trainer can adjust the frequency variable in resistance training per the clients training experience. The higher the training experience, the more sessions they can have per week.

Training status	Frequency guidelines (session/week)
Beginner	2-3
Intermediate	3-4
Advanced	4+

Source: Earle and Baechle, 2004

These frequencies are recommendations only. Going over the above frequency guidelines on a regular basis would not be advisable as it could adversely affect the clients ability to recover.

Good technique - proprioception

A client can be described as having good technique when they can consistently perform the intended movement or exercise pattern without any verbal or physical prompting or correction from the personal trainer.

Proprioception, or motor skills, is an element of fitness that gives a person a sense of the position of where the parts that make up their musculoskeletal system (body) are. It also tells a person what their parts are doing in relation to one another in space and time. The personal trainer should consider these points when formulating the program so that the client makes improvements and can progress safely towards their objectives.

In simple terms, proprioception is a sense of being aware of one's own position, without any outside help. For example, a client in a rowing position will have good proprioception if they can be sure they have formed a neutral spine position without having to look at a mirror (the mirror being the external help). In this case, the proprioceptive components of the neuromuscular system provide the continuous feedback needed, informing the central nervous system (i.e. and so the client) of the position of the spine and surrounding joints during the activity.

Understandably, clients new to resistance training usually show signs of limited proprioception and a general lack of exercise technique. This is mainly due to their sedentary lifestyle choices and because they have limited experience of exercise. Such a client needs to take this into account while exercising as it could affect their safety and overall impact of the workout. Good technique should always be established before starting any progressive intensity resistance training. An example of poor technique is when the client tries to work with a load that goes beyond their strength capacity. For example, exercising the biceps (e.g. dumbbell curls) before any upper body exercise (e.g. lateral pulldowns) is an unsuitable order of exercise. This results in an ineffective workout for the larger muscles and restricts the progress made by the client in these areas of the body.

Program aims for beginners

Any type of resistance program designed for beginners should meet a certain standard. As a minimum, the personal trainer should make sure the exercise program complies with the program design rules. These state that the program should:

- Improve proprioception, posture and core strength
- Provide variety
- Raise tissue tolerance for exercise
- Improve function
- Give the client a sense of achievement

Choosing the most relevant resistance exercises and consistently maintaining a routine in which to conduct the program can enhance proprioception, posture, core strength and overall function. The novice client should at first focus on compound, multi-joint, free-standing activities like squats, deadlifts, bent over rows and overhead presses. This enables the client to progressively learn functional movement patterns which they can also use in daily situations. This is an excellent way of learning a good exercise technique which can be applied outside the fitness environment. The beginner should also start their resistance exercises within the muscular endurance repetition range, which is 12 or more repetitions per set. This enables exercise to involve a high number of repetitions while using a low level of resistance. This combination ensures maximum safety when learning these techniques.

The clients tissue tolerance for resistance based exercise will also gradually increase by using these exercises. It sets the groundwork to let higher loads be applied to the client as they progress in their training program.

To vary the beginner program, several isolation exercises and fixed path machines can be added. This may give the client a sense of achievement as accomplishing exercises that are a little more challenging than usual will help them feel they have performed well, thus benefiting them overall.

Program variables

Sadly, many people do not accomplish their long-term fitness goals. One of the main reasons is because they are prone to follow workouts that have limited variety.

When the personal trainer reaches a stage where they want to change a resistance training program, they may choose from variables, including:

- The number of sets
- The number of exercises
- The range of the target repetition
- Recovery periods between sets
- Workout frequency
- Movement speed – slow to fast
- Different exercises
- Stable to unstable
- Simple to complex
- Different methods, including advanced training methods

Resistance training equipment

There are various resistance training equipment that can be used, including:

- Free weights such as dumbbells or barbells with which various muscles can be worked.
- Weight machines: These are devices found in most gyms. The machines have adjustable seats with handles attached to weights and the resistance can be adjusted.
- Medicine balls: These are weighted balls that can be used at home and other environments.
- Resistance bands: These are like giant rubber bands that provide resistance when stretched. The provide continuous resistance throughout a movement and as they are fairly small portable, they can be adapted to most workouts.
- Cable machines: These are pulley devices where the exerciser holds handles that can move in any direction.

Basic resistance progression

If the personal trainer wishes to develop the progress of a client over a long period, they must develop a long-term training plan. As mentioned earlier, the client's end goal does not always tally with their present level of fitness. A close look at the client's experience of exercise, training routines and maintenance patterns will indicate how well suited they are to each type of resistance training.

Progress in resistance training should be gradual. Intensity should be increased gradually within each training goal by including smaller increments in intensity while staying within the muscular endurance repetition range. A good example of this is when a client wants to mainly focus on muscular endurance, the guidance on 12+ repetitions per set can be further divided into smaller repetition ranges. As the client progresses, later training stages would then increase the repetitions.

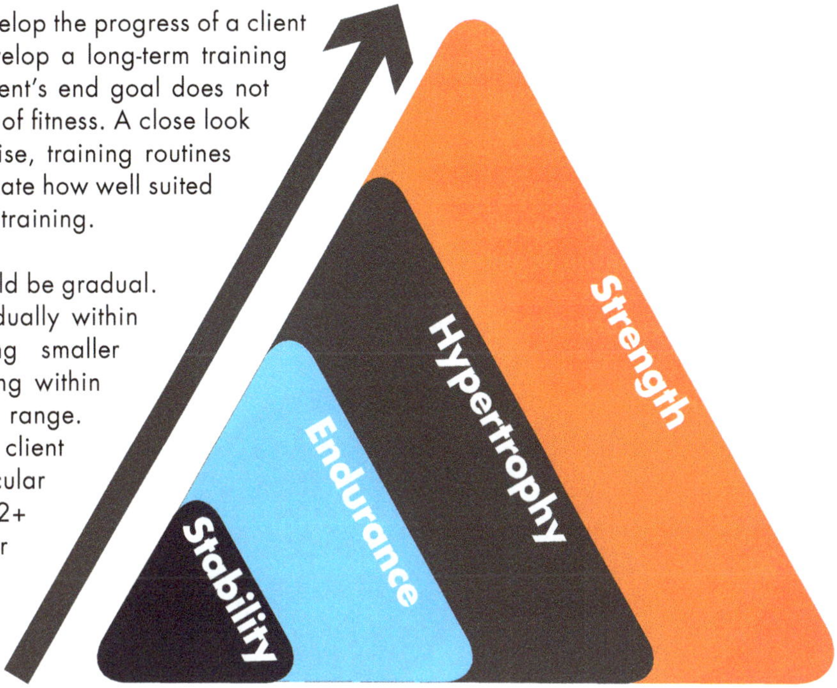

Above is a basic progression pyramid, which must be followed when planning to progress a client from a beginner's level through to the most advanced, intensive types of resistance training:

The basic pyramid is only applicable to resistance training progression if training towards strength or hypertrophy are part of their program. Many clients may not want to concentrate on these areas of muscular fitness. If this is so, then the personal trainer has a couple of options:

Option 1: Intensity can be increased gradually within each training goal by including smaller increments in intensity while staying within the muscular endurance repetition range. A good example of this is when a client wants to mainly focus on muscular endurance, the guidance on 12+ repetitions per set can be further divided into smaller repetition ranges. As the client progresses, later training stages would then increase the repetitions from 18-20, 15-18, 12-15 reps per set.

Option 2: This is to keep the repetition range as it is, but change other variables from the list given earlier. For example, increasing the movement complexity from stage to stage while working with the endurance repetition range is one possibility.

Further information on resistance training can be obtained from: https://www.bodybuilding.com/content/guide-to-resistance-training-7-things-you-need-to-know.html

Resistance training and periodization

The principle of periodization can also be applied to resistance training, where the training program can be divided into training blocks to be performed for a set period of time in order to stimulate a specific adaptive response. Periodization concept is based on Hans Selye's General Adaptive Syndrome (GAS) developed in 1956.

GAS describes the body's specific response to stress whether it is physical or emotional and the responses seem to be similar regardless of what is stimulated according to GAS. The theory has been helpful over the years to explain adaptive responses to stimulus.

There are four phases of responses according to GAS after training commences.

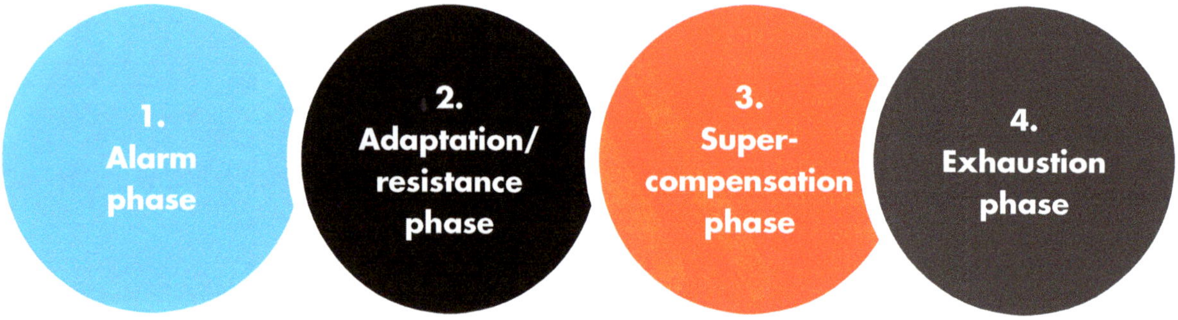

The beginning of training is the introduction of stimulus according to GAS and this stimulus may result in a decrease of performance during the alarm phase. Thus, clients may experience fatigue, soreness and stiffness. Enduring the stimulus leads to the adaptation/resistance phase when the body starts a mixture of biochemical, neural, structural and mechanical modifications which result in improved bodily output. The rate at which modifications and changes occur will decrease after being regularly exposed to the same stimuli. Ultimately, the supercompensation phase will be reached. When this happens, being subject to the stimulus will lead to the exhaustion phase. The reason why this happens is because the body is unable to cope with the progressive stress and pressure of the same stimuli repeating over a course of time (Kraemer, 2004; Wathen et al, 2000).

Signs that a person is in the exhaustion phase include a decline in physical performance, boredom, being sore and feeling tired (Wathen et al, 2000). Maintaining the application of the same stimuli throughout the exhaustion phase can progressively result in many adverse ailments. Not changing or stopping the training stimulus can mean the client becoming ill, suffering injury or they could experience overtraining (Kraemer, 2004). The main goal of any set exercise program is to make the most of the adaptation phase and neglect the exhaustion phase. In order to meet this goal, it is imperative that rest times are diarised into the program and that the stimulus is adjusted regularly. Letting the body rest for a short time after each phase of training allows it to prepare and adjust itself for the upcoming training stimulus.

In addition, it should also be noted that sticking to the same stimulus over the course of time may result in no progression for a different reason. Not making noticeable changes to a workout over a course of time and regularly failing to work hard within each session may make the stimulus insufficient enough to trigger an alarm stage. This situation would build up to a halt in progress as there would be no key stimulus to facilitate changes within the body. Practically, this scenario happens more in overtraining situations.

Practical application of periodization

Applying periodization necessitates the intensity and volume of exercise to be moulded so that a long-term objective can be achieved.

The rationale behind 'progressive overload' is that the client should seek to enhance the productivity of their last workout, and that this should be done often. For example, this could be performing one extra repetition or undertaking the usual amount of reps, but with a heavier resistance or load.

A long-term training program, for example 12 months, can be divided into specific terms. The periodization and precise terminology can be used to divide the program into the stages or cycles listed below:

To develop an effective training program and apply the concept of periodization, it is important to understand its three cycles: macrocycles, mesocycles and microcycles.

Macrocycles

The lengthiest of the three cycles is the macrocycle. It has four phases to its training schedule and these are intensity, recovery, endurance and competition. Macrocycles include all 52 weeks of the year in its annual program and it is for this reason that they give the client an overall picture of the training regime, allowing a long-term plan to be arranged. So, for example, if the client wishes to peak for a special event in a year's time, that date can be earmarked and then the client can work backwards to ensure that they peak at the desired time. The same strategy can be used for other upcoming events during the year.

Mesocycles

The mesocycle features a training program that seeks to complete a specific objective. For example, whilst in the endurance stage, the client may begin a mesocycle formulated to improve muscular stamina on the bike, pedaling the higher gears for a sustained period. This mesocycle could be made up of six workouts over the course of three weeks. It could centre on the client pedaling on the big gears with a week's recovery. Likewise, a mesocycle can be drafted for the intensity stage. It could be constructed to enhance the FTP (Functional Threshold Power). This is the highest average power (in watts) that can be maintained for one hour. This mesocycle may feature threshold intervals lasting three weeks and then a week of recovery.

A mesocycle can be constructed in the competition phase. This mesocycle could enhance neuromuscular strength, which is the capability of pedaling a very high gear, at an equally fast rhythm, in a short time (in other words, sprinting). This mesocycle could include four lengthy sprint interval sessions over the course of three weeks. A mesocycle can be designed for the recovery phase of training. The main aim of this mesocycle will be to relax and recover. In addition, it will include many much easier parts to help with the recovery stage.

Mesocycles are commonly three or four weeks long, with 21 and 28-day training periods. An example of this could be a 25 year old client on a 23/5 training cycle (or a 28-day mesocycle). This would be made up of 23 days of tough work and then 5 days of recovery and simple spinning. On the other hand, an older client may choose a 16/5 training cycle, so a 21-day mesocycle. This would consist of 16 days of tough training and then 5 days of recovery. If the client is confused about which mesocycle to choose, they should start with a 21-day mesocycle, moving on to a 28-day one if they need more of a challenge. If the client is finding the 28-day cycle too challenging, or are fatigued, they can switch to the shorter mesocycle which provides more recovery time.

Microcycles

This is the shortest of the training cycles. It commonly lasts a week and its main aim is to deliver a specific chunk of training. For example, a cyclist during an endurance phase puts together three or four long rides in the space of a week to gradually overload training volume. Another example is to combine block training which is made up of very difficult workouts, lasting two or three days with the same number of recovery days. The recovery days could consist of either very light activity or complete rest days. This would establish an intensity microcycle where the aim is to enhance important physiological capabilities like lactate threshold. Lactate threshold is the greatest intensity that a fit cyclist can sustain for one hour. It would also constitute aerobic ability. Aerobic ability is the largest amount of oxygen that the body can use up during high intensity exercise. Usually, three or four microcycles are bound together to make up a mesocycle.

So to conclude, a sound understanding of the three cycles of periodization can help a client get the most out of their training program. Applying the cycles to formulate a plan lets the client peak at their most crucial events of the year.

Stimulus-fatigue-recovery-adaptation (SFRA) model

A solid understanding of the importance of recovery in between workouts is essential when formulating training programs. Enough recovery time should be allocated and incorporated into the microcycle plan.

The SFRA model states that fatigue is accrued according to the power of the stimulus and according to how long the stimulus lasts. So, for example, where stimulus is an exercise session, then after it has finished, the body can rest, allowing the fatigue to be spent and for changes (supercompensation) to happen. This theory also indicates that if the stress is not applied often enough, then involution or 'detraining' will happen. The length of the preparation period affects the involution time. The longer the training program, the more residual outcomes.

The SFRA suggests that the supercompensation system depends on three important factors:

- The stimulus must be enough to be the reason for fatigue and trigger an adaptation. So, an overload should be progressively applied within the microcycles workouts.
- The recovery time period (time in between each workout) must be sufficient enough to let the client recover and for adaptation to happen.
- The client must have adequate nutrition to get through the training and the recovery periods.

Recovery weeks

If a client has undergone a number of training stages, then an entire week or even longer recovery is recommended. In this time, the body is able to fully recover from the stresses of the lengthy resistance training. Scheduled recovery weeks in long-term exercise plans can be made up of invaluable activities which encourage recovery. For example, activities such as massage, swimming, walking, flexibility sessions or light to medium activities which are non-resistance based should all be encouraged during the period of rest. Reminders about correct nutrition in the recovery period and training phases should be given to clients. Clients who have solid sleeping routines are also more likely to recover better from a period of intense resistance training.

Muscle hypertrophy program design

Muscle hypertrophy is another form of training that falls within the umbrella of resistance training.

Muscle hypertrophy is a term for the growth and increase of the size of muscle cells. The term is often associated with weight training. The most common type of muscular hypertrophy occurs because of physical exercise such as weight lifting.

As is the case with any training goal, hypertrophy demands a long-term plan so that progression can be made over time. The personal trainer should first make sure that the client has physically prepared themselves to a certain degree before starting a hypertrophy program. The personal trainer can achieve this by determining the training experience of the client, and then choosing a relevant starting level. The client can then work up the basic progression pyramid, as illustrated earlier.

Clients will notice a marked difference in training in muscular endurance and training in hypertrophy. Generally, guidelines for muscular endurance programs state that the whole-body routines should be structured around compound exercises. It is quite typical when training for endurance to repeat the same workout twice or three times per week. The number of sets performed under hypertrophy per muscle group is much more than for muscular endurance. Many studies have stated that multiple exercises (i.e. three or more per muscle group) is the most productive way of increasing hypertrophy. Training intensity (% of 1RM) is also much higher for hypertrophy than it is for muscular endurance. So, it can be said that the main quality of hypertrophy training is high volume coupled with moderate and high intensity exercises.

Strength endurance

The increase in volume and intensity from an endurance based program to one of hypertrophy, may prove too much for some. If this is the case, the personal trainer can apply their own sound judgment and basic principles of progression to the programs they formulate for the client. Instead of diving head first into a hypertrophy phase, the personal trainer can phase in a training stage. This would help the client ease into the demands of hypertrophy training. This blend of endurance and hypertrophy can be called 'strength endurance'.

Training guidelines

Guidelines for hypertrophy, muscular endurance and muscular strength exercises are provided in the table below, taking into consideration loads, repetitions, volumes and rest periods.

Training	Load (%RPM)	Repetitions	Sets	Rest period
Muscular endurance	≤67	Lower body	2-3	≤30 seconds
Hypertrophy	67-85	Upper body	3-6	30-90 seconds
Muscular strength	≥85	Lower body	2-6	2-5 minutes

Source: Adapted from Earle and Baechle (2004)

It should be stressed that the total volume per muscle should only be moderate. So, the exercises selected should be inversely proportionate to the sets per exercise. For example, if three exercises are chosen for an individual muscle group, no more than one or two sets per exercise should be performed when training for strength endurance.

The sets assigned do not include warming up and apply to core exercises only.

The %1RM loads for muscular strength applies to core exercises only and assistance exercises should be 8RM or lighter.

Changing the stimulus

The personal trainer needs to plan well ahead to make sure that the program progressively changes on a regular basis. This is because the body has an amazing way of adapting to an exercise stimulus. Boredom could also set in if programs are not modified regularly, which in turn could result in the client quitting the program altogether. To resolve this, the personal trainer should vary the program every four to six weeks in such a way as to generate a new and refreshing exercise stimulus for the client. Trainers should take great care in making sure that volume and intensity progressions from one program to another are as smooth and as manageable as possible for the client. For example, implementing a strength endurance phase in between endurance and hypertrophy phases.

Resistance training methods

There are many established resistance training methods that a personal trainer can adopt to train clients. A number of common training programs are explained below. Some methods are suitable for beginners whilst others are regarded as advanced training methods.

Circuit training system

This method requires the completion of a number of resistance workouts in a circuit but with a very short rest period of around 30 seconds between each workout. Usually, these exercises are undertaken using medium weights (around 60% of 1RM). The number of exercises to be undertaken at each point are 10 to 15 repetitions. As well as improving muscular fitness and local muscular stamina, circuit training may also enhance CRF. It should be noted however, that advances in maximum oxygen usage produced from aerobic exercising are much more than those produced from circuit exercises. When a participant is new to circuit training, it is recommended that they begin with a rest of one minute between each exercise, then slowly decreasing the remainder to the range that is wanted, as the body adjusts.

Express circuit system

Express circuits have been formulated by personal trainers for clients who don't have much time for resistance training and other kinds of exercise. Usually, the participant takes part in a set of 6 to 12 repetitions, then 30 to 60 seconds worth of rest between exercises. Multi-joint and single-joint activities make up express circuits and usually consist of a minimum of one exercise using each main group of muscle. The outcome of this is around 8 to 10 exercises in a session, depending on which exercise is chosen by the participant.

Split routines system

Eventually, the trainer will practically be unable to sustain the progression from the use of whole body routines towards hypertrophy. This is due to the sheer volume of work needed in the time available. Most clients do not have the time and lack the resilience to train for hours at a time. Therefore, an alternative view to resistance training will need to be adopted.

Professionals such as body builders, strength athletes and recreational trainers all use the split routine system. This routine rejects the whole-body approach by categorizing the body up into two or more groups of muscles. These groups of muscles can subsequently be trained on separate days in a cyclical system. The table below illustrates examples of training splits:

	Example 1	Example 2	Example 3
Day 1	Lower body	Lower body	Deltoids, legs, abdominals and chest
Day 2		Upper body	
Day 3	Upper body		Back, triceps, abdominals and chest
Day 4		Lower body	
Day 5	Lower body	Upper body	Chest, biceps and abdominals
Day 6			
Day 7	Upper body	Lower body	Deltoids, legs, abdominals and chest
Day 8 - Restart the exercising cycle			

Split routines considerations

Some points to be considered when formulating a split routine:

- The schedule should match when the client is available.
- The number of times the workouts are repeated should not be more than the maximum advised for every training goal.
- The activity outlined for any day should not be negatively impacted by the previous day's workout. Split routines need clever planning and mental preparation. Abstaining from even one workout will possibly destabilize the week of training.
- Sufficient recovery time should be penciled in the weekly alternation. This is normally two days off for every part of the body or muscle group.

Difficulties with split routines

The personal trainer and client need to know of some possible disadvantages of changing to a split routine.

Exercise selection

It is essential to know that challenging and fatiguing the maximum numbers of fibers is the main aim when choosing exercise programs to train for hypertrophy.

When choosing exercises to form part of hypertrophy activities, the personal trainer needs to include a range of the following:

- Free weight compound workouts
- Free weight isolation workouts
- Machine and workouts based on cable
- A higher workout frequency

Abstaining from even one workout will possibly destabilize the week of training. Split routines need clever planning and mental preparation.

When choosing fixed path resistance equipment to amalgamate into the hypertrophy system, the personal trainer should use their common sense and have an eye for detail. One flaw of fixed path machines, identified by many, is that they are sometimes not accommodating enough for all types of body shapes and sizes. Subsequently, a machine which works well for one person may not be suitable for another.

Putting together the workouts

A straightforward procedure can be followed to create resisting training programs which are free from harm and productive. This procedure is outlined below:

- Establish the training target (e.g. hypertrophy)
- Formulate a weekly split according to the aim and time that the client can allocate
- Choose set and rep schemes suitable to the client's present physical capacity
- Choose exercises for every muscle (activities should match the training goal)
- Arrange the exercises to be undertaken every day after the basic system planning rules
- Consider that the amount of work will be sufficient for the time available in each session

Body part system

These programs are not indifferent to a split-body system as the precise parts of the body or muscle groups are trained on particular days. But with a body-part system, usually only one or two body parts or main muscle groups are exercised at each training session. Commonly a body part program would focus on the muscle groups on particular days of the week:

Day 1	Day 2	Day 3	Day 4	Day 5	Day 6	Day 7
Back	Quadriceps and deltoids	Chest and triceps	Hamstrings and glutes	Back and biceps	Hamstrings, glutes and biceps	Chest, quadriceps & abdominals

Fitness fanatics and body builders prefer body part systems. Usually, for each body part, multiple exercises and multiple sets are undertaken. This gives way to the execution of a great volume of training for a particular muscle group in one training session, after which there are a few days rest for that muscle group. Those in favor of body part systems say that this type of high volume training with a few days rest is vital to encourage optimum increased strength in hypertrophy.

Isolated split system (blitz)

This is a variant of a body part system. Instead of training a few body parts during each training session, the participant focuses on just one body part per training session. The length of the training session is not decreased. So, more sets and exercises for each body part can be carried out.

A brief blitz program can also be suitable if an athlete's attainment can be restricted by a specific muscle groups' strength; for example, an athlete who performs the long jump may undertake a varied version of a blitz program for the legs prior to the beginning of the sessions. This may mean focusing on just the legs, twice a week.

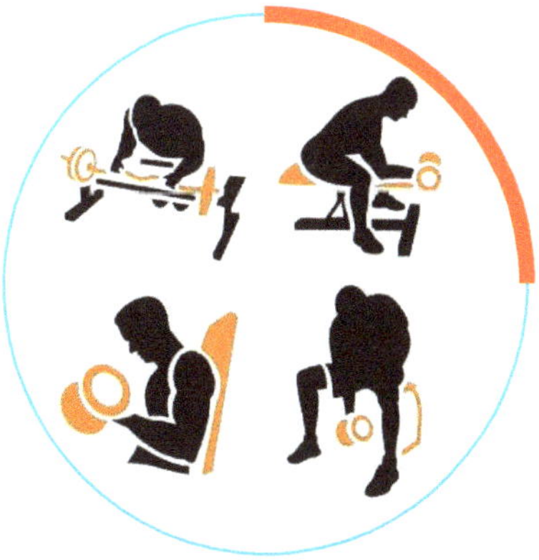

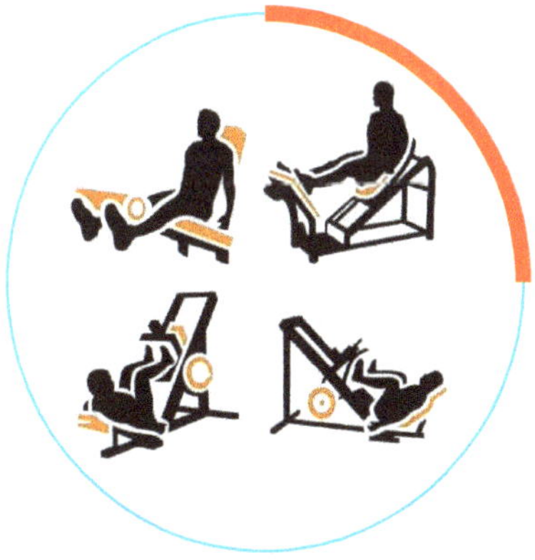

Single-set system

This is one of the most dated programs of resistance training. It is made up of one set of repetitions, for example 8-12, until the participant reaches the point in the set where they can't lift one more rep without cheating (this point is also known as volitional fatigue). This streamlined method of resistance exercise can be productive for people with little or no experience in training. These significant changes due to resistance training (i.e. 6-12 weeks) are mainly from neuromuscular changes. A single-set process is an ideal way to train those people who are new to exercise. This method may increase take-up and boost the number of people sticking to the program, as opposed to further time-heavy training programs. Single-set programs are a good choice for people with time restrictions and for athletes who find they are time constrained in the course of a program or training phase they may be following.

Participants in a single-set program can expect to make notable increases in strength, more so during the first 6 to 12 weeks of training. Over the course of longer training periods, multiple-set training results in better improvements in strength and could be required to boost enough training capacity to keep the increase in strength levels going. (American College of Sports Medicine cited in Fleck and Kraemer, 2014).

Multiple-set system

The multiple-set system is an effective training method for enhancing strength and power.

A multiple-set system can mean undertaking multiple sets where resistance is the same or multiple sets with changing resistances (light to heavy, heavy to light), with differing or an equal number of repetitions for every set. These are carried out with all, some or no sets carried to the point where the participant can't lift one more rep without cheating (volitional fatigue). Any training program with one or more sets of exercises can be classed as a multiple-set system.

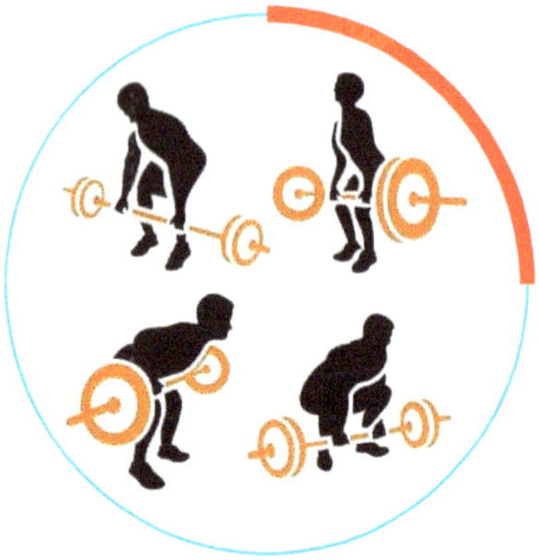

Meta-analyses have shown that multiple-set systems have the effect of a higher level of strength (Fleck and Kraemer, 2014) boosts than single-set systems. When deciding the amount of sets, personal trainers need to differentiate between the number of sets per exercise and the number of exercises per muscle group. Therefore, if two sets of two variations of bicep curl are carried out, the biceps perform four sets.

Over time, several multiple-set systems have progressed using many variants of sets and repetitions. The pyramid system (see below) is an example of a multiple-set system where weight rises gradually over many sets so that fewer repetitions can be executed. For continuous progression in a resistance training system, multiple sets should be utilized. But to cut down the chances of overtraining, the participant will need to progressively boost the total number of sets executed in each training session. Also, every exercise does not need to be undertaken for the same number of sets.

Pyramid training system

This system is about influencing the load and repetitions during a program of multiple sets of an exercise. Here, the load is steadily increased (therefore the number of repetitions will reduce) with each consecutive set. The personal trainer needs to make sure BEFORE starting each subsequent set that the participant has rested and that this rest period is long enough to achieve the training goal.

There are three kinds of pyramid systems, as outlined below:

Ascending pyramid: A light to heavy strategy. Each subsequent set is executed with a weightier resistance for less repetitions. An example is provided below.

Set	Repetitions	Resistance (kg)	Rest time
First	12	60	Up to 2 minutes
Second	10	80	Up to 2 minutes
Third	8	100	Up to 2 minutes
Fourth	6	120	Finished

Descending pyramids: Heavy to light strategy. So, the participant begins with the heaviest load (after a suitable warm up). Part of the load is then taken away from each following set. An example is provided below.

Set	Repetitions	Resistance (kg)	Rest time
First	4	80	Up to 2 minutes
Second	8	60	Up to 2 minutes
Third	12	50	Up to 2 minutes
Fourth	15	40	Finished

Complete pyramids: Light to heavy, then back to light. Here, the participant works up to a peak over the course of a number of sets and then tries to perform the same repetitions with each wearing load on the descending phase. An example is provided below:

Set	Repetitions	Resistance (kg)	Rest time
First	10	60	Up to 2 minutes
Second	8	70	Up to 2 minutes
Third	6	80	Up to 2 minutes
Fourth	4	70	Up to 2 minutes
Fifth	6	60	Up to 2 minutes
Sixth	8	50	Up to 2 minutes
Seventh	10	50	Finished

Supersets, tri-sets and giant sets

Superset

This comprises of two exercises targeting the same muscle group, one immediately after the other. So, for example 12 squats with 12 lunges immediately after would be seen as one superset for the quadriceps, hamstrings and gluteals. This episode can be performed again after a normal rest period. The second exercise in the superset is always undertaken with a substantial amount of muscular fatigue present. Because of this fatigue, the load in the second exercise has to be a lot lower than if the muscle had been permitted to recover during a normal rest period. This kind of training is largely unproductive for strength training. Performing two exercises in this way however is good for local muscular stamina and hypertrophy. This is because the amount of work performed is comparatively high (a hypertrophic reaction would most likely happen if the initial set was executed within the bounds of the hypertrophy repetition).

Antagonist muscle pair supersets
These are alternatives to the supersets mentioned above. They involve undertaking two exercises including the opposing pair of muscles, i.e. biceps brachii/triceps brachii or quadriceps/hamstrings), one immediately after the other. This type of sequence lets a considerable load be put on the relevant muscle while the set is being performed. This can happen because the antagonist is in recovery while the agonist works, and the same in reverse. More strength is used because each set is undertaken from a comparatively rested condition. There have been considerable increases in strength by participants who are trained using this adaptation of the superset program (Fleck and Kraemer, 2014).

Tri-sets

This is completing three exercises back to back with little to no rest. The complete sequence of exercises form one set. Rest is followed after each set before performing the sequence again.

Giant sets

This is four or more exercises back to back with little to no rest. The complete sequence of exercises form one set. Rest is followed after each set before performing the sequence again. An example of a giant set is provided below.

Set	Exercise	Resistance (kg)	Repetitions	Rest time
First	Upright row	20	10	No rest
Second	Shoulder press (dumb bells)	10	10	No rest
Third	Dumbbell lateral raise	10	10	No rest
Fourth	Front raise	20	10	Finished

Pre and post exhaustion system

This training system is made up of executing consecutive sets of two exercises for the same target muscle or muscle group.

Pre-exhaust: The isolation part of the training is executed before the compound exercise, for example the chest fly immediately prior to the bench press with no rest periods in between.

Post-exhaust: The isolation exercise is executed after the compound exercise, for example the bench press, promptly followed by the chest fly and no rest period in between.

Both of the above systems mean that the muscle being focused on does more work. Guidance for pre-exhaust:

- Choose a target muscle – this muscle must perform as a prime mover in a minimum of one compound exercise.
- Choose an isolation (single-joint) activity for the targeted muscle.
- Choose a compound exercise (multi-joint) for the targeted muscle. Conduct the isolation exercise straight away followed by the compound exercise. Take a rest in between sets and perform again as necessary. For post-exhaust, conduct the isolation exercise after the compound exercise.

Drop sets

This is also known as a 'strip set' and is a common choice amongst bodybuilders. This method permits the participant to carry on beyond the point where it would normally end. When utilizing the dumbbells, the weights are 'stripped' off the bar or 'down the rack' as the participant goes from heavy weights to the lighter end. The method consists of conducting a set to the brink of failure, then quickly (sometimes with help) taking away a small amount of the weight and then carrying on with the set. This method can be conducted again quite a few times. An example of sequence of exercise is provided below:

Set	Resistance (kg)	Repetitions	Rest time
First	100	To Failure	No rest
Second	80	To Failure	No rest
Third	70	To Failure	No rest
Fourth	60	To Failure	Finished

Guidance for formulating and conducting drop sets:

- Choose a basic repetition scope within the guidance of the phase of training formulated.
- Determine the number of drops the participant will undertake (a higher number of drops will boost feelings of fatigue and uneasiness.
- Choose which exercise/s will be combined with the drop sets system. Conduct all formulated sets of the exercise as usual. When a parallel failure is reached, reduce the load by a small quantity (5-20%) and promptly carry on with the set.
- Do this again for as many drops as is needed. A point to note is that only when the weight has been descended can the participant conduct a small number of repetitions with the new load. If the participant finds the exercise to be quite easy and if over 3 to 5 extra repetitions can be conducted, it signifies that too much weight has been taken away and the technique has been unproductive.

Forced repetitions

Here, the participant conducts the maximum amount of reps possible alone. The personal trainer / spotter gives a minimum quantity of assistance to allow the execution of 3-4 more full reps. This process is simply a development of normal spotting methods. The personal trainer must not partake in more work than the participant. If this happens it indicates that the load is too high or the set has been lengthened beyond the range of failure. This approach should be used with caution as it can result in DOMs and possibly overtraining as well. For safety reasons the personal trainer should be capable of lifting the resistance alone.

Negative training

The descending phase of a lift is known as the negative phase and also known as the eccentric phase. Here, the muscles being worked are lengthening under tension and control to lower the weight. It is feasible to lower more weight than can be lifted. Therefore, negative repetition training can mean using resistance which exceeds a participant's 1RM. This approach should not be used every session for the same muscle area as it causes DOMs and sufficient rest days in between its use are required to prevent injury.

Negative reps can be used in two ways. The less commonly used way is a purer form and is riskier. Here, a supramaximal load is put on a bar after the participant conducts a warm up set. Usually, a load which is slightly more than the 1RM is utilized with the help of a spotter to conduct the concentric part of the lift. When the bar is in a secure position at the top of the movement, the spotter stays in place but takes away all help as the participant manages the bar though the eccentric phase of the movement. Even when pushing against the bar, it will unavoidably shift through the descending phase of the movement. The spotter can help to move the bar back to the top of the movement and a second or third eccentric repetition can be concluded. Typically, there are a maximum of three repetitions if a real supramaximal load is utilized. The power being pressed on the muscles, connective tissues and skeleton are larger than the body is familiar with. This is a good incentive for variation but there comes with it a greater risk of injury. This method can only be used with particular exercises where the spotter/s can if necessary lift the load, for example during the bench press.

There are several slightly varied and safer ways to the supramaximal loading method. These can be conducted using arms and legs and then descending with just the legs.

Partial repetitions program

This training approach centres on a mixture of full and partial reps in sets to excite an alternative reaction to lifting weights. It is generally used with an isolation exercise and can be performed with many different training approaches. Following a set of reps to failure using a full ROM, further partial reps are completed using a partial ROM. This allows further overload to be created which is sometimes known as 'the burn'.

Matrix

The Matrix consists of a speedy warm up of ascending weights to arrive at workout weight. Three to four exercises for each group of muscle is selected. Key elements of the Matrix are listed below:

- 3 sets made up of 7 reps per set
- 7 half reps from the stretch or bottom stance
- 7 half reps from the squeeze or top position
- 7 full reps using full ROM
- Total of 21 reps all together
- There should be a rest period of 30 seconds between each full set of 21 reps
- Other variations of reps can be used if appropriate to the client and their goal

There are many reasons and benefits to this type of training. Firstly, focusing on partial movements can accentuate movements over routine sticking points in many participant's movements – it can be used to supersede these stages of plateau. Secondly, this system's greater rep number and decreased rest count will counter an alternative energy system; the majority of weight training programs work against the ATP/PC system. However, the Matrix uses mainly the glycolytic or lactate system. The third advantage of this type of training is that the reduced weight also excites the kinds of fibers not encouraged by the greater thresholds of heavy weight training. The Matrix likes to stimulate type 2A and 1A muscle fiber types, with a reduced incentive of the type 2X fibers that we generally try to activate. Finally, the reduced weight will ease pressure on the participant's joints and adjoining tissue while at the same time encouraging the muscles and energy system to grow.

Cheat system

Bodybuilders favor this program. And yes, it does involve cheating as the name suggests, or going against strict exercise form (Fleck and Kraemer, 2014).

For example, instead of preserving an upright upper body when conducting standing barbell arm curls, the participant uses a mild torso swing to begin barbell shifting from the elbow-extended position. The torso swing is not highly executed, but it is enough to let the participant pick up 4.5 to 9.1kg more resistance than is feasible with stringent exercise form. There is a bell- shaped strength curve on the barbell curl and so the arms being fully protracted makes it a weak position to be in. The position with the most strength is when the elbow joint is angled at 90-degrees. When barbell curls are conducted with stringent form, there is a limit to the resistance that can be lifted, and this is dependent on the resistance that can reasonably be shifted from the weaker, fully protracted position.

There is a continuous resistance with the muscles related to flexing the elbow, and so these muscles are not actively used to their full potential in the course of the exercises more stronger stances. The aim of cheating is to permit the utilization of heavier resistance. This compels the muscle/s to establish a force nearer to maximal via a higher part of the exercise's scope of movement. This improves strength and hypertrophy attainment. Cheating may also be conducted at the end of the set once the participant reaches the point of failure where they can't perform another rep without cheating (volitional fatigue).

WARNING

Participants need to be wary when using this cheating method. Risk of injury is increased because of the heavier resistance. For example, the lower back area can be susceptible to added stress when conducting the torso-swinging action.

Combining aerobic training with resistance training

Most clients have little experience of regular exercise so a varied training strategy, combining resistance and aerobic exercise will be most suitable for them. Most clients will not be athletes so won't need a specialized plan in their program.

Encompassing resistance and aerobic training is a skill the trainer will need when formulating the program. For example, training well for aerobic fitness is an obvious different stimulus to a client's overall aim of muscular strength or hypertrophy. These conflicting components affect different parts of the body. Trying to train for both areas to their maximum capacity will decrease effective results for both areas of fitness.

Conversely, if the central aim is aerobic then the same principles will be applied. The resistance training volume and intensity will reduce as the aerobic stages become more of a challenge. It is recommended to incorporate some resistance training in the exercise plan of a client who enjoys aerobic-based exercises more. The same principle applies to resistance based clients – their goals should have a small amount of aerobic conditioning. The client may need to be persuaded to embrace this approach. The best way for this is for the trainer to outline the advantages of it, and to then ensure that the volume and intensity of both modes of training are shaped suitably, thus guaranteeing results.

Sample resistance training program

Overall goal summary

Strengthen multiple muscles to improve overall body strength.

Sets, reps and rest

Sets per exercise: 5
Reps per set: 5
Rest interval: 2-3 minutes between sets and exercises

Session 1

Day and place	Muscles to work on	Exercise type
Monday (gym)	• Pecs • Deltoids • Triceps	• Lying down bench presses using barbell • Deltoids • Triceps
Wednesday (gym)	• Trapezius • Lats • Biceps	• Upright row using barbell/ seated row using rowing machine • Lateral pull down • Bicep Curls
Friday (gym)	• Legs • Hamstrings • Abdominal	• Deadlifts • Recumbent leg presses • Sit ups

Notes

Select a weight that allows you to perform all five sets with five repetitions. In the last two sets, if you find that you can only manage less than four in either of the two, reduce the weight.

Health and medical considerations

A level of fitness, strength and knowledge is essential before training at this intensity. This is not suitable for beginners or unfit individuals.

Activity

Activity 4.2: **Design two basic strength workouts for a client who is new to resistance training. The client wants two workouts that can be alternated, training three times per week. The focus of the program should be to improve basic strength. The plan should cover the whole body and incorporate exercises, sets, reps and recovery periods and resistance approaches.**

Workout 1

Workout 2

Flexibility training overview

Flexibility training can be defined as the range of motion about a joint and its surrounding muscles during movement. By increasing this joint range of motion, performance may be enhanced and the risk of injury reduced. The rationale for this is that a limb can move further before an injury occurs.

Lack of flexibility training results in the exerciser being restricted in movement. A marked reduction in flexibility can have a great effect on posture as well as the output of force that a joint can produce. It can reduce ability and day to day function.

Some exercises, which don't require muscles to be worked using their full motion range, can decrease flexibility, for example football, jogging and cycling. This may result in tight muscle and progressive shortening.

Some resistance exercise plans concentrate too much on one group of muscles and therefore deprive the opposite group of muscles (antagonists). This can result in imbalanced muscles which hinder flexibility.

L2

Benefits of flexibility training:

- Muscle tightness, which has been associated with an increased risk of muscle tears can be reduced before training or competing with stretching
- Help re-balance the body preventing chronic, over-use injury when repetitive training of other sorts creates disparities
- Movement with greater ease and dexterity
- Increase in body awareness and a promotion of relaxation in the muscle groups stretched
- Improved posture
- Stress management
- Improved sports performance

Factors affecting flexibility:

Various factors can affect our flexibility and some of these are summarized below, although there may be additional factors for different individuals and special groups of the population.

- Structure of the joint
- Ligaments and tendons supporting the joint
- Muscle and its connective tissue
- Opposing muscles
- Temperature

Types of stretching

DYNAMIC STRETCHING uses speed of movement, momentum and active muscular effort to bring about a stretch e.g. a walking lunge.

STATIC ACTIVE STRETCHING involves stretching muscles groups without moving the limb itself and the end position is held for up to 30 seconds.

BALLISTIC STRETCHING is similar to dynamic stretching but includes a bouncing or jerking movement to increase the stretch e.g. toe touching with a bouncing movement.

ISOMETRIC STRETCHING involves adding tension to muscles without changing length using for example a chair, or wall as resistance

Stretching with another person: One advantage of personal training is the method of stretching with a partner to help static stretching methods. Slowly helping the client to move their body to a stretch position is one way to help the client in passive stretching. Good communication and consideration is needed to make sure that the muscle doesn't stretch excessively. This type of stretch however, is not advised for those at the beginner stage. This is covered later on.

Dynamic stretching

These must be undertaken during the warm up and at no other part of the workout. Stretches that work the whole body should be chosen. For split routines however, the stretches should focus on the specific areas that will be used during the workout. Practice-type stretches, like the workout exercises should be used during the workout. Only eight to ten repetitions of each stretch are needed – anything more may tire out the client before the actual workout has even begun! Two to three different stretches are enough to prepare the body for exercise. The movement speed should be steady and smooth.

Static stretching

This type of stretching exists to preserve the normal length of the muscles. These are normally completed at the end of an exercise session. Static maintenance stretches carry the muscle to the top of its normal range and it is held there without bouncing. Such stretches are held for 10 to 15 seconds. After repeating contractions during exercise, the muscle becomes shorter and thicker. A 'maintenance stretch' is then performed to revert the muscle back to its usual length. The number of stretches should be enough to cover the major muscles of the body worked during the main session.

Usual practice:

- Take the stretch to the point of bind, whilst preserving good alignment and posture
- Hold for 10-15 seconds until the tension within the muscle has eased
- Repeat stretch if desired

Static developmental stretches

Static developmental stretches are used in flexibility exercises, to promote the length of the fiber themselves. This boosts the range of movement at a joint. The following guidance should be followed:

STEP 01
Stretch the muscle until you feel tension whilst maintaining good alignment and posture.

STEP 02
Hold the stretch in the same position for 10 to 15 seconds, until the tension within the muscle reduces.

STEP 03
Relax and slowly increase the range of motion (ROM) of the stretch until tension is felt again and hold for 10 to 15 seconds, until the tension within the muscles reduces.

STEP 04
Repeat step 3 but once again increasing the ROM and hold until the tension reduces and then slowly return the limb to its normal position.

Static stretching is when a person stretches their muscle while the body is still. It is advised during cool down following an exercise session but has its own benefits if done regularly and some stretches are also helpful for warm up. Static stretching is made up of several different techniques that slowly lengthen a muscle to a protracted position (until it starts becoming uncomfortable). The person then holds this position for up to 10 seconds in a warm up and up to 30 seconds in a cool down.

Stretching exercises can help to:

- Boost the range of motion of a joint to reduce the risk of damage to tendon and muscle during the exercise
- Alleviate tightness and firmness of muscle
- Develop blood flow in the area where muscles are being stretched
- Potentially reduce muscle soreness after heavy exercise
- Develop any imbalances in posture to help decrease chronic back pain

Static exercises can involve the following:

- Stretching calves
- Stretching hamstrings
- Stretching groins
- Stretching quadriceps
- Stretching triceps
- Stretching shoulders
- Stretching chest
- Stretching back
- Stretching abdominal muscles

Isometric stretching

This form of stretch is static as it doesn't require movement. It does however, require the muscle groups to show resistance via isometric contractions. This can be described as a tightening of the muscles which have been stretched. Isometric stretching is one of the quickest ways to promote increased static-passive elasticity. It is much more productive than passive stretching or active stretching. The tensed muscles can also be strengthened and it has been shown to reduce the level of pain usually related to stretching. There are several common ways to create the resistance needed for this stretch. One way is to do so manually to oneself. For example, a person could hold onto the ball of their own foot to stop it from flexing. At the same time, they could use the calf muscles to straighten out their instep, to point their toes.

Another way to create resistance would be to seek the assistance of a partner. For example, Person A could hold Person B's leg up high, keeping it there while Person B tries to lower the leg back down to the ground.

A complete set of isometric training should NOT be completed more than once a day for one set of muscles, the ideal limit being once every 36 hours.

The correct procedure for an isometric stretch is outlined below:

- Form a passive stretch for the targeted muscle
- Tighten the stretched muscle for 7-15 seconds (resist using a static force, like a wall or a training partner)
- Rest the muscle for a minimum of 20 seconds

Some advice has suggested to pause the isometric contraction for over 15 seconds. However, other research has concluded that this is unnecessary. The latter advice should therefore be followed, to save time.

Ballistic stretching

Ballistic stretching requires the body to bounce in and out of a stretched state. The stretched muscles are used as a type of spring, which pulls you in and out of the stretched position. For example, bouncing up and down repetitively to touch one's toes. Ballistic stretching can be more prone to injuries as the muscles are not able to adjust in the stretched position and then relax. Ballistic stretching will not be covered in any more detail in this course as it is not an encouraged form of stretching.

Frequency, intensity and duration

Some of the points relevant to frequency, intensity and duration in flexibility training are listed below:

- The client should engage in exercise three to five days a week, preferably every day
- The client should stretch until there is slight pressure and they are slightly uncomfortable
- 10-30 seconds is the recommended time to hold a static stretch. It may be advantageous for older clients to hold the stretch for longer
- Specific muscle stretches should be repeated two to four times
- There should be static contractions for 3-6 seconds. This should be proceeded by a 10-30 second static stretch

A time of one minute is advised per muscle group. The client can fill this minute by repeating stretches 2-4 times, for example, 2 x 30 seconds of activity.

Considerations:

- The client should make sure that the muscles are warm before stretching
- The client should stretch all muscles prior to exercise (dynamic or static)
- It is recommended to stretch all the main groups of muscles after activity (static stretching – progressive or maintenance)
- A variety of methods of stretching could be relevant for differing groups
- The client should not exceed stretches or try and supersede the motion range if slight pressure is felt, as this may lead to injury

Even though stretching is always recommended post warm up, it can be carried out throughout the day, at a time that suits the client.

Clients may perform stretches in the comfort of their own home while watching TV, or they may even stretch whilst they are at work! This could potentially balance out times of the day when the client would otherwise be not moving or be in a position which lacked posture. Stretching should make up a sizable part of the warm up and cooling down period. Normally, static stretching should not be performed for the following reasons:

- Research suggests that static stretching does not adequately prepare muscles for energetic activity and could even reduce effective performance, because it decreases the level of power that muscles can produce (Kokkonen et al., 1998).
- Static stretching does not reduce the chances of injury and can even make one more prone to it (Martin, 2003 and Rowland, 2003).

There is however, one exception to the general advice recommending that static stretched be avoided. This is where it is used in a 'corrective' manner. An example of such a stretch is to relax shortened pectorals when training the upper back (rhomboids and middle trapezius) for a more enhanced ROM during retraction. Such corrective static stretching should only be performed on selected shortened muscles. Dynamic stretches can be more readily recommended to make up part of the warm up where exercises copy the movement of the session that will follow. Dynamic stretches should be demonstrated only after a warm up that raises the pulse and temperature of the person exercising (Alter, 1998). After training has finished, during the cool down part of the session, it is recommended that any kind of static stretching, like static maintenance or developmental or a PNF stretch be performed.

Partner stretching

Partner stretching involves a partner moving the joint to the point of tension in the muscle and holding it for the athlete, whilst they relax. If using this type of stretching, communication is important to ensure the partner is aware of any discomfort in the muscle and eases off accordingly. Partner stretching can be a good way to get the most out of static stretches. One advantage of working with a personal trainer is that they can assist with stretching. The key point to note is that the personal trainer should assist to gently ease the client's body into a stretch position. It is important to communicate with the client throughout the stretch to ensure that a muscle is not over stretched.

Partner stretching is not recommended for beginners.

Core stability

The term 'core stability' is used to describe how stable the spine, pelvis and shoulder girdle are to make sure that exercises are carried out in the right manner and safely. The core muscles cover the deep abdominal muscles, spinal muscles, the pelvic floor and the shoulder girdle muscles.

Mechanisms that impact on stability

Core stability is impacted by several mechanisms. Some of these are the transversus abdominis (TVA), the thoracolumbar fascia (TLF), the pelvic floor and the intra-abdominal pressure.

Transversus abdominis (TVA) engagement

This muscle envelopes the trunk, similar to that of a girdle, and secures itself to several main structures that are around the spine and pelvis.

- When functional, the TVA works and sets in motion before other limb movements, and has a positive effect on the spine.
- When dysfunctional, (for example, in incidences of lower back pain), the TVA is activated less often, leaving the spine with reduced protection during other limb movements.

Thoracolumbar fascia (TLF)

The TVA contracts and pulls against the TLF. Subsequently, this gives a lateral fascial tension/stabilization push to the vertebrae.

The pelvic floor

These muscles contract alongside the TVA. Many factors can cause the pelvic floor to weaken including childbirth, pregnancy, obesity, being less active and too much coughing (respiratory infections).

Intra-abdominal pressure

Stress is added to the abdominal cavity when the core or 'inner Chapter' is pressurized from four directions (top, bottom, sides, front and back). This produces a solid base in the trunk making the spine stable and level.

When the contractions of each wall progress simultaneously, the system can potentially break down. Any sign of instability in any region will damage the effectiveness of the Chapter. For example:

- A formerly unfit client who didn't exercise previously may lack muscle tone and extended abdominal muscles (anterior wall).
- Some senior adults and new mums may suffer from weaker pelvic floor muscles (inferior wall).
- Clients with back issues or who have been operated on in this area will generally be weaker in this region (posterior wall).

Balancing the core

Exercises that stabilize the core should be undertaken. This can be performed starting with a neutral spine, with the abdominal muscles engaged. Neutral spine is when the spine keeps its assumed 'S' shaped curves. The absence of pressure on the spine means it is one of the least dangerous positions to be in. Normally, it is the half way point between a flat back and a sunken back position. The spinal muscles are not contracted (where muscles are extended and discs are compressed), neither are they lengthened (where anterior muscles are extended and the facet joints are compressed). Abdominal bracing is where the abdominal muscles are made stiff and tight (likened to being ready for a punch in the stomach. McGill (2002) has concluded that this is one of the most productive ways of balancing or stabilizing the core. This method triggers a contraction of the abdominal and lumbar extensors to run at the same time. The abdominal wall isn't pulled or pushed, just made tighter, similar to when the arm muscles are tightened.

Core balance exercises may be inserted into a training program. The table below details some examples of such exercises, at varying fitness levels, that may be included in such programs.

Adaptation and for varying capabilities

Intensity Variable	Beginner	Advanced
Number of exercises	Less exercises needed	Exercises can be added
Start positions	More even positions to be used e.g. horizontal lying.	Positions which command less support and need more composure e.g. being on all fours.
Equipment	Avoid use of equipment, to start off with.	Move on to the use of equipment such as discs or balance balls.
Complexity	Use basic exercises which are less complex.	Gradually factor in more complex exercises to counteract motor skills.
Teaching time	Longer time is needed in order to explain and showcase practical examples.	Increased experience with the exercise formation will decrease the teaching time. Confirm and repeat exercises which client is familiar with.
Repetitions, sets and rest	Decreased repetitions for each exercise. Exercises may be conducted again after rest period. Increase rests between exercises.	Exercise repetition may be a little higher, but concentrate on technique. May conduct exercises again or a wider variety of exercises can be shown. Rests can be more active.

Core stability exercises

Below are a selection of exercises that can be performed to improve core stability. These exercises do not require any special equipment, so a personal trainer can instruct a client to perform them at home or anywhere else they prefer.

Exercise	Teaching points
The plank 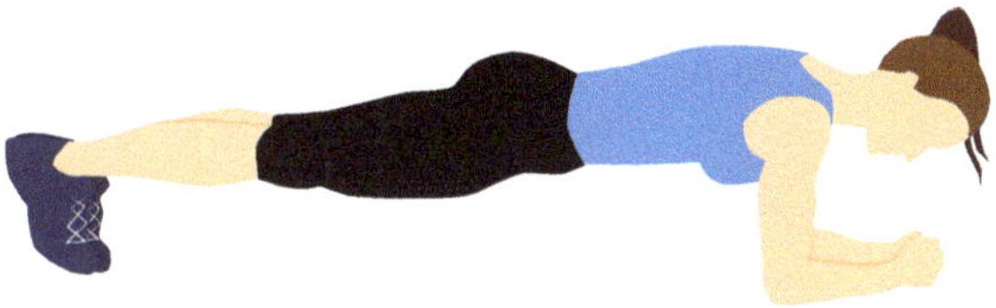	1. Place forearms on floor mat with your elbows under shoulders. 2. Make straight your legs from behind. 3. Raise hips to make a very straight line from shoulders to ankles. 4. The body should be resting on forearms and toes. 5. Lower abdomen area and the back should be keeping the body upright. Hold this position for 60 seconds.
Oblique plank 	1. Assuming a side position, rest on the right forearm with elbow under your shoulder. 2. Legs should be straightened out on the left. 3. Raise pelvis so that body is balanced on forearm and feet. 4. You should be in a straight line. You should be able to feel in the side of your torso the oblique muscles working. 5. Maintain this position for 60 seconds and do this again on the other side.
Abdominal crunch 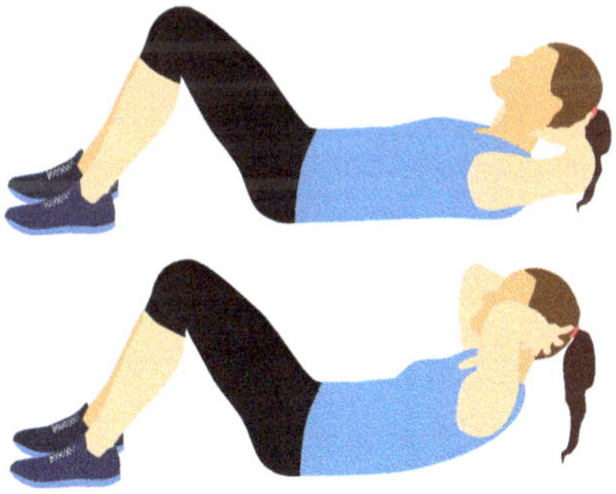	1. Laying on your back, bend knees with feet flat on the mat. 2. Lifting the shoulders off the floor, enable the stomach to perform a 'crunch' or a curl so it slightly rises above the floor. 3. Avoid use of the hip flexor muscles while performing this. 4. You may pull your head up with your arms.
The bridge 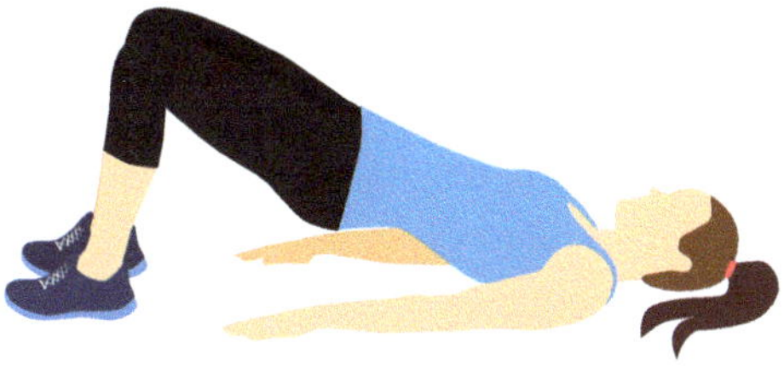	1. Laying on your back, place hands by your side. Bend your knees. 2. Width of feet should match shoulder width. 3. Using mainly the force of the heels against the mat, raise your hips off the mat. Make sure your back is straight. 4. Whilst breathing in, return to the starting position. Do this slowly.

Superman 	1. Assume a balanced hands-and knees position on the mat. 2. Your back should be straight and hips should be opposite the floor. 3. Lift your right arm to the front, and extend leg behind you. Maintain its straight position. 4. Keep in this position for 30 seconds and do the same for the other side.
Static leg and back 	1. Laying on your back, bend your knees, keeping feet flat on the mat. 2. Raise your pelvis, making a bridge-like stance. 3. It should seem like a straight line starting at the shoulders through to the knees. 4. There should be some feeling in the left buttock, back, lower abdomen as these are the areas being worked. 5. Keep a hold of this position for half a minute before repeating on the other leg.
Dynamic leg and back 	1. Repeat the same starting position as the 'static leg and back'. 2. Concentrate to slowly lower the pelvis. Be careful not to let it dip or make contact with the mat. 3. Revert to the starting position, keeping a straight line between shoulders and toe.

Many other exercises can assist with core stability such as oblique crunches, squats and lunges, hamstring raises, leg extensions, static straight leg and leg raises.

Tips to maximize efficiency of core stability exercises

1. Do not allow all of the stomach to become too firm and rigid. If the upper muscles in the abdomen are protruding outwards, then this indicates that you have not followed the correct method and instead performed the exercise with the large rectus (six pack), in place of the transversus abdominus or lower abdominals.
2. Avoid tensing up the lower abdominals; a gentle contraction is enough. The aim is to try and boost stamina, not strength. Grip them for approximately 50%.
3. You must not hold your breath as this indicates that you are not at ease. Breathing normally should be a habit and practiced as a matter of routine, as you must breathe whilst running!
4. It is good practice to perform core stability exercises as part of the cool down routine after running or on a day when you cross-train.

Motor skills

Motor skills are related to activities of the muscles. Motor skills are carried out when the nervous system and muscles work together to perform large or small manoeuvres leading to movements of the body parts.

The six components of motor skills related to fitness are shown in the diagram below (Glencoe /Mcgraw Hill Education).

Motor skills improve with practice and the six components determine a person's level of athletic ability. Training guidance to boost the quality of motor skills or neuromuscular health will differ according to which precise skills a client may want to work on, as well as for what purpose. Distinct motor skills are needed to play certain sports and various skills are required to preserve and boost function whilst undertaking regular activities. An elderly adult training to work on their balance and co-ordination, for example, to lower their risk of falling will be markedly different to training to improve the quality and co-ordination for a specific sport, for example trampolining or gymnastics.

End of Chapter activit

Activity 4.3: Create a set of smart goals for yourself and then design a training program combining aspects of aerobic training, resistance training and flexibility training. List the exact type of exercises you will perform in relation to each objective. Ensure you incorporate duration, frequency, rest and any equipment required.

Based on the plan, make a list of food / drink to have before, during and after exercise.

Goals

Food for exercise

Activity 4.4: Plan a periodised six month training program for a friend or family member based on the client profile created during activity 3.5. Use the table to fill in their progression over time, starting with their current fitness level.

Objectives:

Timeframe:

Training modes:

	Month 1	Month 2	Month 3	Month 4	Month 5	Month 6
Phases						

Notes and specifics:

Activity 4.5: Create a resistance training for an advanced exerciser who wants to enhance their strength and power. Include some methods not selected for other activities.

End of Chapter checkl

1. When designing the training program, consideration should be given to what variables?
2. Why should you warm up before exercise?
3. Why should you cool down after exercise?
4. What are the principles of training?
5. What is the difference between aerobic training and anaerobic training?
6. What is flexibility training?
7. What are the benefits of cardiovascular fitness?
8. What exercise types improve cardiovascular fitness?
9. What is the Borg Rating of Perceived Exertion (RPE) Scale used for?
10. What is interval training?
11. What is the meaning of periodization, macrocycles, mesocycles and microcycles?
12. In what order should exercises be performed in when training muscles?
13. What are motor skills?
14. What is partner stretching and why is it used?
15. What does the stimulus-fatigue-recovery-adaptation (SFRA) model state?
16. What is muscle hypertrophy training?
17. Why is it important for a personal trainer to change the exercise stimulus?
18. What are the benefits of flexibility training?
19. What does isometric stretching involve?
20. What is the core and which exercises are good for core stability?
21. What is resistance training and what are its benefits?
22. What methods can be used to strengthen muscles? Name at least three methods.

Chapter 4B: Delivering PT sessions

Chapter summary

This Chapter will cover the essence of delivering personal training programs, building on the teachings of Level 2 on instructing gym based sessions. The Chapter will also cover monitoring clients during sessions and supporting clients throughout a training program.

Aim

The aim of this Chapter is to teach personal trainers to keep clients motivated and deliver training sessions based on programs designed, monitor clients as well as provide feedback on their performance.

Learning objectives

After completing this Chapter, personal trainers will be able to:

1. Prepare for a training session, including help a client to warm up and cool down.
2. Give visual and verbal instructions to clients to complete exercises and to correct techniques.
3. Monitor clients during sessions, including the intensity of the exercises.
4. Adapt communication techniques depending on a client's preferences.
5. Act as a spotter.
6. Discuss motivation theories and select methods to motivate clients depending on the issues identified.

Delivering personalized training is a key part of a personal trainer's job. Each session with the client needs to be carefully planned and the training environment selected needs to be prepared. For example, if the session involves jogging in the park, the route needs to have been already planned by the personal trainer. Likewise, if the session is to take place in a gym, the environment needs to have been prepared with the equipment selected before the session starts and before clients arrive. Such preparation involves making sure equipment is safe to use and that alternative equipment is available for clients in case they need to use it too.

All equipment should be assessed to make sure it is completely safe. This will prevent any accidents and injuries during the session, ensuring the safety of clients. Good preparation also ensures that the personal trainer can concentrate and focus on the session.

Preparation

After the introductory consultation, the trainer is then ready to plan the first exercise session. Factors such as client goals, health, present fitness status and way of life can all have an impact on the exercise program. For example, the type of activities, exercise surroundings and physical and technical requirements can all be decided upon once the factors mentioned are known. The exercise program must be drafted according to the client's exact needs and requirements. However, it should still accommodate the core areas of physical development, like the client objectives previously agreed upon. A suitable time, quantity and intensity level should reflect the client's capacity and performance as well as their goals.

The exercise surroundings and the tools available to the trainer should help the trainer to gauge how they can conduct their session. A good trainer will be able to safely think on their feet and be able to pick the most relevant exercise to match the requirements of the client. It is imperative that the trainer has the exercise program ready and has prepared the exercise surroundings in advance of the exercise session starting. Such preparation may include:

- Drawing up the program card before the session so that the trainer is able to speak to the client, at the beginning of the session about how the physical and technical content of the session will adequately meet the client's aims. Any tweaking of the program may be recorded fully after the session has finished.
- Surroundings being prepared, making sure it is safe and suitably equipped.

These measures allow the trainer to concentrate on the client during the session and adapt to any changes should they be required. The personal trainer must not write their program cards, look for equipment or deal with administrative tasks during the session, as it is unprofessional to do so.

Preparing the client

1. Welcome the client

Upon arrival, the personal trainer should introduce themselves, making the client feel welcome. They should inform the client of the building's emergency procedures, for example positioning of all fire exits, nearest First Aid box and First Aider and nearest telephone point.

2. Explain reasons for the choice of exercises

The personal trainer should then explain to the client the reasoning and impact of the exercise planned for them. This advice should also include any physical and technicalities that may affect the client. Keeping the client informed of all necessary information will make them more likely to follow the program as they will know the purpose of each activity and how they are benefiting from the program. After describing the warming up and cooling down procedure, the client should be asked if they are happy to proceed with the program that has been designed for them. The personal trainer should relate the whole program back to the client's objectives. Often it may become clear that a client is feeling apprehensive about taking on a new fitness program. They may feel daunted, and any fears should be discussed, with possible solutions considered. Sometimes the client's concerns may only be due to a misunderstanding and once this has been clarified they are happy to proceed with the planned fitness program.

3. Establish rapport

The personal trainer should establish a good rapport in the initial meetings with the client. This will help the personal trainer decide how ready the client is for exercise, both mentally and physically. For example, the client may be excited at the prospect of undertaking the program. Or in contrast, it may seem that the client has a busy home life which is likely to distract them or even reduce attendance. These points should be considered when assessing the physical demands that the session will entail, making any alterations if necessary.

4. The warm up

Before the beginning of any exercise, the personal trainer must explain the importance of the warm up. The personal trainer must make sure the client fully understands its importance and relevance to the whole program. An adequate warm up will benefit the client physiologically as well as reduce the chances of injury. It will also result in a better overall performance in the beginning of the main activity. Understanding the impact of the warm up will encourage the client to include it in future programs without having to be prompted by a professional. All warm-ups must include:

- Pulse-raising and body warming exercises
- Mobilization exercises
- Muscle stretching and lengthening
- Rehearsal of movement patterns the main session will build on

L2

Warm up suggestions:

- Dynamic stretches
- Lunges at different directions
- Multi-directional lunges with reaches
- Jogging on the spot
- Jogging around the exercise area (with a clearly marked route, avoiding any hazards)
- Jogging combinations e.g. wide strides, cross-over strides, short & long strides, heavy & light feet
- Jogging with alternate punches e.g. up in the air, punches out to the side and rotational upper cut
- Jogging with waist to shoulder height alternate arm movements e.g. hammer curls, lateral raises and upper cuts

Instructional skills

Instruction means 'giving information on how to perform something'. Clear advisory skills will ensure clients better understand what is required, resulting in a safe workout, reducing the chances of accidents and injuries.

Verbal instructions

Use of words are one of the most powerful tools for a personal trainer to successfully engage his/her audience. The personal trainer should use simple generic terms. For example, 'chest up' instead of saying 'maintain neutral spine'. Personal trainers may want to prepare a list of non-technical words to describe any planned exercises. This will mean all clients can understand the instructions as they are succinct and easy to understand.

One of the key qualities needed to succeed in keeping to a long-term fitness program is motivation. It is therefore vital that the personal trainer is motivated themselves if they are to motivate the client. It may go without saying that a good personal trainer will show confidence, be enthusiastic and show immense passion in their manner with an intention to encourage the client to be the same!

The ability to motivate is particularly important when trying to 'tempt' new clients out of their comfort zones or current sedentary habits.

During exercise sessions, praises and motivational words of encouragement should be regularly used to help the client. A typical client would feel a sense of achievement when told that a goal has been reached, or that they have just delivered a great performance. Terms such as 'well done', 'great job!', 'you can do it!' are examples of encouraging language one can use to help the client succeed. Personal trainers should never use discouraging or negative language. Even the slightest of criticisms could dent a client's self-belief and confidence, which may result in them dropping out of the program altogether.

However, personal trainers should be careful not to be too generous with words of praise as it could potentially lessen its impact. The personal trainer should establish a relationship with the client whereby they indicate what is expected, and rewarding with praise when it has clearly been 'earned'. Praise given when not actually deserved reduces its impact and effectiveness. For example, if the client is praised for every move they make, they are unlikely to want to improve on their performance.

Tone of voice

'It's not what you say, it's the way that you say it' is a common phrase which summaries the importance of voice intonation. Voice intonation is the way information is relayed and is a vital part of exercise instructions. For example, training for hypertrophy uses up a lot of strength and energy. Using words such as 'explode' will only be appropriate if spoken with passion and at the right volume, otherwise it would not have the intended motivational effect on the client. In the same way, the level of intonation may need to be adjusted when speaking to a novice, or elderly person who is a lot slower so may not be motivated with highly pitched terms like 'come on, faster, faster!'

Essentially, the personal trainer should be adaptable enough to change his voice intonation according to his audience.

Ways to promote voice intonation:

- Practice in varying the tone
- Develop a wide choice of instructions
- Practice in varying the speed
- Practice in varying the volume

Teaching points

Teaching points are used to reinforce a visual demonstration. When used appropriately, teaching points facilitate easier instructions and allow personal trainers to express, correct and fine-tune clients' exercise technique. However, to use teaching points effectively the personal trainer must themselves be fully proficient in exercise technique.

Teaching points can usually be logically broken down into two categories:

- Setting up exercise / introducing equipment
- Execution of movements

Teaching points should always be kept positive to build confidence. It may help to make teaching points creative using metaphors and similes or referring to objects. All this may help clients to visualize, focus and better understand the exercise and how it should be performed. However, it is important to note that overuse of teaching points can confuse a client due to having to concentrate on too many variables. It is up to the personal trainer to find a balance when working with their clients.

In Level 2, how to introduce equipment and exercise types was covered. Teaching points on using equipment and performing various movement types were highlighted. Personal training involves using the same teaching points to deliver training to clients usually on a one to one basis. It involves taking the same approach to introducing exercise types. A summary of the approach is provided in the figure below:

Introduce the machine/equipment by name → Demonstrate how to use it → Explain the key teaching points → Allow the client to have a go at using the machine/equipment while the trainer watches

How to use machines can differ depending on the manufacturer and therefore before teaching clients, personal trainers should learn to use the machines in the fitness centre they are working by reading any instructions provided with the machines.

Visual instruction

Demonstration

Personal trainers should be wholly proficient not only in exercise technique but also to give demonstrations properly. Demonstrations give the client the best example of how an activity is to be correctly performed. For best results, clients should be positioned so that they can witness all the major joints in motion. For example, the client is best placed to the side of the demonstrating personal trainer if they are to view fully all the joints, especially the lower back, during the bent over row exercise. A good demonstration will include three to five repetitions slowly, in a controlled way (unless it is power training). This should ideally be done before the main teaching points.

Body language

Body language is a form of non-verbal, visual communication and can indicate a person's emotional and psychological state. Something as simple as the crossing of arms can be a sign of being bored and disinterested. In contrast, open arms and hand gestures help to create an enthusiastic, energetic and open atmosphere. Eye contact and facial expressions can also be used to praise and motivate. Lack of eye contact can have the opposite effect on a client. As such, a personal trainer needs to be fully aware how their body language can impact on a client. It can affect a client's mood, in a good or in a negative way, therefore influencing the overall result. The personal trainer should disregard any matters that may be affecting them in their personal life and always be self-aware of their body language and do as much as possible to ensure their body language is a positive one.

Adapting communication to meet client needs

All types of communication should be tailored to serve the requirements of the client. Some clients are more receptive to being spoken to (being verbally motivated or being told how to conduct a certain exercise). However, other people may respond better to visual communication (for example, practically being shown how to conduct an activity). Some clients may even like a mix of both kinds of communication. Being adaptable when communicating with a client is an essential quality to have. It helps to form a good relationship with the client and helps the trainer to figure out client needs and preferences with regards to communication and learning methods. It is widely accepted that there are three main ways in which people learn and digest information:

1. Visual

Clients with this preference learn better by watching practical examples or pictures explaining the relevant exercise method. In addition, these clients react positively to eye contact, expressions of the face, as well as other gestures which help to encourage or explain. These techniques stimulate the client's favored neurological route. Productive training techniques may be to:

- Provide a visible demonstration of the exercise to be taught.
- Keep eye contact with the client, staying in their line of vision (perhaps by using a mirror) when making corrections.
- Being more self-aware of facial expressions and other body language, as visual learners are particularly in tune with such types of communication.
- Use pictures where relevant, to help elaborate on exercises. Terms such as 'light as a feather' or 'bracing for a punch' may be used.

Identifying

There are two sub-types to visual learning – linguistic and spatial. Visual linguistic learners prefer to be taught via written methods, like reading and writing tasks. They recall anything they have seen written down even if they have only read it once. Visual linguistic learners like writing down any directions given and are more likely to pay more attention to lectures if they are watching them. On the other hand, visual-spatial learners find written language methods challenging, and perform better with tools like charts, demonstrations and videos, amongst other visual methods.

Plan of action

In an exercise environment, such clients will benefit more from demonstrations rather than lots of teaching points. If you are going to give instructions, give them visuals like illustrations, photographs, videos.

2. Via audio

Clients with this preference learn much better when a system is explained to them. The varying degrees of pitch, volume and tone of voice help the client to absorb the information even further.

Identifying

People who benefit from this type of method often like talking to themselves. They like to move their lips and read aloud. They could find reading and writing challenging. They usually perform better when speaking to a colleague or a recorder to hear what was just said.

Plan of action

- Keep the visual demonstration short and to the point.
- Clear verbal words should be used as well as instructions to correct the client.
- Encouraging sentences should be spoken like "You can do it!"
- Being aware of other background sounds within the surroundings (for example, music), as these can distract the client, especially because they are sensitive to sound.
- Any new topics should be introduced with a short introduction as to what will follow. End the session with a recap of what has been covered.

3. Kinaesthetic

Clients who prefer this method like to get 'stuck in' and learn best when they are physically doing the exercises and activities themselves. Such a learner can be part of the demonstration, which is better being kept short and succinct. The trainer can adjust the learning style by practically showing the main muscles that will be used. The trainer may do this during the exercise, or by making some movement in the joints and muscles. The trainer should invite the client to partake in the demo by asking the client to copy what the trainer is demonstrating, as they are demonstrating it. This way, by the time the exercise is performed, the client has already learnt the movements involved.

Identifying

These learners perform best via contact and by moving. It again has two sub-types. These are kinaesthetic (movement) and tactile (touch). Learners here are prone to loss of focus if there is rare or non-existent stimulus or movement. During lectures, they may choose to take written notes just so that they are moving their hands. Before reading a document, they like to skim before concentrating on the finer details. A common trait for them is to use color highlighters **via audio**.

Clients with this preference and note take by using visual aids such as drawing, diagrams or doodles. To blend this style of learning into the atmosphere, the following strategies may wish to be undertaken:

Training techniques

- Encourage the client to move and practice at the earliest opportunity. So, if demonstrating an activity using a weight, allow the client to practice without the weight during the demonstration.
- Perform manual corrections and practical contact to correct a method. So, for example, placing two fingers on the client's lower back so that they remember to preserve lumbar neutral spine during an exercise.

Some clients may like a domineering learning method. However, they can still learn from other methods. Realistically, people learn most when using several methods. So a visual learner for example, may also benefit from using audio and kinaesthetic techniques.

Spotting

Spotting in exercise is the act of one person such as a personal trainer supporting a client during an exercise, with an emphasis on allowing the client to lift or push more than they could normally do safely. The three main roles of a spotter:

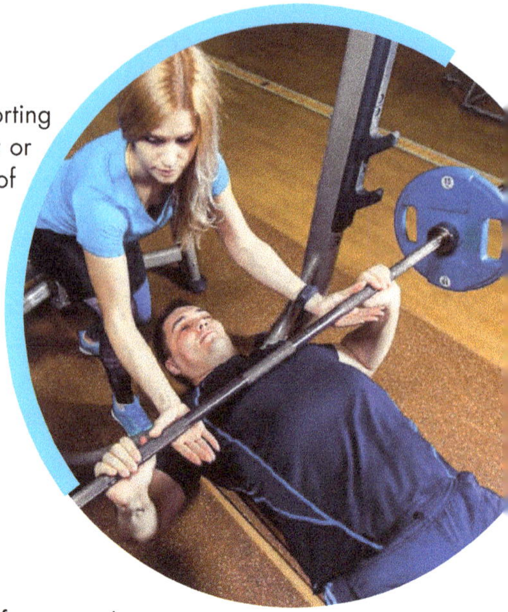

- To help the client if they are in difficulty
- To enforce high intensity training techniques
- To make sure correct technique is being used

Spotting is recommended for the following free-weight exercises (Earle and Baechle), 2004:

- Overhead exercises (e.g. shoulder press)
- Exercises with the bar on the back e.g. back squat, step up, lunge)
- Exercises with the bar rested on the anterior deltoid or clavicles (e.g. front squat)
- Exercises involving the bar over the face(e.g. bench press & lying triceps extension)

WARNING

Spotters should NOT be used during power exercises. For example, exercises like the clean, snatch and the jerk. This is because spotting for these kinds of exercises are dangerous for both lifter and a spotter.

When spotting, a number of points should be considered:

- Good communication is essential, and should be established even before the first session of exercise.
- The spotter should have knowledge of the right exercise technique and how to change this technique if it becomes necessary.
- The spotter should have enough strength to help the client if required, including provide a firm support base and promote a neutral spine, specifically when lifting.
- Some exercises will entail the spotter making sure the client is safe. For example, during heavy back squats.
- Spotters should be aware beforehand of the number of repetitions the client is trying to lift.
- Spotters should always monitor the client and pay close attention to the technique used.
- Spotters should be able to get help immediately if there is an accident or injury.
- When spotting over the face barbell exercises, the spotter needs to alternate his grip when holding the bar. Usually this is inside the client's grip.
- During over the face dumbbell exercises, spotters need to be as close to the dumbbells as possible. It should be mentioned that a lot of clients would rather be spotted under the elbows when supine exercises are taking place.
- Dumbbells should be passed one by one. This will enable the client to grip the handle safely.
- The spotter needs to be as tall as, and have at least the same strength as the lifter when spotting overhead/bar on back on front exercises. They should conduct the exercise in a power rack with the right pin placement.
- Only skilled athletes and spotters with experience should tackle out-of-rack exercises like the lunge and step up, otherwise serious injury can occur.

Correcting techniques

Making sure that clients conduct each exercise in the correct manner is key to successful personal training. Performing an exercise, the way it is designed to be executed, drastically reduces injury risk and increases effectiveness. The first way of promoting the right technique is via the exercise induction; by demonstrating, explaining and advising the client to be in the right start position to begin exercise. Trainers should consider when introducing any new exercise, just how much information a client is likely to remember. It may be more effective to break down instructions into two or three main points to make it easier for the client to retain and recall information. Once the client is used to following these pointers, the trainer can add more precise details needed so that the client can excel in the exercise. The trainer supervises the correction of technique by watching the client closely as they conduct each activity. The teaching position should be changed so that the client can be examined from various aspects, enabling the trainer to provide continuous assessment on their correctional technique.

At the time of correcting the technique, timing is crucial. Firstly, teaching points should be explained before the exercise session begins, and more precise teaching points should be reasserted during the exercise session. This point of teaching should be integrated smoothly during the session, and not serve to disrupt the enactment of the exercise. The trainer should ensure they do not 'bombard' the client with excess information, as the client will be focusing on the practical technique and any excess information may only distract them.

Trainers should correct the client through verbal means, using as much positive language as possible. For example, instead of saying "No! Don't do it like that!", they should say "Do it like this". Positive language boosts the client's confidence, whilst negative comments may hinder their motivation. Both positive and negative language can have an impact on the client's commitment.

It may be appropriate at times to physically correct the client through touch. It is essential that the trainer seeks the client's permission to do this before approaching them in this way. For example, the trainer may ask the client "May I guide your arm during this particular exercise?". The client's response should be honored with sensitivity and tact; if they say yes then force such as pulling and pushing should be avoided, rather the trainer should use gentle movements to help the client.

Phases of correction:

- Give succinct, precise teaching pointers in the beginning stage
- Ask the client if they have any queries
- Position the client into correct starting point
- Watch the client from various angles as they undertake the exercise
- Use positive language to motivate the client, complimenting any areas of achievement
- Give an assessment and guide client on how to improve on any incorrect techniques
- Provide practical help where appropriate and with consent
- Allow the client some independence when their technique gets better
- Review client performance with them and be receptive to any feedback from them

Monitoring

Monitoring during sessions

A crucial part of a personal trainer's job is to monitor the safety of exercise conducted. A good personal trainer will follow good practice when dealing with postural alignment. If a client struggles with good technique or posture, the personal trainer should pause the activity and suggest a different exercise.

During each personal training session, the personal trainer should use their judgment to decide whether a client is ready to progress to the next stage, or whether they have in fact regressed. The following are several ways of monitoring performance, after which a decision on the next stage can be made:

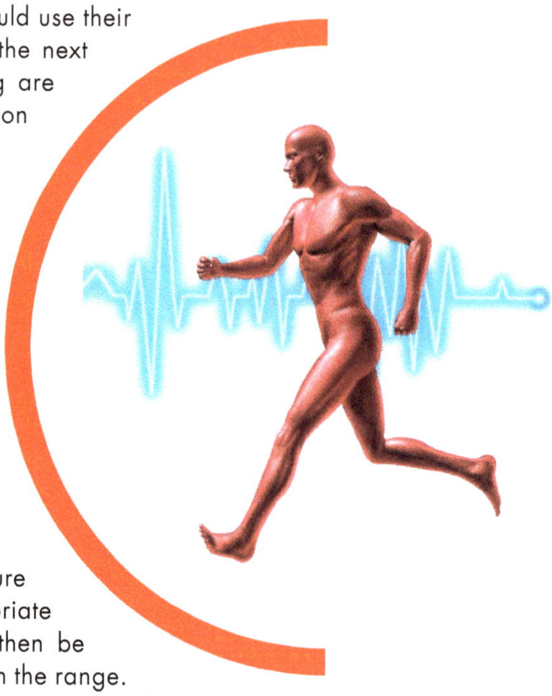

- The rate of perceived exertion (RPE)
- Heart rate monitoring
- Using performance markers
- Physical checking of the pulse
- Talk test
- Observing and asking client

Heart rate monitoring

The heart rate approach requires having the ability to measure your heart rate (BPM) periodically as you exercise. An appropriate target heart rate range is then calculated. The BPM should then be periodically measured during training to ensure that it lies within the range. Elderly and beginners are typically given a range of between 40 to 60% of the MHR. Healthy adults might be advised to aim to stay between 50 and 75% of the MHR. As the program continues, the resting heart rate should drop and it should be possible to work harder or longer whilst remaining within the target heart rate range.

RPE approach

This approach requires the client to rate their level of exertion using a number from 6 to 20 based on the physical sensations they experience whilst exercising, including increased heart and breathing rate, increased sweating and muscle fatigue. The numbers 6 to 20 in the RPE scale (see page 208) relate to phrases used to rate how easy or difficult an activity is perceived to be.

A personal trainer can tell from the RPE scores and peak heart rate whether the intensity targets are being met. They can then adjust any of the required intensities where necessary to achieve the desired result.

Observing the client

Observing the client's technique as well as other indicators such as the strain seen on client's face, sweat levels all help in determining how well the client is performing. Also, by now, the personal trainer should be more familiar with how a client looks after a certain level of intensity.

Talk test

The talk test is also a good method to monitor how hard a client is exercising. If the client can talk and exercise at the same time, the oxygen needs of the exercise are still being met and therefore the exercise intensity can be increased. If the client is out of breath (especially if they have to stop and catch their breath) it is likely that they are working too hard.

Overtraining

Overtraining is as much a possibility for beginners as it is for advanced clients. The personal trainer must be aware of both the immediate effects of overtraining that may occur and the longer-term symptoms so that any issues can be understood, safety maintained and adjustments to the program made accordingly.

Immediate effects include:

- Loss of concentration
- Loss of co-ordination
- Decreased motivation
- Insatiable thirst
- Increases in injury
- Personality changes including irritability and aggressiveness

If overtraining is suspected the client might also disclose effects that occur outside of training.

These might include:

- Insomnia
- Muscle soreness that continues for longer than two days
- Insatiable thirst
- Varying resting heart rate
- Personality changes including depression, irritability, aggressiveness and lower self-esteem

Most issues can be contained by ensuring good hydration, reducing and more closely monitoring training intensity as well as extending rest and recovery periods. It may also be necessary to decrease the pace at which challenges are increased across a training program.

Dealing with injuries

Remaining calm is the key to dealing with injuries and managing an emergency situation effectively. The personal trainer should help the client to be comfortable and keep them calm administering first aid until the emergency services arrive, if they have been called. The personal trainer should give emergency services an account of the incident clearly and accurately.

The emergency services should be called when:

- Casualty is unconscious
- Suspected head, neck or spine injury
- Suspected fractures
- Possible dislocation of bones
- Severe external bleeding
- Suspected internal injuries
- Suspected heart attack/stroke/asthma attack
- Diabetic emergencies
- Casualty's condition is worsening

Training logs

To maintain a comprehensive and professional service, the trainer must keep detailed training records for every client. The records need to be completed in each training session and collated to form a record that measures the progress of each client over a period of time. This record might have information about:

- Training sessions which are physically overseen by a trainer
- Training sessions where the client works independently
- A log of the client's day to day activities
- A log of the client's hobbies which may include activity

A thorough training log can help the client achieve their fitness aims as it monitors how the client performs. It can also be used to motivate the client. It is written proof of the client's progression.

Establishing key markers

These are similar to short term goals set for the client, within a session. Some examples are asking the client to focus towards a set distance covered or asking them to complete a set number of repetitions. This type of strategy can give important motivation for them to carry on with the exercise. Towards the end of the session, giving the client an idea of how far he has left to complete his goal will give them a last-minute boost towards achieving the goal.

Praise

Praise for anyone, at any age can be a useful strategy to aid motivation. It is extremely satisfying to be told that a goal of yours has been accomplished, more so where there is a reward. Whilst this is a good tool to use, praise should not be excessively given, otherwise it may not hold any value after a while. Praise should clearly be earned.

Concluding a session

Cool down

The cool down phase is as important as the warm up, mitigating various side-effects of the endurance phase. The impact of blood pooling, muscles soreness and increased body temperature are all more readily alleviated when you cool down using the right techniques.

A cool down should reflect the content of the session that has just finished. For example, if the session concentrated on the leg area, then there is little point in cooling down the upper body area. The level of intensity of the session should also be considered and as such, a high intensity workout will require a gradual cool down starting with brisk actions slowly reaching an eventual stop. Conversely, a session involving only simple core exercises will only require basic stretches as a cool down, and nothing more vigorous.

Suggestions for cool downs:

- Multi-directional lunges
- Multi-directional lunges with reaches
- Slow lunge walking
- Bodyweight squats
- Bodyweight squats with anterior arm reaches, overhead posterior arm reaches, overhead sideways reaches (both sides), arms together rotational reaches at shoulder height (both sides)
- Static stretches
- Fixed stretches of all the muscle groups that have been burdened during the conditioning phase

Other factors determining the type of cool down a personal trainer leads include the client's health. For example, a pregnant lady will only need to perform some minimalist stretches that affect the relevant muscle groups related to pregnancy, such as hip flexors, lumbar erectors and pectorals. Another example could be the older lady with arthritis in her knees. She would need to have a more controlled cool down. Overall, it is essential that the cool down is tailored to the client's needs. Gym equipment should always be left in a satisfactory condition for other clients and future gym users.

Give feedback

The cool down is a good time to give the client feedback based on their performance. Feedback should be positive and honest, offering constructive criticism without demotivating or offending the client where they have failed to reach the required goal. Tone of voice and choice of words can all affect the client's reaction to feedback. The following are some examples of poorly constructed feedback, and a better, motivational one:

'You failed to get the last three repetitions for the last lunge exercise. Your spine was not neutral and your knee was edging inwards during the end of the exercise. Give it your all next time!'.

Contrast this with:

'That was a great effort. I'm sure you'll be able to reach three repetitions in the next session. Try and focus on keeping the chest lifted, with your knees in line. This will help improve your performance'.

Both statements are more or less saying the same thing but impact differently on the client. The first statement is more likely to have a demotivating effect and the client may be prone to give up hearing these words. The second statement detracts from their poor performance, instead focusing on the their efforts and expectations of the next session. The personal trainer also indicates the belief they have in the client to reach their objective. This is very important in helping the client to stick to the program.

After giving feedback the client should then be invited to:

- Evaluate the overall session – did they enjoy the session, how hard did they feel it was, was it enjoyable, where they feel their strengths and weaknesses were, are all points that can be discussed at this stage.
- Ask questions – the client may be uncertain about a few areas of the programme or may ask the personal trainer for an overview of how they performed.
- Share thoughts on how they feel physically – they may have found some of the session difficult, or have comments about the motivation employed by the personal trainer.
- Identify further objectives – participating in the session may encourage the client to tell the personal trainer of other objectives they may have. They may ask the personal trainer for more help later and may ask to help them remember the program they have just finished.

The personal trainer should ensure that the client fully understands how to continue with the program without supervision. If the client is still uncertain about a follow up, they should make an appointment with the personal trainer.

Review and reflect on personal trainer's part

It is good practice for the personal trainer to reflect and review their own performance, at a quiet time after the session has ended. They can consider any feedback given by the client as well as their own thoughts. A good personal trainer will be able to critically evaluate a session and pinpoint areas of success and areas which may need to be improved. Reflection of a session could include:

- How the exercises matched the client needs
- How effective and motivational the rapport with the client was
- How well the instructing style matched the client's needs
- Whether the client enjoyed the session

TIP

A personal trainer who is honest with themselves and can review their work will in the long term be more successful, as they will be able to rectify any issues early on. They will be able to further enhance their teaching methods and make future sessions even more successful.

Clearing up

Finally, the personal trainer should ensure that the environment is left in a condition acceptable for future use. They should educate the client in terms of health, safety and cleanliness to ensure that:

- Machines, benches and mats are wiped clean after use
- Mats, handles and other equipment are clean, tidied up and put in their allocated place
- Free weights are put away in their allocated place
- Any fault or damage has been reported to the relevant person
- Clear away any drinks and water bottles

Activity

Activity 4.6: Make plans for a one-hour aerobic session for a client whose main objective is to tone arms, legs and lose 2kg. Include warm up and cool down exercises.

Breaking barriers

Taking note and responding to any barriers which are holding the client back helps them to keep on track.

Taking part in more exercise can be positively viewed as beginning a new life of good habits, instead of the loss of old ones. The client should feel fulfilled and successful regularly, because of their new exercise plan.

The personal trainer should help the clients name and remove any barriers that are preventing them from progressing. This will assist them in moving forward. The following is a list of barriers that often prevent a person's desire to exercise. Strategies to help resolve these issues are also provided. Common barriers can be:

1. Physical

Not being fit enough is one reason used by people to refrain from exercise. Good practice is for a personal trainer to develop a plan for a person who is not very fit. The personal trainer can counteract this barrier
by telling the client that 'doing even a little is still better than nothing'. For clients who are not in good health, it is best to refer them to a suitable professional who can formulate an appropriate exercise program for them.

2. Emotional

Some people can feel self-conscious or too aware of themselves, perhaps more if they are extremely overweight. They may not want to exercise in front of others, feeling that 'all eyes will be on me'. This barrier can be removed by presenting to the client some exercises that they can do at home. This will increase their confidence. Another suggestion would be for the client to exercise amongst friends with whom they may feel more comfortable as opposed to exercising amongst strangers.

3. Barriers relating to experience

A lot of people have failed to stick to exercise plans in the past. This may affect their attitude to exercise now. They may have previously tried to follow the latest 'fad', and failed or only resulted in short-term results (they put the weight back on soon after). The experience may have put them off exercise all together. Here, the personal trainer should address this and design a more suitable plan for the client, creating short-term goals which produce long-term results. The personal trainer can explain that some programs are unsuitable for certain people and that a different route should be taken to have the maximum impact. This approach may help the client to overcome this barrier, ensuring closer adherence to the newly designed program.

4. Motivational

Exercise is enjoyed by many but not for all people. For such clients, it is more of a chore that they must endure rather than enjoy. Here, the trick is for the personal trainer to find an exercise that they will like doing. This will start off their journey and formation of a new exercise habit all together. The personal trainer should analyze what the client likes and doesn't like so that they can pinpoint the reason for the client's lack of motivation. A solution can then be sought. One example is where the client is bored of the same exercise routine. The personal trainer can offer alternative exercise which will inspire the client. This would hopefully reignite their desire to get fitter.

5. Time barriers

In these modern times, life for a typical person is much busier compared to, say a decade ago. Having 'no time' for exercise is a common reason given for one's lack of fitness. This barrier can be lifted by incorporating physical activity into the client's daily life. Taking the stairs is just one example of doing this. There are even some exercises that can be performed whilst watching T.V! These exercises will save travel time to and from a gym and can be easily built into a daily routine.

6. Financial barriers

When speaking about exercise, people often immediately think of an expensive gym membership. A client should be advised of ways to reduce costs. For example, there are many exercises that can be done from home, reducing the number of gym sessions. Running or walking in the park are activities which cost nothing. They may like to form a walking group amongst their peers. This in turn will encourage them to be more active and stick to a program.

7. Change training frequently

Making changes to variables like intensity, duration and frequency helps the client to stay interested in the exercise plan, and they are less likely to become bored of it.

8. Suggest group exercise

Personal training often tends to be solitary which can at times be a lonely experience. Therefore, if the personal trainer senses this, it may help to suggest some group exercises and incorporate them within the training program. E.g. one class of yoga per week in a fitness centre. At times where their motivation is dipping, attending a group session may be just the thing to fix these feelings. They may not want to let the other group members down and attend for their sake, for example.

9.Track progress

The client may feel very satisfied seeing on paper how much they have improved over time.

Motivating clients

Client support involves motivating the client and keeping them motivated. It is the personal trainer's job to keep the client motivated to adhere to the training program designed to achieve the goals that have been established.

"Motivation is a psychological construct that arouses and directs behavior" and "a construct is simply an internal drive or neural process that cannot be directly observed but must be indirectly inferred from observation of outward behavior" (Earle and Baecle, 2004). An example of motivation is a person that goes running first thing in the morning. The definition of motivation above suggests that there are two aspects of motivation a 'directional' aspect that leads to the choices the client makes about their time and commitment and the 'intensity' aspect which is the level of effort they put in to pursue their choices (Earle and Baecle, 2004).

Motivation concept requires studying behavior change and the theories of behavior.

Behavior change

Behavior, the action of an individual or more than one individual, is an important factor that influences health. In Europe, the way we live contributes to morbidity and mortality. Definitive evidence suggests that leading a healthy lifestyle leads to a longer and healthier life. Actions that encompass such a lifestyle include:

- Regular exercise
- A balanced diet
- Controlled blood pressure
- Not smoking

People in many professions, including personal trainers, seek to help and support people trying to change their behavior in order to become healthier. It is therefore necessary to establish ways and techniques of encouraging change and to help people maintain newly learnt healthy behaviors.

There are three levels encompassing the range of personal, social, and environmental factors that affect behavior:

- Personal or individual: Beliefs, knowledge, attitudes, skills and genetics
- Social: Interaction with other people including friends, family and the community
- Environmental: The area in which a person lives, e.g. school, shops, place of employment, other factors including the economy (such as prices) and technology

All of the above factors should be taken into account when formulating any plan to change behavior. A mix of these interventions conducted over time will have the maximum long-term effect. Taking into account factors solely on an individual level will most probably be least effective in impacting on behavior as it doesn't take environmental or social influences into account. Taking into consideration and implementing all three factors will be most effective at bringing about change in behavior long-term.

Theories of behavior

The study of psychology, economics and sociology has in recent years brought about much discussion around the theories and models of behavior. These theories take into account a number of psychological, social, societal and contextual factors like emotions, habits and routines. The theories of change recommend interventions by illustrating how behaviors evolve over time. Behavioral models exist to explain behavior and establish the components that influence it. Both aspects need to be understood in order to promote interventional strategies that work.

There are more than 60 socio-psychological models and theories of behavior. Many health promotion programs have used these models. Success has been varied. Definitive evidence suggests that using theory when formulating and applying behavior change interventions, improves the effectiveness of interventions.

Examples of popular models are:

- Transtheoretical Model (also referred to as the 'Stages of Change' model): Divides the audience and applies the intervention to their stage of change: precontemplation, contemplation, preparation, action, maintenance, and termination.
- Social Cognitive Theory: Centres on observation and learning from others, positive and negative reinforcement of behavior.
- Theory of Planned Behavior: Considers people's behavior to be determined by intention, and is predicted by attitudes, subjective norm (beliefs about whether other people approve or disapprove), and perceived behavioral control (beliefs about whether it is easy or difficult to do).

It is not within the scope of this course to look at behavior theories in more detail. However, further information can be obtained from the following sources:

World Health Organization (WHO) (2008). Behaviour change strategies and health: the role of health systems. EUR/RC58/10.

National Institute for Health and Clinical Excellence (NICE) (2007). NICE Public Health Guidance 6 'Behaviour change at population, community and individual levels'.

Willingness to change

As exercise professionals, it is important to learn and promote methods that positively influence people to adhere to their exercise program and recognize that different approaches work on different people. If you know someone is reluctant to give up smoking, pressurizing them on every occasion is unlikely to work. As personal trainers, you need to recognize whether people are willing to change.

Some people are self-motivated and are willing to change. This could be due to one of four reasons:

- Encouragement from a person in authority e.g. a doctor or nurse.
- Observing the positive effect of exercise on people they know e.g. weight loss, more energy.
- Physical changes – e.g. clothes feeling tighter or negative comments on appearance may motivate someone to take up exercise.
- Previous success in exercise – if goals have been easily reached it can motivate a person to continue with the exercise plan.

It is essential that a client is self-motivated and able to take personal responsibility for their own health and fitness. A client of this nature is more likely to be independent and much more able to maintain an exercise plan in order to reach their fitness targets. Being heavily reliant on another person like a doctor or personal trainer to motivate oneself is not advisable as the client may find it easy to use them as a 'scapegoat' if they fail to achieve the results they want. The client may 'lean' on the other person too much to do the work for them, leaving the client incapable of looking after their health and fitness without someone else being there.

Stages of behaviour change

Research has shown that there are several stages of behaviour change. A personal trainer should be fully informed and familiar with these stages so that they can devise ways in which to assist the client as they go through each step. The following list will describe each stage of behaviour change. It should be noted that these stages are sometimes referred to differently by some researchers.

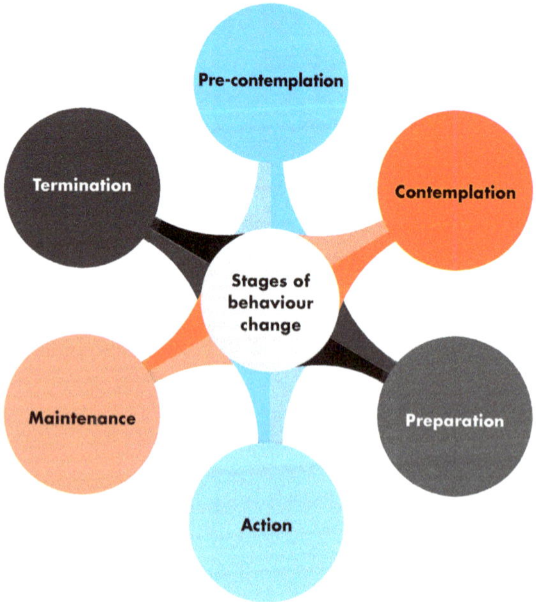

1. Pre-contemplation

Here, the client has no desire to change and so does not wish to start any kind of activity. They don't feel there is any need to change their life and may be defensive when speaking about their lack of interest. They do not acknowledge that their life can improve. They may dismiss any information presented to them that challenges their attitude. When presented with this scenario, the personal trainer should try and inspire the client by ensuring that any information to counteract their thoughts can be easily obtained. This information should be easy to understand and jargon-free. The personal trainers should do their utmost to reassure the client and deal with any concerns they may have about exercise.

2. Contemplation

At this stage, the client is not active but has the intention to begin exercising within six months. The personal trainer here presents the client with goals. The personal trainer also proposes to the client activities and packages which they know the client will enjoy taking part in, and which are not too rigid. This would inspire the client to begin exercising. It is quite common at this stage for the client to reflect on the issue and identify that they need to change their life for the better. There may be an event in their life that triggers this change. For example, they may have had a health scare after a routine medical check-up. This type of client is at the stage of realization that the behaviour they have previously displayed needs to change. One of the reasons behind their perceived apathy is that they are considering the advantages and disadvantages of any future change. This set of people would feel a sense of loss by a change but at the same time are open to information and are willing to research into their options.

3. Preparation

Here, the client is preparing to change their behaviour or is trying out small changes. They are ready to change and at this stage firm and sure about their decision. This is often seen as a transitory phase that lasts only a short amount of time.

4. Action

This is probably the hardest time for the client. They can see the effect of exercise and the change that it is making but they may reach the 'plateau' stage where the instant results they initially saw when they first took up exercise momentarily stagnates. This may demotivate the client and they may need extra support and attention during this stage in order to carry on with the change in behaviour. This stage of action is applicable to those who have made firm changes and are beginning to enjoy this new phase of their life. This is a pivotal stage, in that there is a high chance of relapse. However, the client is equally willing to accept guidance to help them through this stage. This is also known as the 'willpower' stage. A common strategy to motivate the client is to offer short-term rewards. Clients are also more likely to evaluate changes in their behaviour so that their self-belief is increased. This also supports them in their plans to resolve any personal or external stresses in their life. It is common to see the client move from this to the next stage (maintenance) after around six months.

5. Maintenance

This is often known as the 'wobbly' stage, as motivation levels can dip. Plenty of support and a reminder of goals should be communicated to the client. Fitness diaries are a useful tool that a personal trainer can use to help the client preserve their behaviour. Clients at this stage are often focusing on amalgamating any changes in their behaviour in order to continue with the changes made. Several coping mechanisms are put in place to prevent a return to previous habits. These strategies are usually successful. Clients at this stage need to persevere and exercise, being careful not to give in to external temptations. They need to remind themselves of what they have already achieved. Chances of relapse are smaller than in previous stages.

6. Termination

The work of Prochaska and DiClemente has had an influence on researchers. Such researchers have sought to build on the initial work of the above-named academics by adding this stage to the model. This stage recognizes that returning to previous behaviors would feel strange to the client, and that such behaviors are no longer desirable. This stage encourages some to 'broadcast' the change to their family, neighbors and even the local community. This kind of promotion is extremely helpful in moving people along the stage they are at. It is good for this act to be encouraged. A client may show signs of relapse. However, this is turned around and viewed as part of the 'learning curve', and a chance to make strong existing coping mechanisms and strategies of support.

Methods to motivate clients

There aren't any set ways to motivate clients and not all approaches will work with every client. It is therefore vital for the personal trainer to 'know the client' and find ways to motivate them. Below are some methods that can be used.

Use a fitness management software

There are many aids on the market, devised to help personal trainers motivate and encourage more people in the least amount of time. Using personal training software helps trainers to formulate training programs and nutrition/diet plans. They can even make these accessible to the client via their smartphone. The software enables the trainer to set the client goals in a way which appeals to the client. Yet another feature of the software is that it provides a way to collate client feedback, respond to the feedback in good time so that the software can be as responsive and as motivating as possible.

The software can also be downloaded on smartphones and tablets as an app and so can be sent direct to clients.

Agree short-term and long-term goals

Just being more active and eating well cannot be classed as goals. Nobody wants to be just active – they may want to live longer and being active is one of the realistic ways in which they can achieve this. Other goals could be to look better, weigh a little less than present amongst other things. The danger however is when these goals become too overwhelming for the client. It is for this reason that firm, short-term and long-term aims and objectives should be decided for the client. It is easy enough to say a long-term goal is to lose 10 kilograms in weight. However, this will take time and so it is better to also set short-term goals, for example to lose a pound of weight a week. This will help to keep the client motivated and on track to achieve their long-term goal.

Working out the whys

A lot of trainers fail to connect with their clients and don't form a bond with them. It is important that a personal trainer does a mental assessment of the client as well as a physical one.

A good personal trainer should be full of positivity and be there for the client, through their good and bad days. The trainer should make an appointment with the client if necessary, to evaluate progression and objectives. It is imperative that findings are relayed to the client. The question 'why' should first be asked to discover why the client has started a fitness program in the first place. It is then easier to tailor the fitness program to them.

The trainer should be aware of the client's mood and if they appear to be downcast at any point, the trainer should make an effort to ask why they are feeling the way they are. Reminding the client why they started training in the first place and of any achievements they have made so far may help lift the client's mood.

Recognizing myths

The following questions may be put to the client to see how they perceive fitness:

1. What is your best way to get in shape?
2. How have you tried to meet your fitness goals in the past?
3. What exercise methods and nutrition plans do you think are necessary?
4. How can you improve your health and fitness levels and body shape?

Keep positive

It is perhaps obvious that a prerequisite of being a personal trainer is to stay positive! We all have bad days, even personal trainers, so it is important that the trainer is effective in compartmentalising any worries they may have in their personal lives. This may be one of the hardest parts of being a trainer but it is vital that they stay positive. Clients bounce off the good energy a trainer brings to the session.

The client should also be around people that share the same positive energy and the personal trainer should ensure the client is in this kind of environment.

Workouts should be enjoyable

It is important for workout sessions to have a good balance between fun and challenging. If the client is not enjoying the session, it would be difficult to keep them in a positive frame of mind. Personal trainers should therefore design a program that includes a variety of exercises. A good personal trainer will include in the plan a good peak and finish. This doesn't have to be anything complicated. Changing a sequence in sets or saving a liked exercise for the end of the session are just some simple ways of doing this. It is good practice to regularly change the content of the plan to keep exercising fun.

Get online

It goes without saying that it is almost compulsory nowadays to be online. A simple social media account like Twitter or Instagram should be created and used. This is an excellent way of building a relationship with the client, post quotes or sayings that motivate them. The trainer can even start a discussion relating to exercise promoting services.

Life experience throws many curveballs at a person, and it is the personal trainer's role to educate the client ways in which they can hold the bat and turn the curveball in to a home run.

Develop and award the practical advantages of exercising

The most rewarding part for many when exercising is seeing the results. Seeing practical improvements in movement is an example of this, especially when it impacts the client daily.

Burgess states that teaching clients the short-term and lasting advantages of exercising is a main aspect of training. When client can see the practical benefits of exercise, they are more likely to stick to the program.

Rewards systems can be used as a motivational tool when meeting goals. For example, the client can treat themselves to a new item of clothing instead of with food. The importance of emotional and practical advantages of regular exercise should be stressed.

A reward system should be designed and be based on goals tailored to the client. A visual aid can be used towards the end of every month with all clients included. One of them can receive a reward such as a voucher for a sports store.

Self-determination theory (SDT)

This theory was initiated by Edward L. Deci and Richard M. Ryan. It seeks to analyze a person's ability to be driven by goals. It focuses on our instinctive tendency to be healthy. Some professional health workers are using this theory as a motivational tool for their clients.

http://selfdeterminationtheory.org/theory/

The crucial part of the theory relates to the extent to which a person completes their fundamental emotional needs. The more they meet these fundamental needs, the more their actions will be self-determined. These three needs are **autonomy, competence and relatedness**.

Autonomy

Autonomy essentially is a freedom to choose. When people feel they take part in exercise out of choice and not under any pressure, then autonomy is high. Hopefully, clients exercise because they enjoy doing so. But the reality is that most people exercise to purely improve their bodily appearance. Whilst this is perfectly acceptable, it is best that clients also motivate themselves by thinking about the parts of exercise that they do enjoy. This will keep them on track when exercising. A personal trainer can control how much autonomy the client has by:

1. Asking the client to choose the kinds of exercise they wish to take part in.
2. Reinventing how they perceive exercise.

Competence

This is largely a person's perception of how they feel they can perform their best in any given activity. Evaluating a client's performance and feeding back how they have done is an excellent way to manage the competence of a client. The following are some hints on how to facilitate feedback:

Positive use of words

Use positive phrases a few times a session. Phrases like "Great work!", "Yes, that's it!" go a long way in keeping a client motivated. The trainer should be careful however, not to overuse praise as it can reduce its impact on the client.

Give targeted comments on the first few occasions that a client correctly performs a specific type of exercise. For example, "You're doing really well keeping your arm still" during a bicep curl or "You managed to keep the upper half of your body nice and tight – well done" during a lunge. This kind of feedback should be given as soon as the client has performed it. This type of feedback should also only be given when the client is nearer to performing it perfectly.

Relatedness

This is linked with giving the client a feeling that the trainer understands what they are going through. A client's motivation can be improved if they feel they are in a warm environment. This atmosphere can be created by the trainer spending more time with the client and showing them that they care.

The following list explains how a personal trainer can bond with their client:

- Ask the client if they prefer to be spoken to while they are exercising and adjust the program depending on what they say. For example, they may find it helps them when the trainer repeats the number of repetitions while they are exercising. The trainer should be able to gauge how chatty the client is and adjust the program accordingly.
- The client can be telephoned twice a year. The trainer can praise the client by highlighting two commendable personality traits of the client.
- The client can be emailed once a month. They can be commended for a specific achievement in the last month. The trainer should make sure the client feels like they have had control over their achievements.

Encouraging and maintaining motivation

Once a client is motivated, preserving this motivation is vital to promote commitment and to ensure lasting results. Instructing in a domineering manner usually helps to motivate the client, helping them to perform better. Some elements of motivation contribute to performance, and choosing the most productive methods for the client can impact their success in repetitions, weight or time in a session.

Loudness of voice

Some people respond well to an extrovert trainer with a loud voice, thriving off the enthusiasm shown by the trainer as motivation to 'keep going'. However, other clients may prefer a less direct attitude, and a trainer who is less forceful and quieter, someone who does not attract attention from other gym users or those in the surroundings of an outdoor location.

Visual aid

Some clients react better to images used as a tool to motivate during a session. For example, during an indoor cycling class, trainers may use a description of a terrain with uphill and downhill incline levels as well as distances to different checkpoints. Doing this may assist in breaking down the workout into bite-size chunks. Comparable techniques can be used by the trainer to help motivate the client during certain exercises that need focus. For example, describing a fartlek program on a cardiovascular piece of equipment. Visual imagery may also be used when the trainer is assisting with certain movements. For example, the trainer may ask the client to visualize lowering their body to sit on a chair and lifting themselves up when leaving a chair during a squatting activity.

Supporting beliefs

Other ways for the trainer to motivate the client include stressing to them their belief in them and their ability to achieve their goals. Use of positive and encouraging statements like "you're doing so well!" or "well done" are an example of how this can be achieved. Some clients however will not respond well to this type of motivational tool and may even find it hinders their progress, especially clients with low self-esteem.

Inverse motivation

This can be applied where the client works better when faced with a challenge. Inverse motivation should not offend the client but it should compel them to concentrate and focus on the session more. Terms like "this weight is better than you" or "you performed better last time round" may drive the client to improve performance. The point of this is not to demotivate the client and this method should only be used on clients who are used to exercise. It should not be used on clients who are new to the gym.

Diet and nutrition support

Many clients that start an exercising program also tend to or would like to make some changes to their eating habits for the better. They want to eat food that are considered healthy. The type of food and amount of food one consumes will directly impact their body and the efficacy of a training program. The significance of diet control whilst exercising and the type of food recommended is dependent on the client's objectives. For example, if the objective is to lose five kilograms then a change in diet will most likely become necessary. However, if the objective is to simply tone the muscles without losing much weight, a less vigorous change in diet may work. Dieting is therefore very much dependent on the client's fitness level, current body composition and exercising goals. A personal trainer needs to assess the need for dieting on a case by case basis.

Only fully qualified dietitians can legally give this kind of advice. Dietitians must have a degree, which takes four years to complete, to earn their job title. This is unlike the job of 'Personal Trainer' whose job title does not afford such legal protection. Check what is your country's body responsible for regulating dietitians.

WARNING

If personal trainers give nutrition advice to alleviate real or suspected medical conditions, then they are operating outside of their professional boundaries and may find themselves in trouble if problems with clients occur.

What diet and nutrition support to provide?

- Personal trainers can only give general advice on eating healthily. They must not give precise or prescriptive/medical advice.
- Personal trainers may promote a good diet to their clients and inspire them to change their eating patterns in line with proven healthy eating guidance.
- Personal trainers should not give advice on 'fad' diets, latest trends or any diets with a celebrity following.
- Personal trainers should refrain from giving advice which omits or restricts food types, for example, advising client to avoid all forms of protein. They should also not endorse eating patterns which are severely limited.
- Personal trainers should never formulate their own tailored nutritional plan for the client unless of course they are a fully qualified dietitian.

The information provided in Chapter 2, can be used to provide general dietary and nutrition advice and support.

End of Chapter activities

Activity 4.7: Work with a friend or family member to give them visual and verbal instructions on how to use and perform two exercises or pieces of equipment from the list below. Point out the muscles worked.

- Gym ball
- Step machine
- Treadmill
- Rowing machine
- Abdominal crunches and plank
- Bench press
- Squats and lunges
- Back stretch

Activity 4.8: Prepare 60 seconds on how communication should be adapted to meet a client's needs.

Activity 4.9: Work with a friend on a set of exercises and then give them feedback. Write down the feedback and make recommendations for improvement.

Activity 4.10: Consult a friend or family member to identify possible barriers to exercise and propose ways that the barriers can be addressed.

Barriers	Solutions

End of Chapter checklist

1. What are teaching points?
2. What is spotting?
3. What are the three ways that people learn and digest information?
4. What methods can a personal trainer use to monitor clients?
5. What are some of the effects of overtraining?
6. Why is it important to keep training logs?
7. What factors can affect motivation?
8. What are theories of behaviors?
9. What are the stages of behaviour change?
10. What is the self-determination theory (SDT)?

Chapter 4C: Training special populations

Chapter summary

This Chapter will look at the differences between the bodies of groups of people classified as
special populations compared to an average adult's body, with the view to understand specifics to select suitable exercises when working with these groups of people.

Aim

The aim of this Chapter is to allow personal trainers to identify factors that need to be taken into consideration when working with children, pregnant women, elderly and disabled clients.

Learning objectives

After completing this Chapter, personal trainers will be able to:

1. Train special populations – children, pregnant women, elderly and disabled clients.

2. Discuss the differences between the bodies of the special populations and an average adult's body.

3. List areas of vulnerability with respect to special populations and take this into consideration when designing programs and delivering training.

Definition of 'special populations'

As a personal trainer, you may need to support clients with special needs such as the elderly, children, disabled individuals, pregnant women and those with illnesses that impact the body. It is important for a personal trainer to understand the body of these special groups of the population in order to support them the best you can with the exercise and fitness programs.

Anyone whose body functions differently to the way described in the earlier sections, would fall under this 'special populations' category. Examples would be:

- Younger clients: Their body functions slightly differently to adults until they reach adulthood.
- Older clients: As we age, our body starts to function slightly differently mainly due to parts of our body and organs becoming tired and slowing down.
- Pregnant women: During pregnancy, a woman's body goes through a number of changes which has an impact on them physically.
- Disabled individuals: Some people are born with disabilities which affects their body on a day-to-day basis.
- Individuals suffering from illnesses: Many people's body changes due to diseases and illnesses which makes the body function slightly differently to the way described in the earlier sections.

In the sections to follow we will examine the bones, joints and muscles of these special groups of people as well as look at how their special needs impact the energy system, cardiorespiratory system and the nervous system.

Younger clients

Bones, joints & muscles

Our bones are not fully formed until the age of about 18 to 25, varying between individuals. This bone development process, known as ossification starts in the womb. By the time we are born many of our bones have partly ossified, but there is still a lot of development yet to take place and therefore children's bones are more vulnerable to fractures. Injuries to bones in childhood can affect the growth and development of bones as well as make joints unstable. Therefore the exercises and physical activities children participate in should always be well thought out and monitored.

The muscular system we have has actually been genetically inherited to some extent and muscle growth varies in children depending on their age. Muscle growth does not correlate with bone growth and therefore extensive growth of muscles can make children clumsy as well as limit movements in other ways.

All children will go through a stage in their life where their bones will grow drastically at an advanced rate. This is often referred to as a 'growth spurt'. Growth spurts occur at varying rates and at different ages, with gender being a factor. Generally, growth spurts start for females between the age of 10 and 12. The speediest growth stage for them is between the ages of 12 and 13. The spurt usually finishes aged 18. On the other hand, boys can expect a growth spurt between the ages of 12 and 14, the speediest growth being between 12 and 14 years of age. Boys grow most rapidly between ages 14 and 15 and their spurts finish later than girls, usually at approximately age 20. Growth cartilage in children may be susceptible to trauma and have tendencies to be used excessively. This can interrupt the supply of blood and nutrients to the bones, and can subsequently mean lasting interruptions in growth. With adults, ligament injuries can happen after constant stress or trauma from a previous fall. In children, this type of injury amalgamates itself in the form of an epiphyseal growth plate fracture.

Growth plate fractures:

- Occur more to boys than girls
- Mostly happen to 14 to 16 year old boys and 11 to 13 year old girls
- Are more likely to be damaged because growth plates are the weakest region of a developing skeleton

It is for this reason that the personal trainer should deal with children sensitively and with extra care. Trainers should refrain from using heavy loads which require repetition when instructing this group.

Cardiorespiratory system

Children's blood volume is considerably less than adults and this is one of the reasons why children are less efficient at regulating their body temperature and thus more easily overheat than adults. Children also have smaller and less powerful heart chambers than adults and so their maximum heart rate is higher and stroke volume is lower compared to adults. Children are also less efficient at processing oxygen and so require a higher uptake of oxygen for aerobic activity.

Average pulse rates

The average pulse rate of an adult ranges from 60-100 beats per minute, which is slower than an average child's heart rate. The average pulse rate of a child depends on their age as listed below:

- Newborn: 125 beats/min (ranging from 70-190 beats/min)
- Infant: 120 beats/min (ranging from 80-160 beats/min)
- Toddler: 110 beats/min (ranging from 80-130 beats/min)
- Preschooler: 100 beats/min (ranging from 80-120 beats/min)
- Six years old: 100 beats/min (ranging from 75-115 beats/min)
- Eight years old: 90 beats/min (ranging from 70-110 beats/min)
- Ten years old: 90 beats/min (ranging from 70-110 beats/min)
- Twelve years old (girls): 90 beats/min (ranging from 70-110 beats/min)
- Twelve years old (boys): 85 beats/min (ranging from 65-105 beats/min)
- Fourteen years old (girls): 85 beats/min (ranging from 65-105 beats/min)
- Fourteen years old (boys): 80 beats/min (ranging from 60-100 beats/min)
- Sixteen years old (girls): 80 beats/min (ranging from 60-100 beats/min)
- Sixteen years old (boys): 75 beats/min (ranging from 55-95 beats/min)
- Eighteen years old (girls): 75 beats/min (ranging from 55-95 beats/min)
- Eighteen years old (boys): 70 beats/min (ranging from 50-90 beats/min)

Nervous system

Children's nervous systems work the same way as adults. However, some research based on brain scans have found that children's brains are organized differently than those of adults. Further information can be obtained from the sources below.

General approach to training

The bodies of clients younger in age are not fully developed, and younger people are often not fully aware and lack co-ordination. Younger adults need greater guidance to make sure they are correctly aligned. To reduce the chances of injury, basic exercise should be undertaken, that are made up of lower resistance activity. Where applicable, movements which mirror daily activities should be used.

Preventing injuries relating to growth

The following steps should be taken to stop injuries linked with growth:

- Refrain from too much exercise, for example playing the same sport
- Refrain from participating in unsuitable sport for the body or using excessively heavy weights
- Gender should be accommodated as well as the varying phases of development
- Avoid unsuitable pairing sizes when working with a partner
- Refrain from excessive motions on the spot which are strong in impact
- Relevant warm up and cool down should always be administered and taught
- Suitable equipment for the activity should always be provided (e.g. size & weight)
- The client should only be moved to the next stage once their technique is correct

Adaptability

Great care should be taken when delivering an exercise session featuring stretch exercises. This is especially applicable whilst the youngster is experiencing a growth spurt. Bone growth rates exceed the speed of muscle growth, making the soft tissue around joints sufficiently stretched as it is. This leads to a higher chance of injury.

Gym Equipment

Machines seen in gyms are tailored for adults to use. Therefore, any weight increments are usually too large for younger people to use. Free weights could be a more a useful alternative as they have smaller weights which younger clients can use. Attention should be given to ensure correct technique.

Utilizing energy

Children are able to utilize oxygen more effectively because they use more mitochondria in their muscles. Have you ever wondered where children get so much energy from all day? It is because children have a higher anaerobic threshold compared to adults and therefore they can continue with activities as long as it is at an appropriate intensity. However, children have a smaller storage of anaerobic fuel and less capacity to use it. They also have a limited supply of muscle and liver glycogen. All these limitations mean children are not able to tolerate short bursts of intense exercise that requires intensive usage of energy, although this improves as they get older.

Aerobic capability

A child's aerobic ability increases with age, in relation to the increased capability of their growing lungs and heart. In males, VO_2 max calculated in L/min rises from 6 to 18 years and 6 to 14 years for females. But when VO_2 max is standardized with the use of body weight, few changes are seen with age. VO_2 max is lowered in girls after they reach puberty. This is due to a rise in muscle mass. A lack of appropriate technique by children results in limited endurance in children, having the effect of poor quality exercises such as running. Compared with adults, children have limbs which are shorter as well as lower muscle mass. This results in lesser technical strength. Whilst a young person is going through a growth spurt, they may have legs which are out of proportion resulting in a lack of balance and possible loss of co-ordination.

Anaerobic capability

As with aerobic activity, anaerobic capacity also rises with age. However, it is still not sufficiently developed until approximately age 20. Trainers therefore must be aware that:

- Young people have a lesser amount of glycogen in storage, per gram of muscle.
- They also have less storage capacity of creatine phosphate compared with an adult. This has the effect of producing less anaerobic work.
- Children do not have as much natural fatigue process for intense exercises that adults have.
- Children are prone to overheating much more than adults.

Teenagers do not usually need any power training built in to their program, but it can be relevant to their sport on occasions. Children yet to reach their adolescence and teenagers themselves should refrain from activities such as bodybuilding, maximal lifts and power lifting until they are physically and skeletally mature enough (American Academy for Paediatrics, 2008).

WARNING

Although on the surface it may seem that a younger person can 'keep going' at high intensity workouts, their muscles may be suffering from fatigue, resulting in them overheating. Trainers MUST therefore be conscious of these factors when training youngsters.

Body temperature and dehydration

Children have a less effective cooling process because of decreased blood volume and increased temperature of the skin. Because children consume more energy per kilogram of body weight compared to an adult, they are at an increased risk of dehydration whilst exercising. When it is cold, children tend to lose heat much more quickly than with an adult. This is down to the bigger surface area in comparison with adults. Young people need to therefore have regular water breaks, lower-intensity warm up as compared to an adult's, shorter cool down elements, and allocated rest periods built in to their program in between sections of strenuous exercise.

Older clients

Skeletal changes

As we age, changes occur to bones, joints and muscles. A decrease in activity along with changes in hormone levels can affect bone remodeling. The articular cartilage also tends to become thinner as we get older and the synovial fluid which lubricates joints tends to diminish slowly. Similarly, the ligaments shorten and become less flexible and tendons become weak and less elasticated with age. Overall joints become stiffer and less flexible and the number of muscle fibers and the size of muscle fibers reduces. All this has an impact on our movement abilities, slowing down movements and making it difficult to accomplish certain movement types. The changes in muscles also affect our posture which is why we often say we shrink as we age.

A balanced exercise program focused on strengthening ligaments and tendons can help to offset some of the inevitable changes to the body as we age.

Osteoporosis

As seen in Chapter 1, many people develop osteoporosis as they age and this is due to the gradual loss of bone mineral. This loss of minerals is inevitable with old age and not necessarily caused by diseases and infections. When bones lose minerals, they remain the same size but just become fragile and porous. The loss of bone minerals can be offset to some degree with medication, good intake of nutrition and exercise that stimulates increased bone formation to improve the bone mineral density (BMD).

The type of exercise chosen should be tailored to the individual's needs and abilities. People with osteoporosis must take special care when exercising to reduce the risk of fracture from impact or falls.

Neuromuscular changes

For many members of the elderly community, aged over 70, it is a task to even get up and stand after being seated. This is usually due to a general loss of muscle function because of growing older. The process of ageing reduces the amount of fast twitch (FT) muscle fibers and also gives rise to slow twitch (ST) muscle fibers. Getting older is also related to a decrease in muscle mass. This is called sarcopenia. To combat this, taking part in resistance training is advised. This would lessen the impact of ageing on the neuromuscular structure. Routine weight-bearing activities has been proven to help preserve and construct bone mass. Muscles are made stronger by exercising. Composure and nimbleness are also improved, and this may help in preventing an elderly person from falling.

Because of the fragile nature of the older client's (aged 70+) musculoskeletal structure, the personal trainer needs to be more conscious when working with these clients. Even though weight-bearing activities are advised, personal trainers should opt for exercises which are low impact. This will prevent avoidable stress on the skeletal and muscular structures.

Guideline for training older clients

A standard exercise session can cater for the average 50 to 64 year old adult, with relevant age-related adjustments. Clients of this age bracket who have additional medical needs would have to be signposted to a doctor because they may need to be referred to a trainer who specializes in their health condition. The same would apply for any adult over the age of 65.

Guidelines for different parts of a training session are provided below:

Warm up

- Conduct a lengthier warm up, one that progressively builds up. This should last about 15 minutes.
- Take part in more mobility activities.
- Progressively increase the scope of the mobility exercise. For example, start with smaller shoulder rotations and then gradually raise the shoulder range of motion to arm circles.
- utilize gradual, composed movements.
- Centre attention on stance, positioning and the right method.

Cardiovascular

- Gradually increase intensity.
- Reduce the functioning intensity.
- Adopt low impact exercises.
- Perform less complicated actions.
- Include a lengthier, more progressive cool down.
- Share information in stages rather than all at one time.
- Any exercise the client does not feel comfortable with doing, suggest alternatives.

Resistance

- Decrease resistance and power for some of the exercises.
- Include less repetitions and sets and increase rest.
- Include more firm and secure stances.
- Include allowances for time it takes to go down to the floor and get up again.
- Have a generally slower tempo.
- Allow more time to adjust exercise and starting positions.
- Reinforce the right technique.
- Make stronger the pelvic floor and muscles relating to posture.
- Any exercise the client does not feel comfortable with doing, suggest alternatives.

Cool down

- Spend longer on cool down.
- Use a higher number of stretches for certain muscles.
- utilize more solid positions.
- Have a smaller range of motion.

Pregnant women

Pregnant women are more prone to changes in hormones and posture, which makes them more susceptible to several things, mainly:

- Being injured
- Misaligning of the joints
- Imbalance in the muscles
- Loss in motor skills
- Morning sickness

These changes may begin at the very beginning of pregnancy, becoming more and more apparent during the pregnancy. The needs of pregnant and post-natal client's changes according to the phase of pregnancy and the various physical reactions. Some of these reactions may include:

- Cardiorespiratory system changes
- Body shape changes
- Hormonal changes
- Energy utilizing changes
- Nervous system changes
- Weaker pelvic floor

These are not the only changes a pregnant client may experience. Every woman's experience of pregnancy can be different and there are likely to be other changes which a personal trainer can identify by gathering the relevant information.

Other changes can include

- Changes in centre of gravity
- Reduced pelvic girdle stability
- Diastasis recti (abdominal separation)

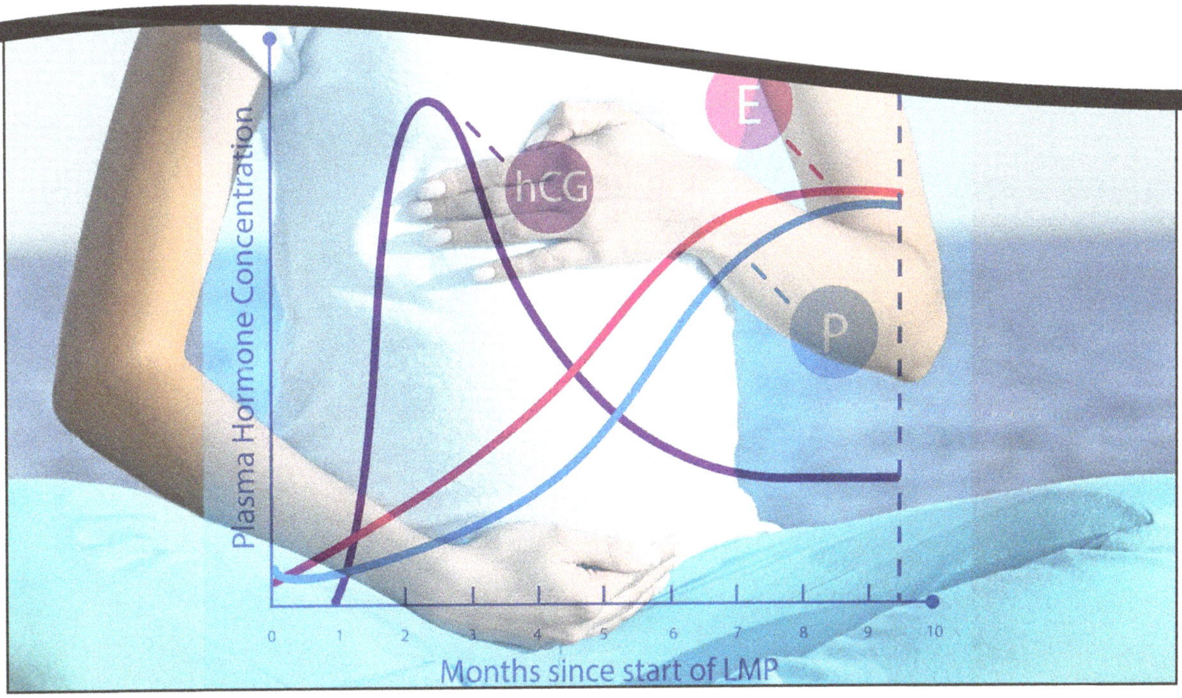

Body shape changes

As the foetus grows, the pregnant woman's abdominal muscles begin to increase in length, altering the body's centre of gravity. This could have an impact on balance. It may also change the mother's posture, for example an increase in the lordotic curve of the lumbar spine.

Other postural shifts during pregnancy may be:

- Shoulder girdle protraction
- Kyphosis
- Short, tight pectoral muscles

These tend to be related to weight gain and having to carry the weight of the baby. The posture shifts can cause lower back, shoulder or neck pain.

Pelvic floor changes

Exercises which help to make the pelvic floor muscles stronger should be offered before and just after birth. The uterus muscles start to droop as the uterus grows, because these muscles start to become overly burdened. This may result in health issues like incontinence as the muscles related to this group regulate the bladder.

Cardiorespiratory changes

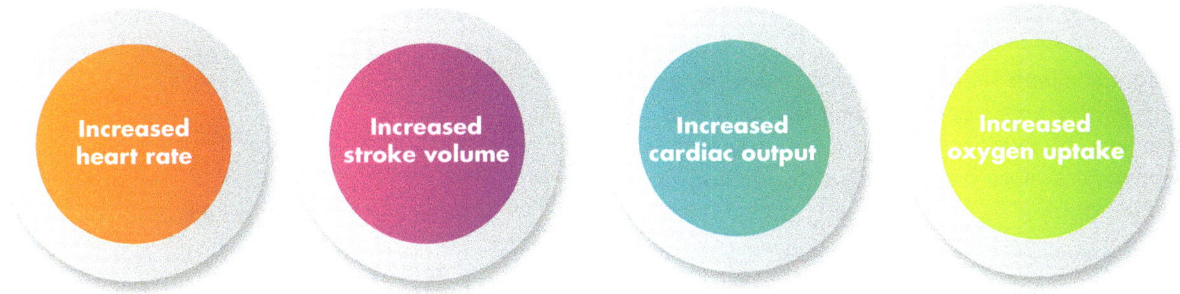

The respiratory system is affected by pregnancy. Whilst pregnant, a woman's blood volume increases by approximately 30% and there is a reduction in red blood cells as the blood becomes more dilute. The extra muscle tissue accumulated around the heart due to oestrogen also increases the stroke volume and cardiac output. Similarly, the heart rate increases and at rest the heart rate is approximately 10 - 15 beats higher per minute. Moreover, blood vessels are dilated by the relaxing effect of progesterone and venous return can reduce due to the foetus pressing on the blood vessels of the pelvic area, in particular when lying down, which can lead to dizziness.

Some women also suffer from increased blood pressure, which is known as pregnancy hypertension. From the 18th week of pregnancy the oxygen requirement of the foetus increases and at the same time carbon dioxide receptors in the brain also become more sensitive. Consequently, pregnant women tend to become more easily breathless and some may even hyperventilate. The growing foetus also forces the diaphragm to move up in later stages of pregnancy, reducing lung capacity and the ribs move outwards and upwards to assist breathing.

Nervous system changes

The nervous system can be affected in some cases of pregnancy and there are many neurological conditions and diseases that can affect pregnant women. This is a complex area that requires specialized knowledge and therefore outside the scope of this training course.

Hormonal changes

Relaxin is a hormone triggered in the first trimester of pregnancy. It relaxes the ligaments, cervix and cartilage, enabling them to extend during childbirth. This especially helps the pubis symphysis and the sacroiliac joint to move the desired length during this time. Relaxin also has the consequence of softening joints throughout the body, making them more susceptible to damage if overused. It is therefore very important that pregnant clients are careful not to aggravate it, for example through heavy stretching. The length of time that relaxin stays in a new mother's body differs from person to person. It can be in a woman's system for three months, and as much as 12 months, although it is often stated to be for five months. Lactating mothers often find the hormone stays in their bodies as long as they are breastfeeding, which could be up to two years. The mother herself is the best indicator to assess when her joints stop feeling so soft and relaxed.

Utilizing energy changes

As pregnancy advances, so does the usage of energy. Pregnant women exercising utilize more carbohydrates than fat during moderate exercises and therefore sometimes blood sugar levels can drop quickly. As a result, pregnant women should carefully plan exercises depending on their general well-being during pregnancy.

Training approach – before and after birth

Before birth

Pregnant clients should 'listen to their bodies' and only ever exercise depending on how they feel at the time of exercise. This is because pregnant women are more prone to nausea, fainting and feeling dizzy.

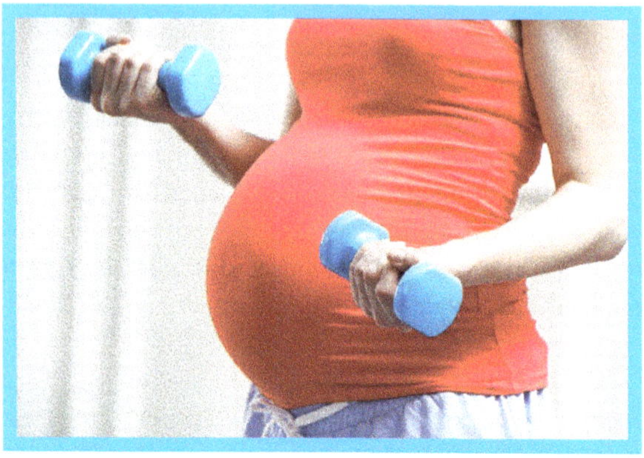

Understandably, pregnant women need to refrain from any exercise which requires them to lie down after 16 weeks of pregnancy. They should also avoid exercise which involves them to stand for long periods. Pregnant women should see exercise as a way of keeping active as opposed to increasing fitness, so they should never exercise till they are exhausted. Any exercise involving the abdominal area should be avoided as well as any activity which may increase the likelihood of them falling. Focus should be given on exercises which improve posture, movement and pelvic floor. Any activity requiring heavy, resistance based exercise work above the head should be avoided as well as leg adduction and abduction that works against a resistance. Isometric exercises, those requiring fully forward flexion, any quick changes to direction or stance, rampant twisting of the body and too much unregulated balance techniques should all be abstained from during pregnancy.

If a pregnant client experiences any of the following symptoms, exercise should be stopped immediately and medical help sought if necessary:

- Unusual pain in the pelvis, buttocks, legs, groin legs or back
- Any loss of blood or loss of amniotic fluid
- A feeling of being dizzy, faint or feeling nauseous
- Pain in the abdomen, chest or any feelings like a contraction
- Too much shortage of breath or palpitations

After birth

Women must not start exercise after the birth of their baby until their doctor or health professional authorizes them to do so. This normally happens at the routine 6-8 week check. Medical professionals in general advise that women who have given birth should not take on any excessive physical activity for two weeks. If they have a caesarean delivery, they should not partake in physical activity for 12 weeks. This will allow their caesarean wound to heal fully. Once permission to exercise is given by the medical professional, the new mother needs to first focus on:

- Adjusting her posture and alignment of her joints
- Giving attention to any imbalance in muscles
- Promoting the recruitment of transversus abdominis (TA)
- Improving the pelvic floor mechanism

It is vital that a woman refers herself for medical treatment if she experiences any incontinence or feels a decline in strength of her pelvic floor muscle. She should also seek medical help if she feels a 'dragging' sensation in the abdominal area, or if the lower part of her abdomen or pelvic floor feels heavy. Any type of groin, lower back pain or difficulty in walking is also an indicator that she needs medical help. Attention should be paid to the abdomen. If any of the following symptoms are present in this area, then medical aid should be sought:

- Increased softness in the area or any abdominal separation
- Dips in the umbilical midline or umbilical hernia

Advice to follow after birth

The following advice should be given when a woman starts to exercise soon after giving birth:

Warm up

- Obtain the suitable posture at the very beginning and maintain this all through the session
- Movements should be slower and under greater control than normal
- Add mobility exercises into the program
- Warm up the muscles by undertaking a complete range of mobility exercises and movement patterns
- Gradually increase movement intensity to prevent quick increase in blood pressure
- Accommodate stretch positions and be careful not to transgress into an uncomfortable range of motion

Cardiovascular activity

- Keep to low-medium intensity levels
- Reduce impact and choose uncomplicated moves
- A slow, progressive increase and decrease of intensity
- Women who are unfamiliar with exercise need to begin with short bursts (usually 15 minutes, increasing slowly to 30 minutes)
- Keep hydrated
- Don't exercise in extremely hot environments
- Don't measure heart rate – rely on the 'talk test' method instead

Muscular fitness

- Take part in low intensity exercises
- Choose starter positions which are comfortable
- Refrain from lying on your back or lying face downwards
- Refrain from exercises which stress the pelvic girdle area
- Select movements that reflect daily life
- A small number of repetitions is best
- Avoid exercises such as sit-ups which bear weight on the abdomen

Cool down

- This should include relaxing activities
- Refrain from activities which may excessively stretch the ligaments
- Choose to be in a well-balanced and relaxed state when conducting passive stretching
- Make use of shorter-hold stretches to preserve flexibility
- Avoid choosing stretches which may promote flexibility

Disability and illnesses

There are a range of disabilities and medical conditions that can have an impact on bones, joints and muscles, causing limitations to movements. These conditions can also affect energy production as well as impact the cardiorespiratory system. Similarly, there are hundreds of neurological conditions leading to disabilities that impact exercising.

As a personal trainer, if you are supporting individuals with disability and illnesses, it is vital to take into consideration their conditions and specific requirements of the body prior to exercising as well as asking the individuals to seek professional advice.

Some detail on common conditions are provided below.

Physical differences

Wheelchair user

Regular aerobic exercise and muscle-strengthening exercise are just as important for the health and wellbeing of wheelchair users as they are for other adults. However, the personal trainer will have to assess and find a pace suitable for the client and select movements that they can do comfortably. There are a range of options available for taking cardiovascular exercise in a wheelchair, such as seated exercises and wheelchair sprinting in a studio or track and using rowing machines adapted for wheelchair use. The aim is to raise the client's heart rate and get them warm enough to break a sweat.

When it comes to muscle-strengthening, the personal trainer should pay special attention to certain muscle groups. The repeated pushing motion required to push a wheelchair can make the chest and shoulder muscles tight and therefore prone to injury whilst the back muscles can become weaker because they are not worked when pushing the wheelchair. It is therefore a good idea when working with wheelchair users to focus on exercises that work the smaller muscles that support the pushing motion. The back muscles can also be strengthened by doing exercises that involve a pulling motion, such as a pull-up. Gyms with equipment adapted for wheelchair users are a great place to do muscle-strengthening activities. Some wheelchair users also find they can do muscle-strengthening exercises at home using resistance bands.

Disproportioned weakness

Some disabilities display disproportional weakness – for example, cerebral palsy. Where a client has contrasting strength levels between the left and right side of their body, the personal trainer should concentrate on making the disadvantaged side as strong as they can, without neglecting the other side of the body. It should be noted that if the nerves regulating the disadvantaged side is partly or fully damaged, then only limited improvement in the affected muscle can be achieved.

Spastic muscles

These muscles are extremely taut and rigid. Many people with a disability have a fair amount of spasticity, so such training will be significant. However, medical advice must be sought by the personal trainer, on how to stretch a muscle that is spastic without causing harm to the client.

Progressive disorders

Physical disabilities like multiple sclerosis come under this category. Here, the condition of the sufferer deteriorates gradually over time. Such disorders need to be observed closely to make sure the clients condition does not worsen as the exercise program progresses.

Sensory nerve damage

Many kinds of disabilities cause damage to sensory nerves. The body loses its ability to sense pressure against the skin and this may cause pressure sores. The use of a wheelchair boosts the chances of the client getting pressure sores; the client will usually already know the relevance of regular checks. Using gym equipment attaches similar risk so should also be checked regularly.

Neurological disorders

These conditions adversely affect the central nervous system (CNS). An example of such a condition is muscular dystrophy. Muscles can progressively become more fragile alongside a declining neurological function. The effect of this can be minimized through a training program which focuses on broad levels of fitness. Advice from the client's GP should immediately be sought if there is a drastic reduction in function.

Depression

This is a debilitating condition in its own right, but it can also be brought about because of living with a disability. Depression often demotivates a person, depleting their levels of energy. It can even result in them completely dropping out of the program. Prescribed medicine given to patients with depression often cause them to put on weight.

Understanding client's conditions

The personal trainer MUST complete a health form prior to any exercise, in order to screen the client. This will reveal any conditions(for example, stage 3 hypertension or heart conditions) and will give the opportunity to seek advice from a GP or medical professional, should the need arise. A specialist trainer may be hired for clients with very precise medical conditions. For the client to participate, they may need to consider the following factors when tweaking the program to accommodate the needs of the client:

- Simplify several of the exercises.
- Reduce levels of intensity, for example less repetitions and resistance, a suitable range of motion.
- Adjust positions in exercise, for example, enabling wheelchair users to use their chairs or other persons to use chairs where they have issues with balance.
- Oral instructions should be clear for those who have none or weak hearing and sight.
- Clear practical demonstrations for those who may need visual aid or those who have difficulty hearing.
- Capture the interest of those who may have a learning disability, for example Downs Syndrome.

Health and safety considerations

The personal trainer should give thoughts to facilities within the building, including procedures to evacuate the building in an emergency. They should also be able to meet relevant legislation which regulates clients who have specific needs, for example safeguarding weaker adults.

Safety in an emergency

Any employer or organization that provides ser-vices to the public must take responsibility for peo-ple from all sections of society. An employer should consider the needs of disabled people when for-mulating its evacuation procedures from a build-ing; it would be discriminatory not to. It is also mandatory to consider the needs of other vulnerable people, like younger clients and the elderly. The personal trainer should have full knowledge and training on how to execute such procedures in the event of an emergency. The fol-lowing are general guidelines covering emer-gency procedures in relation to vulnerable people:

Younger clients

When a younger client finds themselves in such a situation, their behavior may change and they may even regress. Good preparation for emergency situations will minimize this reaction and make for a smoother task. A good example of preparation could be to rehearse the emergency procedure with them. Any complex language or terms would be simplified to suit the age of the younger client.

Younger clients naturally become more dependent in an emergency. They look to an adult for help and support, and for feelings of safety and security. These feelings and needs should be acknowledged and embraced by the personal trainer. The personal trainer should not patronize the younger client and stay calm. They should try and placate the younger client and make them feel like they are in-cluded and that everything will be all right.

Younger clients should be kept informed about what is happening. Any questions from the younger client should be answered truthfully, considering their feelings. The personal trainer should always have a positive and optimistic attitude as this will impact on the younger clients.

Disabled people

The procedure for this will be dependent on the level of disability in the people or person concerned. If possible, the number of disabled people should be recorded as well as the location within the building.

Evacuation routes, and any necessary equipment need to be evaluated. Procedures for when an alarm goes off should also be set. Roles and actions for all staff members should be allocated also in relation to handling those with a disability.

Staff members should help anyone who is visually impaired by guiding the person to hold their arm. On stairwells, the personal trainer or staff member should lead the disabled person by guiding them to place their hand on the staff member's shoulder whilst slowly walking down the steps.

There may be people who cannot walk up or down stairs. They may need equipment to safely transport them to their destination. Such equipment is highly recommended, especially for high rise buildings as lifts are not allowed to be used in emergencies. There are however, specialist lifts known as evacuation lifts or firefighting lifts. These could be used to evacuate disabled people. This lift can also be used to evacuate wheelchairs, guide dogs and other 'equipment'.

The elderly

It is increasingly common nowadays to see older people at the gym, so this group should be accommodated when planning an emergency procedure. Much of the above advice can be applied to the elderly, as it is common for this group to have restricted mobility. As a person ages, they often see a gradual decline in their physiological and psychological state. This could lead to a reduction of their independent life. It may be wise therefore, for a member of staff to partner up with an older person in the event of an emergency.

End of Chapter activities

Activity 4.12: Complete this table on how the body of special populations can be different and the factors to take into consideration when exercising.

	Difference	Factors to consider by a personal trainer
Younger Clients		
Elderly		
Disabled		

Activity 4.13: List the do's and don'ts of maintaining safety of special populations in an emergency.

Do	Do not

Activity 4.14: Summarize the factors to consider when training a client before birth and after birth.

	Factors
Before birth	
After birth	

End of Chapter checklist

1. Who would fall under the definition of 'special populations'?
2. Is an average child's heart rate slower or faster than an average adult's?
3. How can injuries relating to growth be prevented?
4. Does a child's aerobic and anaerobic capability increase or decrease with age?
5. Why are children's bodies less effective at cooling down?
6. What causes osteoporosis?
7. What neuromuscular changes occur as we age?
8. What is relaxin and what triggers it?
9. How soon should women start exercising after birth?
10. What are spastic muscles and what are their implications on exercising?

References

Books and articles

Note: The web based references listed here are based on availability of the web pages at the time of writing and are subject to change or removal by their respective owners.

ACSM (2013). Resistance Training for Health and Fitness from www.acsm.org Alter, 1998).

ACSM (1998). The recommended quantity and quality of exercise for developing and maintaining cardiorespiratory and muscular fitness, and flexibility in healthy adults

ACSM (2001). ACSM's Guidelines for Exercise Testing and Prescription, 4th Edition. Lippincott Williams & Wilkins, Philadelphia

American Academy of Pediatrics Committee. (2008). Sports Medicine and Fitness Strength training for children and adolescents

Bassey, J.Dinan, S. Hunter, F. and Gow, E. (2011). Strong Bones for Life, National Osteoporosis Society, Carrol & Brown Publishers

BBC. (2005). Many labels on food 'misleading' in http://news.bbc.co.uk/1/hi/health/4311087.stm

Boundless. (2016). "Basic Principles of Gas Exchange." Boundless Biology. Boundless, from https://www.boundless.com

British Nutrition Foundation. (2016). Nutrition Requirements

BUPA (2002) High blood pressure. http://www.bupa.co.uk/fact_sheets/html/ hypertension.html

Costill D, King D, and Thomas R. (1985). Effects of reduced training on muscular power in swimmers.

Hawley, J. A., & Burke, L. M. (1998). Peak performance: Training and nutritional strategies for sport, Allen and Unwin

Dalgleish, J. and Dollery, S. (2001). The Health and Fitness Handbook. Longman

Durstine, J.L. and Moore, G.E. (2003). ACSM's Exercise Management for Persons with Chronic Diseases and Disabilities, 2nd Edition, Human Kinetics

Earle, R.W. and Baechle, T.R. (2000). Resistance Training and Spotting Techniques. In Essentials of strength training and conditioning. NSCA

Earle, R.W. and Baechle, T.R. (2004). NSCA's Essentials of Personal Training. Human Kinetics

Fleck, S.J. and Kraemer, W.J. (1997). Designing Resistance Training programs. 2nd Edition. Human Kinetlcs

Gavin, J. (2005). Lifestyle Fitness Coaching. Human Kinetics

Golding et al. (1989). The Y's to Physical Fitness, 3rd Edition, Human Kinetics

Health Promotion Chapter (2007). Stages of behaviour change: Queensland Stay On Your Feet® Community GoodPractice Toolkit.

Hoeger, W.K & Hoeger, A. Principles and Labs for Fitness and Wellness (2015). Cengage Learning

HSE (2013). Adult Anthropometric Measures, Overweight and Obesity, Vol.1 Ch.10

HSCIC (2016). Statistics on Obesity, Physical Activity and Diet

Institute for, Cancer Research. (2007). Food, Nutrition, Physical Activity, and the Prevention of Cancer: A Global Perspective

Kokkonen, J. Nelson, A.G. Cornwell, A. (1998) Acute muscle stretching inhibits maximal strength performance. Research Quarterly for Exercise and Sport. no.69

Kraemer, W. (2004). Kraemer W. Roundtable discussion: periodization of training (part 1) Strength and Conditioning Journal

Kris-Etherton et al. (1999). High monounsaturated fatty acid diets lower both plasma cholesterol and triglycerol concentrations

Martin, C. (2002) Functional Movement Development. (2nd ed.). W.B. Saunders Company

McArdle, W.D., Katch, F.I. and Katch, V.L. (1996). Exercise Physiology. 4th Edition, Williams and Wilkins

McArdle, W., Katch, F. and Katch, V. (2001). Exercise Physiology: Energy, Nutrition & Human Performance, 5th Edition. Baltimore, Lipincott, Williams & Wilkins.

McGill, S. (2002). Low Back Disorders, Human Kinetics

McGill, S (2002). Low Back Disorders: evidenced – based prevention and rehabilitation. Human Kinetics

McMillan, Beverley. (2006) Human Body. Reader's Digest

Naderi, S. MD, & Ozgen, S. MD. (1998). Cervical spondylotic myleopathy surgical results: Factors affecting results. Neurosurgery

National Institute for Health and Clinical Excellence (NICE) (2007). Public Health Guidance 6 'Behaviour change at population, community and individual levels'.

NHS. (2011). Supplements Who needs them?

New Studies in Athletics, no. 2/2008. The Lactic Acids System

NHS. (2016). Procedure for Measuring Bioelectrical Impedance Using the Bodystat 1500. NIHR Southampton Biomedical Research Centre

O'Connor, J. (2001). NLP Workbook. Element

Panjabi, M.M., Abumi, K., Duranceau, J. and Oxland, T. (1989). Spinal stability and intersegmental muscle forces. A biomechanical model

Reader's Digest, (2010). Foods that Hard Foods that Heal

Roberts, M. and Ingram N. (1995) Biology, 2nd Edition, Nelson Science

Rowland, P. (2003) In The stretching debate. Journal of Bodywork and Movement Therapies. April: 80-96

Siff, M. (2003). Supertraining. Supertraining Institute. Denver

Stafford Brown, J, Rea, S, and Manley, C. (2016). BTEC First Sport. 2nd Edition, Hodder Education

Stafford Brown, J. Rea, S. Manley, C. and Janaway, L. (2011). BTEC First Sport for Performance, Exercise and Fitness and Outdoor Recreation, Hodder Education

Stuart, A. and Webster, S. Biology, Heinemann

The Cooper Institute for Aerobics Research, The Physical Fitness Specialist Certification Manual, Dallas TX, revised 1997 printed in Advance Fitness Assessment & Exercise Prescription, 3rd Edition, Vivian H. Heyward, 1998. p48. Cited in www.biopac.com

The British Dietetic Association. (2014). Dietitian, Nutritionist, Nutritional Therapist or Diet Expert?

The Food Standards Agency. (2016). The Eatwell Guide

The Food Standards Agency. (2008). Criteria For The Use Of The Terms Fresh, Pure, Natural Etc. In Food Labelling

The Food Standards Agency. (2008). FSA nutrient and food based guidelines for UK institutions

Theory Into Practice Strategies, NCETA in http://nceta.flinders.edu.au/files/2212/4710/5738/Goal_Setting.pdf

Turner, A. (2011). The Science and Practice of Periodization: A Brief Review, Lippincott, Williams and Wilkins

Tortora, G.J. and Grabowski, S.R. (1996). Principles of Anatomy & Physiology, 8th Edition. New York, Harper-Collins.

UK Active, The Health Commitment Statement from www.ukactive.com

Wassung, Keith. Cervical Curve, Structure, Function and Optimal Health, Research Report #9 in https://www.nrchiro.com/

Wilmore, J. and Costill, D.L. (1999). Physiology of Sport and Exercise. Champaign, Illinois: Human Kinetics

Wilmore, J.H. and Costill, D.L. (2004). Physiology of Sport and Exercise. Champaign, Illinois: Human Kinetics

Wong, D. and Faithful-Willams, K. (2016). The Feel Good Plan, Ebury PressWorld Health Organization (WHO) (2008). Behaviour change strategies and health: the role of health systems. EUR/RC58/10.

Zatsiorsky V and Kraemer W. (2006) Science and Practice of Strength Training (2nd ed). Human Kinetics

Zestco, Great Communication: The power of influence

Zickerman, A. and Schley. Bill. (2003). Power of 10, The Once a Week Slow Motion Fitness Revolution, Harper Collins

Websites

Note: The websites and web pages listed here are based on availability of the web pages at the time of writing and are subject to change or removal by their respective owners.

https://bmcpediatr.biomedcentral.com/articles/10.1186/1471-2431-14-249
http://webarchive.nationalarchives.gov.uk/+/http://www.dh.gov.uk/ab/Archive/COMA/index.htm
http://selfdeterminationtheory.org/theory/
www.acsm.org
www.bbc.co.uk/news/science-environment-37450953
www.bda.uk.com/
www.b-eat.co.uk/
www.bhf.org.uk
www.bloodpressureuk.org
www.bloodpressureuk.org/BloodPressureandyou/Yourlifestyle/Beingactive/Whatkinds
www.bodybuilding.com
www.bodybuilding.com/fun/guide-to-resistance-training-7-things-you-need-to-know.html
www.bps.org.uk/behaviourchange
www.bupa.co.uk/health-information/directory/f/food-for-exercise
www.fda.gov/food/nutrition-food-labeling-and-critical-foods/standards-identity-food
www.food.gov.uk
www.free-online-calculator-use.com/skin-fold-test.html
www.glencoe.com/
www.gov.uk/government/groups/scientific-advisory-committee-on-nutrition
www.gov.uk/government/publications/sacn-vitamin-d-and-health-report
www.hcpc-uk.co.uk/
www.innerbody.com
www.heart.org
www.hse.gov.uk
www.hse.gov.uk/pubns/indg449.pdf
www.hse.gov.uk/quarries/education/powerpoint/topic4.ppt
www.legislation.gov.uk/ukpga/1974/37/section/2
www.livescience.com
www.livescience.com/3616-child-brains-organized-differently-adult-brains.html
www.mstrust.org.uk/
www.nice.org.uk
www.nhs.uk
www.nhs.uk/Livewell/fitness/Documents/adults-19-64-years.pdf
www.nspcc.org.uk
www.nutrition.org.uk
www.nutritionsociety.org
www.physiotheraphyclinic.com.au
www.smamiddennederland.nl/wp-content/uploads/2014/02/Core_stability-Routine.pdf
www.soilassociation.org/
www.statisticsauthority.gov.uk/assessment/code-of-practice
www.ukactive.com
www.yourhormones.info/default.aspx
www.yourhormones.info/hormones/relaxin.aspx)
www.verywell.com/normal-pulse-rates-for-kids-2634038
www.weightrainer.net/skinfoldbf.html
www.who.int/en
www.uhs.nhs.uk/
www.uhs.nhs.uk/Media/Southampton-Clinical-Research/

www.ingramcontent.com/pod-product-compliance
Ingram Content Group UK Ltd.
Pitfield, Milton Keynes, MK11 3LW, UK
UKHW052010041026
15590UKWH00008B/2261

9 798345 575376